WORKBOOK

S N A P Student Notes and Problems

MATHEMATICS 8
B.C. Edition

Castle Rock
Research Corp

Canadian Cataloguing in Publication Data

Rao, Gautam, 1961 –
STUDENT NOTES AND PROBLEMS – Math 8 (B.C.)

1. Mathematics – Juvenile Literature. I. Title

Published by

Castle Rock Research Corp.

2340 Manulife Place

10180 – 101 Street

Edmonton, AB T5J 3S4

5 6 7 FP 07 06 05

Printed in Canada

Publisher
Gautam Rao

Editors
Mun Prasad
Shirley Wacowich

Contributors
Sandi Sasges
Rob Shkrobot
Linda Spiller
Claire Wilkins
Krista Zirk

Print Production
Phil Beauchamp
Alesha Braitenbach
Tory Braybrook
Nishi Chadha
Markus Chan
Kevin Huenison
Lorraine James
Shawna Kozel
James Kropfreiter
Julie May
David Moret
Suzanne Morin
Jackie Pacheco
Abhinav Rastogi
Diana Seguin
Jan Witwicky
Gary Yaremchuk
Richard Yeomans

Dedicated to the memory of Dr. V. S. Rao

STUDENT NOTES AND PROBLEMS WORKBOOKS

Student Notes and Problems (SNAP) workbooks are a series of support resources in mathematics for students in grades 3 to 12 and in science for students in grades 9 to 12. SNAP workbooks are 100% aligned with curriculum. The resources are designed to support classroom instructions and provide students with additional examples, practice exercises, and tests. SNAP workbooks are ideal for use all year long at school and at home.

The following is a summary of the key features of all SNAP workbooks.

UNIT OPENER PAGE

- summarizes the curriculum outcomes addressed in the unit in age-appropriate language
- identifies the lessons by title
- lists the prerequisite knowledge and skills the student should know prior to beginning the unit

LESSONS

- provide essential teaching pieces and explanations of the concepts
- include example problems and questions with complete, detailed solutions that demonstrate the problem-solving process

NOTES BARS

- contain key definitions, formulas, reminders, and important steps or procedures
- provide space for students to add their own notes and helpful reminders

PRACTICE EXERCISES

- include questions that relate to each of the curriculum outcomes for the unit
- provide practice in applying the lesson concepts

REVIEW SUMMARY

- provides a succinct review of the key concepts in the unit

PRACTICE TEST

- assesses student learning of the unit concepts

ANSWERS AND SOLUTIONS

- demonstrate the step-by-step process or problem-solving method used to arrive at the correct answer

Answers and solutions are provided for the odd-numbered questions in each workbook. A SNAP Solutions Manual that contains answers and complete solutions for all questions is also available.

CONTENTS

Number Concepts

Negative Exponents 3

Scientific Notation 9

Rational Numbers 15

Ratio 23

Percentage 26

Square Root 31

Practice Quiz 1 36

Operations with Fractions 39

Operations with Rational Numbers 52

Ratio, Rate, Proportion, and Percentage 61

Calculating Percentage 66

Ratios and Rates 72

Practice Quiz 2 76

Review Summary 78

Practice Test 79

Patterns and Relations

Expressions and Equations 84

Substituting Variables 91

Relations 94

Graphing Relations 103

Practice Quiz 1 114

Algebra Tiles 118

One-Step Equations 123

Two-Step Equations 130

Practice Quiz 2 138

Review Summary 142

Practice Test 143

Shape and Space

Pythagorean Theorem 151
Perimeter 160
Area 168
2-D Composite Figures 180
Practice Quiz 1 187
3-D Objects 194
Surface Area 201
Volume 211
3-D Composite Figures 217
Practice Quiz 2 228
Enlargements and Reductions 232
Scale Diagrams 239
Maps 244
Networks 249
Practice Quiz 3 259
Review Summary 263
Practice Test 265

Statistics and Probability

Surveys 273
Survey Results 280
Graphing 286
Data Sets 293
Stem-and-Leaf Plots and Box-and-Whisker Plots 301
Practice Quiz 1 310
Probability 316
Independent Events 322
Practice Quiz 2 333
Review Summary 337
Practice Test 338

Answers and Solutions

Answers and Solutions 347

NOTES

NUMBER CONCEPTS

When you are finished this unit, you should be able to . . .

- demonstrate and explain the meaning of a negative exponent (PLO 1, number concepts)
- represent numbers in scientific notation (PLO 7, number concepts)
- define, compare, and order rational numbers (PLO 1, number concepts)
- demonstrate that the product of reciprocal numbers is equal to 1 (PLO 2, number operations)
- express 3-term ratios in equivalent form (PLO 6, number concepts)
- represent and apply fractional percentage and percentage greater than 100, in fraction or decimal form (PLO 3, number concepts)
- represent square roots in a variety of forms (PLO 4, number concepts)
- distinguish between square roots and decimal approximations using a calculator (PLO 5, number concepts)
- add, subtract, multiply, and divide fractions (PLO 1, number operations)
- estimate, compute, and verify the sum, difference, product, and quotient of rational numbers (PLO 2, number operations)
- estimate, use a calculator to compute, and verify square roots of whole and decimal numbers (PLO 3, number operations)
- use rate, ratio, proportion, and percentage to solve problems (PLO 4, number operations)
- calculate percentages (PLO 3, number concepts)
- derive and apply unit rates (PLO 5, number operations)
- express rates and ratios in equivalent forms (PLO 6, number operations)

Lesson	Page	Completed on
1. Negative Exponents	3	
2. Scientific Notation	9	
3. Rational Numbers	15	
4. Ratio	23	
5. Percentage	26	
6. Square Root	31	
Practice Quiz 1	36	
7. Operations with Fractions	39	
8. Operations with Rational Numbers	52	
9. Ratio, Rate, Proportion, and Percentage	61	
10. Calculating Percentage	66	
11. Ratios and Rates	72	

Practice Quiz 2	76	
Review Summary	78	
Practice Test	79	
Answers and Solutions	at the back of the book	

PREREQUISITE SKILLS AND KNOWLEDGE

Prior to beginning this unit, you should be able to. . .

- explain and understand exponents
- distinguish between exponential form, repeated multiplication, and standard form
- read and write numbers using a place value table
- understand how to write numbers greater than 1 using scientific notation
- understand the meaning of ratios
- estimate and calculate percentage
- convert between fractions and decimal numbers
- understand, compare, and order integers
- use arithmetic to solve problems involving decimal numbers and fractions
- distinguish between rate and ratio
- understand proportion
- apply order of operations to solve problems

Lesson 1 NEGATIVE EXPONENTS

You will recall from Grade 7 lessons that *exponential expressions* are mathematical expressions in which a number is multiplied by itself a given number of times.

An exponential expression has two parts: a base and an exponent. The *base* is the number in the power that is being multiplied. The *exponent* is the number of times that the base is multiplied by itself.

In the expression 10^4, the base is 10 and the exponent is 4. The expression 10^4 is read as "10 to the power of 4" or "10 to the fourth."

$$10^4 \qquad = \qquad 10 \times 10 \times 10 \times 10 \qquad = \qquad 10\,000$$

Exponential Form   Repeated Multiplication   Standard Form

There are positive and negative exponents. A *positive exponent* is an exponent that is 1 or greater than 1. A *negative exponent* has a value of less than 1. Negative exponents are written with a negative sign (–) beside the exponent.

In the expression 10^3, the exponent 3 is a positive exponent. In the expression 10^{-3}, the exponent –3 is a negative exponent.

Study the following examples of numbers written in standard form and exponential form.

Standard Form	Exponential Form	Standard Form	Exponential Form
100	10^2	36	6^2
10	10^1 (or 10)	6	6^1 (or 6)
1	10^0	1	6^0
$\frac{1}{10}$	10^{-1} or $\frac{1}{10^1}$	$\frac{1}{6}$	6^{-1} or $\frac{1}{6^1}$
$\frac{1}{100}$	10^{-2} or $\frac{1}{10^2}$	$\frac{1}{36}$	6^{-2} or $\frac{1}{6^2}$

As you can see from these examples, some numbers can be written with either a positive or a negative exponent. If a number in standard form is less than 1 (in the form of a decimal number or a fraction), it can have a negative exponent when it is written as an exponential expression or it can have a positive exponent if it is written as a fraction with an exponent.

The value of an exponential expression that has a positive exponent is 1 or greater than 1.

The value of an exponential expression that has a negative exponent is less than 1.

The exponent 1 is almost never used because any number to the power of 1 is the number itself. The exponents 2 and 3 are very common. We refer to the exponent 2 as "squared" and the exponent 3 as "cubed." Squared is used when referring to area and cubed is used when referring to volume.

Any power than has an exponent of 0 is equal to 1. The 0 implies that there is none of the base.

NOTES

Example 1

Write $\dfrac{1}{100}$ as a positive exponent.

Solution

Step 1

Use repeated multiplication to determine how many 10s are multiplied together to equal 100.

$100 = 10 \times 10$

Two 10s multiplied together equal 100.

Step 2

The number of 10s that were multiplied together is the exponent. The base is 10.

$100 = 10^2$

Step 3

Remember that $\dfrac{1}{100}$ is a fraction. That is, a number less than 1.

Therefore, let the exponential expression become the denominator. The numerator is 1.

$$\dfrac{1}{100} = \dfrac{1}{10^2}$$

$\dfrac{1}{10^2}$ is a positive exponent. $\dfrac{1}{100}$ can also be written as a negative exponent.

Example 2

Write $\dfrac{1}{100}$ as a negative exponent.

Solution

Step 1

Write the fraction with a positive exponent, as explained above.

$$\dfrac{1}{100} = \dfrac{1}{10^2}$$

Step 2

Take the reciprocal of the positive exponent.

$$\dfrac{10^2}{1}$$

Reciprocals are fractions where the numerator and the denominator have changed places. Example $\dfrac{3}{4}$ and $\dfrac{4}{3}$ are reciprocals.

When changing from a positive exponent to a negative exponent, the reciprocal is taken because the negative exponent indicates that the value of the power is less than 1.

Step 3

Insert a negative sign in front of the exponent to indicate that the number is less than 1. When the denominator is 1, it does not need to be written as part of the answer.

$$\frac{10^{-2}}{1} = 10^{-2}$$

Example 3

Write $\dfrac{1}{1\,000}$ as a negative exponent.

Solution

$1\,000 = 10 \times 10 \times 10$

$1\,000 = 10^3$

$$\frac{1}{1\,000} = \frac{1}{10^3}$$

Take the reciprocal $\dfrac{1}{10^3} = \dfrac{10^{-3}}{1} = 10^{-3}$

Example 4

Decimal numbers can also be written as negative exponents. Write 0.01 as a negative exponent.

Solution

Step 1

Say the number aloud or record it in a place value table.

One hundredth

Step 2

Write this number as a fraction.

$$\frac{1}{100}$$

Step 3

Use repeated multiplication to determine how many times 10 is multiplied by itself in the denominator.

$100 = 10 \times 10$

Step 4

Write the number as a positive exponent.

$$0.01 = \frac{1}{10^2}$$

NOTES

Step 5

Write the number as a negative exponent by taking the reciprocal and adding a negative sign.

$$0.01 = \frac{10^{-2}}{1} = 10^{-2}$$

Example 5

Write 0.1 as a negative exponent.

Solution

One-tenth

$$\frac{1}{10}$$

$$10 = 10 \times 1$$

$$0.1 = \frac{1}{10^{1}}$$

$$0.1 = 10^{-1}$$

PRACTICE EXERCISE

1. Complete the following chart.

	Standard Form		Exponential Form	
	Fraction	**Decimal**	**Positive Exponent**	**Negative Exponent**
a)		0.1		
b)				10^{-3}
c)			$\dfrac{1}{10^2}$	
d)	$\dfrac{1}{100\ 000}$			

2. Write the following numbers in positive and negative exponential form.

   a) $\dfrac{1}{100}$

   b) $\dfrac{1}{10\ 000}$

   c) $\dfrac{1}{1\ 000}$

   d) $\dfrac{1}{10}$

3. Write the following decimal numbers in exponential form both as fractions and with negative exponents.

   a) 0.01

   b) 0.00 001

   c) 0.1

   d) 0.000 000 01

4. Write the following numbers in standard form both as fractions, and with negative exponents

   a) 10^{-5}

   b) 10^{-2}

   c) 10^{-4}

   d) 10^{-7}

5. Write the following numbers in standard form as decimals, and as fractions using the reciprocal rule.

    a) 10^{-6}

    b) 10^{-3}

    c) 10^{-1}

    d) 10^{-8}

6. Make each of the following statements true by using the symbols >, <, or =.

    a) 10^{-5} _____ 0.001

    b) 10^{-7} _____ $\dfrac{1}{100\,000}$

    c) 10^{-2} _____ 0.01

    d) 10^{-2} _____ $\dfrac{1}{1\,000\,000}$

Lesson 2 SCIENTIFIC NOTATION

Very large and very small numbers can be written in a shortened form called scientific notation. Any number in standard form can be written in scientific notation.

In scientific notation, a number that is greater than 1, but less than 10, is multiplied by a power of 10.

For example, the number 2 345 is written as 2.345×10^3 in scientific notation.

Example 1

Write 4 509 in scientific notation.

Solution

Step 1

Locate the decimal point in the number.
The decimal point is after the number 9.

Step 2

Move the decimal to the *left* until it is between the first two digits of the number (creating a number that is greater than 1, but less than 10).
$4\,509. \rightarrow 4\,50.9 \rightarrow 45.09 \rightarrow 4.509$

Step 3

Count the number of places that the decimal moved and use this value as the exponent in the power.
The decimal moved 3 places $\rightarrow 10^3$

Step 4

Rewrite the revised number from step 2 (the number that was created after the decimal was moved) and multiply this number by the exponent from step 3.
$4\,509 = 4.509 \times 10^3$

Example 2

Write 12 900 in scientific notation.

Solution
$12\,900. \rightarrow 1\,290.0 \rightarrow 129.00 \rightarrow 12.900 \rightarrow 1.2900$
1.29×10^4

$$12\,900$$
$$\overset{\hookleftarrow}{}_{1\ 2\ 3\ 4}$$

or $12\,900 = 1.29 \times 10^4$

Scientific notation is a method used to write very large or very small numbers.

Recall that powers of 10 are powers that have a base of 10.

If you do not see a decimal point, the decimal point is located at the end of the last number; after the last digit.

When writing the scientific notation form of the number, remember to use the revised number (the number created after the decimal was moved).

In scientific notation, the zeros at the end of the number are not written. It is assumed that the zeros are present.

NOTES

To change a number greater than 1 from scientific notation to standard form, the value of the exponent determines the number of positions that the decimal moves to the right.

Example 3

Change 6.6873×10^5 to standard form

Solution

Step 1

Look at the exponent. This number tells you how many places to move the decimal. The decimal will move 5 places.

Step 2

Locate the decimal. Move the decimal to the right the number of times indicated by the exponent.

6.6873×10^5

66.873 (one time)

668.73 (two times)

6 687.3 (three times)

66 873 (four times)

668 730 (five times)

When changing from scientific form to standard form, zeros are added to the end of the number if there are no more positions to move the decimal to.

Step 3

Write the new number.

$6.6873 \times 10^5 = 668\ 730$

Example 4

Write 8.907×10^7 in standard form.

Solution

$8.907 \times 10^7 =$ move 7 decimal places to the right

$8.907 \times 10^7 = 89\ 070\ 000$

89 070 000
1 2 3 4 5 6 7

Numbers that are less than 1 can also be written using scientific notation.

Example 5

Change 0.058 6 to scientific notation.

Solution

Step 1

Locate the decimal point in the number.

The decimal is between the two zeros (between the tenths and ones position).

Step 2

Move the decimal to the *right* until there is only one number greater than 0 to the left of the decimal (creating a number that is greater than 1, but less than 10).

$0.058\ 6 \rightarrow 00.586 \rightarrow 005.86$

Step 3

Count the number of places that you moved the decimal. Use this value as the exponent in the power (with 10 as the base). Place a negative sign in front of the exponent to indicate that the value of the number is less than 1.

The decimal moved 2 places $\rightarrow 10^{-2}$

Step 4

Rewrite the revised number from step 2 (the number that the decimal place was moved to) and multiply this number by the exponent from step 3.

$0.0586 = 5.86 \times 10^{-2}$

> When writing the final answer, remove any zeros that are in front of the number.

Example 6

Write 0.000 34 in scientific notation.

Solution

$0.000\ 34 \rightarrow 00.003\ 4 \rightarrow 000.034 \rightarrow 0\ 000.34 \rightarrow 00\ 003.4$

3.4×10^{-4}

When changing a number with a negative exponent from scientific notation to standard form, the value of the exponent determines the number of positions that the decimal moves to the left.

Example 7

Change $8.091\ 7 \times 10^{-3}$ to standard form.

Solution

Step 1

Look at the exponent. This number tells you how many places to move the decimal.

The decimal will move 3 places.

Step 2

Locate the decimal. Move the decimal to the left the number of times indicated by the exponent.

$8.091\ 7 \times 10^{-3}$

0.809 17 (one time)

0.080 917 (two times)

0.008 091 7 (three times)

NOTES

When changing a number from scientific notation to standard form,
- if the exponent is positive, move the decimal to the right
- if the exponent is negative, move the decimal to the left

Step 3
Write the new number.
$8.091\ 7 \times 10^{-3} = 0.008\ 091\ 7$

Example 8
Write 23.021×10^{-5} in standard form.
Solution
$23.021 \rightarrow 2.302\ 1 \rightarrow 0.230\ 21 \rightarrow 0.023\ 021 \rightarrow 0.002\ 302\ 1 \rightarrow 0.000\ 230\ 21$
$23.021 \times 10^{-5} = 0.000\ 230\ 21$

PRACTICE EXERCISE

1. Complete each of the following equations by writing the appropriate power of 10.
   a) $80 = 8 \times$ _____
   b) $200 = 2 \times$ _____
   c) $93\,000 = 9.3 \times$ _____
   d) $45\,600 = 4.56 \times$ _____
   e) $6\,770 = 6.77 \times$ _____
   f) $1\,908\,000 = 1.908 \times$ _____

2. Write each of the following numbers in scientific notation.
   a) $4\,600$
   b) 590
   c) $70\,000$
   d) $34\,000$
   e) $2\,430\,000$
   f) $750\,000$
   g) $21\,300\,020$
   h) $901\,000\,000$

3. Write each of the following numbers in standard form.
   a) 3.6×10^2
   b) 10.5×10^4
   c) 5.9×10^3
   d) 8.8×10^5
   e) 6.02×10^6
   f) 7.893×10^4

4. Complete each of the following equations by writing the appropriate power of 10.
   a) $0.005 = 5 \times$ _____
   b) $0.8 = 8 \times$ _____
   c) $0.06 = 6 \times$ _____
   d) $0.43 = 4.3 \times$ _____
   e) $0.009\,8 = 9.8 \times$ _____
   f) $0.000\,005 = 5 \times$ _____

5. Write each of the following numbers in scientific notation.
   a) $0.000\,4$
   b) 0.09
   c) $0.005\,4$
   d) $0.000\,001$
   e) $0.000\,007\,3$
   f) $0.004\,05$
   g) $0.305\,06$

6. Write each of the following numbers in standard form.

   a) 5×10^{-3}

   b) 3.4×10^{-4}

   c) 7.07×10^{-7}

   d) 5.28×10^{-5}

   e) 8.01×10^{-2}

   f) 5.6×10^{-3}

   g) 4.01×10^{-8}

Lesson 3 RATIONAL NUMBERS

Rational numbers include the set of integers {. . . –4, –3, –2, –1, 0, 1, 2, 3, 4 . . .}, all fractions and mixed numbers, and all terminating and repeating decimal numbers.

The following numbers are examples of rational numbers:

$\frac{5}{6}$, $3\frac{1}{2}$, $\frac{43}{4}$, –12, 0, 17, 0.813, 0.454 5 . . .

Rational numbers are defined as numbers that can be written as the quotient (the answer in a division question) of two integers in the form of $\frac{a}{b}$, where b is any value *except* 0.

Numbers that cannot be written as the quotient of two integers are called *irrational numbers*. These numbers are non-terminating, non-repeating decimals. $\sqrt{2}$, $\sqrt{7}$, and π are irrational numbers.

Rational numbers can be expressed in equivalent forms. For example:

$\frac{1}{5}$ is equal to $\frac{2}{10}$, $\frac{3}{15}$, and $\frac{4}{20}$.

–4 is equivalent to $-\frac{12}{3}$, $-\frac{8}{2}$, and $-\frac{20}{5}$.

0.25 is equivalent to $\frac{25}{100}$, $\frac{5}{20}$, and $\frac{1}{4}$.

FRACTIONS

Example 1

Find an equivalent form of $-\frac{3}{8}$.

Solution

Step 1

Select any number, positive or negative. Multiply this number by both the numerator and the denominator. To write equivalent forms, you can also divide the numerator and denominator by a common multiple.

$$\frac{(3x)(-3)}{(8x)(-3)} = \frac{-9}{-24}$$

Terminating decimals are decimal numbers that end. E.g., 5.687 is a terminating decimal.

Repeating decimal numbers are decimal numbers in which one or more numbers repeat indefinitely. E.g., $0.\overline{6}$ is a repeating decimal.

Be cautious when using a calculator to determine if a number is rational or irrational. Some calculators will round the last digit of the number giving the impression that the number has terminated.

Real numbers include all rational and irrational numbers.

Equivalent means equal to.

Recall that a multiple is a number that can be evenly divided by another number. A multiple of two numbers, then, is a number that can be divided by both of the numbers.

To reduce a fraction to lowest form, divide the numerator and the denominator by their greatest common factor. It is also possible to reduce a fraction to lowest form by dividing the numerator and denominator by any factor that both are divisible by. Continue dividing by factors until the fraction is in lowest form.

Step 2

Check the answer by reducing both fractions to their lowest form. If both fractions, in lowest form, are the same, the answer is correct.

$\dfrac{3}{8}$ is in lowest form

$$\dfrac{-9 \ (\div -3)}{-24 (\div -3)} = \dfrac{3}{8} \qquad\qquad \dfrac{3}{8} = \dfrac{3}{8}$$

Therefore, $\dfrac{9}{24}$ is an equivalent form of $\dfrac{3}{8}$.

Example 2

Express $\dfrac{4}{12}$ in an equivalent form.

Solution

$$\dfrac{4 \ (\times 6)}{12 (\times 6)} = \dfrac{24}{72}$$

Reduce to lowest form

$$\dfrac{4 \ (\div 4)}{12 (\div 4)} = \dfrac{1}{3} \qquad\qquad \dfrac{24 (\div 24)}{72 (\div 24)} = \dfrac{1}{3} \qquad\qquad \dfrac{1}{3} = \dfrac{1}{3}$$

Therefore, an equivalent form of $\dfrac{4}{12}$ is $\dfrac{24}{72}$.

MIXED NUMBERS

Example 1

Find an equivalent form of $2\dfrac{1}{4}$.

Solution

Step 1

Change the mixed fraction to an improper fraction. Multiply the denominator by the whole number. Add the numerator. This answer is the numerator. The denominator remains the same.

$$2\dfrac{1}{4} \rightarrow (4 \times 2) + 1 = 9 \text{ (numerator)}$$

The denominator, 4, remains the same.

$$2\dfrac{1}{4} = \dfrac{9}{4}$$

Improper fractions are fractions in which the numerator is greater than the denominator.

Step 2

Select any number, positive or negative. Multiply this number by both the numerator and the denominator. You could also divide the numerator and denominator by a common factor.

$$\dfrac{9 (\times 5)}{3 (\times 5)} = \dfrac{45}{20}$$

Step 3

Check the answer by changing the equivalent fraction to a mixed number. To do this, determine how many times the denominator divides into the numerator. This answer is the whole number. Subtract this answer from the numerator. This remainder is the numerator. The denominator remains the same. If both fractions, in mixed form, are the same, the answer is correct. The fraction in the mixed number may have to be reduced to lowest terms.

$$\frac{9}{4} \rightarrow 9 \div 4 = 2, \text{ remainder } 1 \rightarrow 2\frac{1}{4}$$

$$\frac{45}{20} \rightarrow 2, \text{ remainder } 5$$

$$\rightarrow 2\frac{5}{20}$$

$$\rightarrow 2\frac{5 \ (\div 5)}{20(\div 5)} = 2\frac{1}{4}$$

$$2\frac{1}{4} = 2\frac{1}{4}$$

Therefore, $\frac{45}{20}$ and $2\frac{5}{20}$ are equivalent forms of $2\frac{1}{4}$.

Example 2

Express $3\frac{2}{5}$ in an equivalent form.

Solution

$$3\frac{2}{5} \rightarrow (5 \times 3) + 2 = 17 \text{ (numerator)}$$

Step 1

Create an improper fraction first.

$$3\frac{2}{5} = \frac{17}{5} \text{ (keep denominator)}$$

Step 2

Multiply both numerator and denominator.

$$\frac{17(\times 2)}{5 \ (\times 2)} = \frac{34}{10}$$

$$\frac{34}{10} = 34 \div 10 = 3, \text{ remainder } 4$$

Step 3

Convert improper back to mixed.

$$\frac{34}{10} \rightarrow 3\frac{4}{10}$$

Mixed numbers and their corresponding improper fractions are equivalent.

NOTES

Remember that 1 is the denominator for any number without a visible denominator.

Step 4

Reduce to lowest form $3\frac{4}{10} = 3\frac{2}{5}$

$3\frac{2}{5} = 3\frac{2}{5}$

Therefore, $\frac{34}{10}$ and $3\frac{4}{10}$ are equivalent forms of $3\frac{2}{5}$.

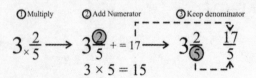

INTEGERS

Example 1

Find an equivalent form of 6.

Solution

Step 1

Select any number, positive or negative. Multiply this number by both the numerator and the denominator.

$\frac{6(\times 7)}{1(\times 7)} = \frac{42}{7}$

Step 2

Check the answer by reducing it to lowest form. If the answer is the same as the original number, the answer is correct.

$\frac{42(\div 7)}{7 \ (\div 7)} = \frac{6}{1}$ or $42 \div 7 = 6$

$6 = 6$

Therefore, $\frac{42}{7}$ is an equivalent form of 6.

Example 2

Express –9 in an equivalent form.

Solution

$\frac{-9(\times 5)}{1(\times 5)} = \frac{-45}{5}$

$\frac{-45(\div 5)}{5(\div 5)} = \frac{-9}{1}$

$-9 = -9$

Therefore, $\frac{-45}{5}$ is an equivalent form of –9.

18

DECIMAL NUMBERS

Example 1

Find an equivalent form of 0.8.

Solution

Step 1

Change the decimal number into a fraction.

$0.8 = \dfrac{8}{10}$ because the 8 is in the tenths place.

Step 2

Select any number, positive or negative. Multiply this number by both the numerator and the denominator. You can also divide the numerator and denominator by a common factor.

$$\dfrac{8 \ (\div 2)}{10(\div 2)} = \dfrac{4}{5}$$

Step 3

Check the answer by reducing both fractions to their lowest form. If both fractions, in lowest form, are the same, the answer is correct.

$\dfrac{4}{5}$ is in lowest terms

$$\dfrac{8 \ (\div 2)}{10(\div 2)} = \dfrac{4}{5} \qquad\qquad \dfrac{4}{5} = \dfrac{4}{5}$$

Therefore, $\dfrac{8}{10}$ and $\dfrac{4}{5}$ are equivalent forms of 0.8.

Example 2

Find an equivalent form of 0.28.

Solution

$$0.28 = \dfrac{28}{100}$$

Reduce by common factor $\dfrac{28 \ (\div 2)}{100(\div 2)} = \dfrac{14}{50}$

Lowest terms

Reduce by common factor $\dfrac{28 \ (\div 4)}{100(\div 4)} = \dfrac{7}{25}$

or $\dfrac{28(\div 2)}{100(\div 2)} = \dfrac{14}{50}$ Reduce again $\dfrac{14 \div 2}{50 \div 2} = \dfrac{7}{25}$

Since $\dfrac{7}{25} = \dfrac{7}{25}$, 0.28 is equivalent to $\dfrac{28}{100}, \dfrac{14}{50}$ and $\dfrac{7}{25}$

Therefore, $\dfrac{28}{100}, \dfrac{14}{50}$, and $\dfrac{7}{25}$ are all equivalent forms of 0.28

NOTES

You use equivalent forms to compare rational numbers; that is, to determine which rational number is larger and which is smaller.

FRACTIONS

Example 1

Which is larger, $\dfrac{2}{3}$ or $\dfrac{3}{4}$?

Solution

Step 1

Find the Lowest Common Denominator (LCD).

$3 = 3, 6, 9, \underline{\mathbf{12}}$

$4 = 4, 8, \underline{\mathbf{12}}$

The LCD of 3 and 4 is 12.

Recall Lowest Common Denominator (LCD) is the Least Common Multiple (LCM) of two or more denominators.

Step 2

Using the LCD, create equivalent fractions, as explained earlier in the lesson, for each fraction.

$$\frac{2}{3} \rightarrow \frac{}{12} \qquad \frac{2(\times 4)}{3(\times 4)} = \frac{8}{12} \qquad \frac{2}{3} = \frac{8}{12}$$

$\times 4$

When recording the answer, remember to use the "original" fractions.

$$\frac{3}{4} \rightarrow \frac{}{12} \qquad \frac{3(\times 3)}{4(\times 3)} = \frac{9}{12} \qquad \frac{3}{4} = \frac{9}{12}$$

$\times 3$

To compare the value of mixed numbers, change the mixed fraction to an improper fraction and follow the same steps listed for fractions.

Step 3

Compare the fractions with the common denominators. The fraction with the largest numerator is the largest fraction.

$$\frac{8}{12} < \frac{9}{12} \qquad \text{Therefore, } \frac{3}{4} \text{ is the larger fraction.}$$

If the whole number parts of the mixed fractions are different, it is also possible to compare the mixed numbers by simply determining which mixed number is larger.

When comparing the values of mixed numbers that have the same whole number, it is also possible to simply compare the fractions – without changing the mixed number into an improper fraction.

Example 2

Which is smaller, $\dfrac{5}{6}$ or $\dfrac{7}{8}$?

Solution

6 = 6, 12, 18, **24**

8 = 8, 16, **24**

$$\dfrac{5}{6} = \dfrac{}{\underset{\times 4}{\longrightarrow} 24} \qquad \dfrac{5(\times 4)}{6(\times 4)} = \dfrac{20}{24} \qquad \dfrac{5}{6} = \dfrac{20}{24}$$

$$\dfrac{7}{8} = \dfrac{}{\longrightarrow 24} \qquad \dfrac{7(\times 3)}{8(\times 3)} = \dfrac{21}{24} \qquad \dfrac{7}{8} = \dfrac{21}{24}$$

$\dfrac{20}{24} < \dfrac{21}{24}$ Therefore, $\dfrac{5}{6}$ is the smaller fraction.

When comparing positive and negative numbers, the positive number is always larger.

INTEGERS AND DECIMAL NUMBERS

Example 1

Which is larger, 12.350 6 or 12.351 6?

Solution

Step 1

Rewrite the integers, lining the decimal points up.

12.350 6

12.351 6

Step 2

Examine the numbers, left to right. If the numbers in each place value position are the same, look to the right at the next number. Repeat this procedure until the numbers differ. The number with the larger value is the larger number.

1	2	.	3	5	0	6
1	2	.	3	5	1	6
Equal	Equal		Equal	Equal	1 is larger	

Therefore, 12.351 6 is larger than 12.350 6.

Example 2

Which is larger, 12 345.069 9 or 12 345.068 9?

Solution

1	2	3	4	5	.	0	6	9	9
1	2	3	4	5	.	0	6	8	9
Equal	Equal	Equal	Equal	Equal		Equal	Equal	9 is larger	Equal

Therefore, 12 345.069 9 is larger than 12 345.068 9.

PRACTICE EXERCISE

1. Identify which numbers are rational numbers.

   a) 776.0   **b)** $\sqrt{121}$ **c)** $\dfrac{0}{8}$ **d)** $4.\overline{76}$ **e)** $\dfrac{7}{0}$

   f) $-\dfrac{3}{4}$ **g)** $\dfrac{66}{99}$ **h)** $\sqrt{23}$ **i)** -2.48 **j)** π

2. Write two equivalent fractions for each of the following numbers.

   a) $\dfrac{5}{8}$ **b)** $\dfrac{9}{15}$

   c) $\dfrac{-3}{10}$ **d)** $2\dfrac{2}{3}$

   e) $\dfrac{7}{5}$ **f)** 4

   g) 0.5   **h)** 1.25

   i) −0.2   **j)** −0.66

3. Fill in the blank with <, >, or = to make each statement true.

   a) $\dfrac{6}{8}$ ____ $\dfrac{2}{8}$ **b)** $\dfrac{0}{4}$ ____ 0

   c) $\dfrac{-7}{2}$ ____ $\dfrac{-3}{2}$ **d)** −2.46 ____ −6.42

   e) 12.457 8 ____ 12.454 8   **f)** $3\dfrac{1}{4}$ ____ 3.75

   g) 0.63 ____ $\dfrac{2}{3}$ **h)** 0.29 ____ $2\dfrac{9}{10}$

   i) $-6\dfrac{2}{10}$ ____ $\dfrac{-31}{5}$

4. Order the numbers from smallest to largest.

   a) 12.5 $\sqrt{49}$ $-3\dfrac{1}{2}$ $4\dfrac{3}{9}$

   b) 2.08 $\dfrac{3}{12}$ $-1\dfrac{4}{100}$ $-\sqrt{1}$

Lesson 4   RATIO

A ratio is a comparison of two or more numbers. In a ratio, each number is called a term and all the terms are separated by either a colon or the word *to*.

In the ratio 4 to 7, the terms are 4 and 7 and they are separated by the word *to*.

In the ratio 2:5:8, the terms are 2, 5, and 8, and they are each separated by a colon.

When writing ratios, it does not matter which form you use, they both represent the same thing.

Consider the following diagram.

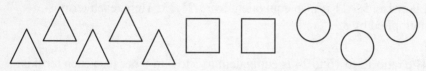

You can write many different ratios about the shapes in this diagram. For example:

The ratio of triangles to squares is 5 to 2 because there are 5 triangles and 2 squares. You could also write this ratio as 5:2.

The ratio of circles to squares to triangles is 3:2:5.

The ratio of triangles to circles to all shapes is 5 to 3 to 10.

When working with ratios, the order in which the terms are written is important because each position in the ratio represents something different.

Consider the following diagram.

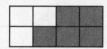

Imagine that you are asked to write a ratio showing the number of shaded sections to unshaded sections. You should write 5 to 3 because there are 5 shaded sections and 3 that are unshaded.

Writing *3 to 5* would be incorrect because you would be saying there are 3 shaded sections and 5 unshaded sections. If the question had been, "*What is the ratio of unshaded sections to shaded sections?*" you would have answered *3 to 5* because there are 3 unshaded sections and 5 shaded ones.

If you are given the ratio 3 to 5 to 8 and asked what it represents for the diagram above, it would be unshaded sections to shaded sections to total sections because there are 3 unshaded ones, 5 shaded ones, and 8 sections in total.

NOTES

Remember that equivalent means equal.

There is an infinite number of possible equivalent ratios because you can multiply by *any* number.

As you know from previous years, you are able to write equivalent fractions. You can do the same thing with ratios and write *equivalent ratios.*

To find equivalent ratios, you multiply or divide each term in the ratio by the same number.

Example 1
3:4 is equivalent to 6:8 because
$(3 \times 2):(4 \times 2)$
6:8

The ratio 5:7:11 is equivalent to 10:14:22 because each term is multiplied by 2.
Likewise, 5:7:11 is also equivalent to 15:21:33. Here, each term is multiplied by 3.

The ratio 12 to 16 to 24 is equivalent to 3 to 4 to 6 because each term is divided by 4.
$(12 \div 4)$ to $(16 \div 4)$ to $(24 \div 4)$
3 to 4 to 6

Ratios are usually written in lowest terms. That means you divide each term in the ratio by the same number until there are no common factors left (when you cannot divide any more).

A factor is a number that when multiplied gives you a specific product.

Example 2
The ratio 16:28 in lowest terms is 4:7 because both terms can be divided by 4
$(16 \div 4):(28 \div 4)$
4:7

Another way to show this is to write the ratio as a fraction, list the factors of both the numerator and denominator, then remove the common ones:

$$\frac{16}{28} = \frac{2 \times 2 \times \cancel{2}^{1} \times \cancel{2}^{1}}{\cancel{2}_{1} \times \cancel{2}_{1} \times 7} = \frac{2 \times 2}{7} = \frac{4}{7} = 4:7.$$

Example 3
There are 12 boys in a class and 14 girls.
The ratio of boys to girls in the class is 12:14. In lowest terms, the ratio is 6:7 because you can divide each term by 2.
The ratio of girls to all students, in lowest terms, is 7:13 (write the ratio as 14:26 then divide by 2).

PRACTICE EXERCISE

1. In a box, there are 4 red marbles, 3 yellow marbles, and 7 green marbles. Write ratios for each of the following combinations of marbles in two different ways (using a colon (:) and the word to).

   a) red marbles to yellow marbles

   b) green marbles to red marbles

   c) yellow marbles to green marbles to all marbles

2. For each ratio given below, write two equivalent ratios.

   a) 8 to 9

   b) 2:11

   c) 2:8:16

3. Write the following ratios in lowest terms.

   a) 36:12

   b) 28:77

   c) 13 to 26 to 52

4. In a particular Grade 8 class, 10 students have blue eyes, 8 have green eyes, 4 have brown eyes, and 1 has hazel eyes.

   a) Write the ratio of students with blue eyes to students with brown eyes. Then write the ratio in lowest terms.

   b) Write the ratio of students with green eyes to students with hazel eyes to all students. Then write the ratio in lowest terms.

   c) Write the ratio of students with brown eyes to students with blue eyes to students whose eyes are not hazel. Then write the ratio in lowest terms.

   d) If the class doubled in size, how many students would you expect to have brown eyes?

Lesson 5 PERCENTAGE

A percentage is a fraction with a denominator of 100.

This is easy to remember by breaking the word *percentage* into two parts. *per* meaning "out of," and *cent* meaning "100."

Percentages help to visualize and compare fractions or decimal numbers. They show how much out of a whole is represented.

The symbol for percentage is the % sign. This is always placed after the number.

When given a fraction where the denominator is 100, the numerator is the percentage. Rewrite that number with the % sign after it.

Example 1

i) $\dfrac{23}{100} = 23\%$

Solution

In a diagram, this could be shown as follows:

ii) $\dfrac{142}{100} = 142\%$

Solution

Here, the percentage is greater than 100, which is acceptable. This is because there is an improper fraction where the numerator is greater than the denominator. As long as the denominator is 100, the percentage is still the numerator. This could be shown in a diagram as follows:

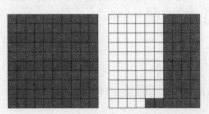

If the fraction does not have a denominator of 100, an equivalent fraction with a denominator of 100 must be made. Then, the numerator will be the percentage.

Example 2

i) $\frac{5}{10}$ is equivalent to $\frac{50}{100}$ because $\frac{5\times10=50}{10\times10=100}$. The denominator is

now 100, so the numerator is the percentage. Therefore $\frac{5}{10}=50\%$

ii) $\frac{17}{25}$ is equivalent to $\frac{68}{100}$ because you multiply both the numerator and

denominator can be multiplied by 4 to get an equivalent fraction with a
denominator of 100.

Therefore $\frac{17}{25}=\frac{17\times4}{25\times4}=\frac{68}{100}=68\%$

If the fraction has a denominator that is not a factor of 100, you need to
turn the fraction into a decimal number and find the percentage by
multiplying the decimal number by 100.

Example 3

i) Write $\frac{5}{8}$ as a percentage.

Solution

There is no whole number that 8 can be multiplied by to get 100;
therefore, turn this fraction into a decimal and multiply by 100.

$$
\begin{array}{r}
.625 \\
8{\overline{\smash{\big)}\,5.000}} \\
\underline{4\,8} \\
20 \\
\underline{16} \\
40 \\
\underline{40} \\
0
\end{array}
$$

To find the decimal equivalent, divide 5 by 8 to get the decimal 0.625.
To convert a decimal into a percentage, multiply by 100 and add the %
sign. So $0.625\times100=62.5$, which is 62.5%.

Therefore $\frac{5}{8}=62.5\%$

ii) Write $\frac{63}{75}$ as a percentage.

Solution

To do this, divide the numerator by the denominator, and then multiply
by 100.

$63\div75=0.84$

$0.84\times100=84\%$

Multiplying by 100 is the
same as moving a decimal
two places to the right.

NOTES

To convert a decimal to a percent, multiply by 100.

To convert a fraction to a percentage, divide numerator by denominator, then multiply the answer by 100.

To convert a ratio to a percent, divide the first number by the last number then multiply the answer by 100.

Percentages can also be calculated from two-term ratios in one of two ways:

1) Write an equivalent ratio with the second term 100, then the first term becomes the percentage.

2) Divide the first term by the second term and multiply the decimal number by 100.

Example 4

Show how to find 46:50 as a percentage two different ways.

Solution

1) 46:50 is equivalent to 92:100 because $(46 \times 2 = 92$ and $50 \times 2 = 100)$ so the first term, 92, is the percentage.

2) $46 \div 50 = 0.92 \times 100 = 92\%$

When comparing fractions, ratios, and decimal numbers, it is easiest to convert them all into percentage. The larger number is the larger percentage because it shows more parts out of 100.

Example 5

Order the following numbers from largest to smallest.

63%, 0.27, $\dfrac{41}{50}$, and 11:25

Solution

Convert all numbers into percentages:

63% = already a percentage

$0.27 \times 100 = 27\%$

$\dfrac{41}{50} = \dfrac{82}{100} = 82\%$

$11:25 = 44:100 = 44\%$

Now, put the percentages in order from largest to smallest.

82%, 63%, 44%, 27%

So the numbers in order from smallest to largest are

$\dfrac{41}{50}$, 63%, 11:25, 0.27

Percentages can also be used to solve problems:

Example 6

In his sock drawer, 55% of Jason's socks are black. His brother Rob has 20 pairs of socks, and 13 of those pairs are black. If Jason and Rob each have 20 pairs of socks, who has more black ones?

Solution

Jason = 55%

Rob = 13:20 black ones = 65:100 black (multiply both terms by 5) = 65%

Rob has more black socks than Jason because his percentage of black socks is higher.

PRACTICE EXERCISE

1. What percentage of each diagram is shaded?

   a)

   b)

   c)

2. Write each number below as a percentage.

   a) $\dfrac{32}{100}$ b) $\dfrac{76}{100}$ c) $\dfrac{16}{20}$

   d) $\dfrac{4}{10}$ e) $\dfrac{23}{25}$ f) $\dfrac{52}{50}$

   g) $\dfrac{4}{5}$ h) $\dfrac{3}{2}$ i) 0.59

   j) 0.125   k) 1.13   l) 0.07

3. Complete the table below(make sure all fractions and ratios are written in lowest terms).

Fraction	Ratio	Decimal	Percent
	1:4		
			100%
$1\dfrac{2}{10}$			
		0.45	
	5:8		

4. Order the following sets of numbers from smallest to largest.

   a) 0.425 $\dfrac{7}{10}$ 39%   39:50

   b) 0.125 $\dfrac{1}{5}$ 0.5%   2:25

5. Greg had 3 nickels, 2 quarters, and 5 pennies in his pocket.
   a) What percentage of his coins were nickels?

   b) What percentage of his coins were not quarters?

   c) What percentage of a dollar did he have in his pocket?

6. There are 4 vowels and 6 consonants in the word PERCENTAGE.
   a) What percentage of the letters are vowels?

   b) What percentage of letters are Es?

Lesson 6 SQUARE ROOT

The square root of a number is a number that when multiplied by itself gives you the original number.

The symbol showing square root is $\sqrt{}$.

$\sqrt{}$ is known as the radical sign.

$\sqrt{36}$ means find what number that when multiplied by itself gives you 36. Here, the answer is 6 because $6 \times 6 = 36$.

$\sqrt{121} = 11$ because $11 \times 11 = 121$

Any number that has a square root that is a whole number is called a perfect square.

A whole number is 0, 1, 2, 3, 4, 5 . . .

The first 15 perfect squares are

1 because $1 \times 1 = 1$
4 because $2 \times 2 = 4$
9 because $3 \times 3 = 9$
16 because $4 \times 4 = 16$
25 because $5 \times 5 = 25$
36 because $6 \times 6 = 36$
49 because $7 \times 7 = 49$
64 because $8 \times 8 = 64$
81 because $9 \times 9 = 81$
100 because $10 \times 10 = 100$
121 because $11 \times 11 = 121$
144 because $12 \times 12 = 144$
169 because $13 \times 13 = 169$
196 because $14 \times 14 = 196$
225 because $15 \times 15 = 225$

Knowing the perfect squares helps you estimate square roots. Perfect squares can be visualized with a square where each side length is the square root, and the perfect square is the area.

NOTES

$A = 36 \text{ m}^2$ $l = 6$ m

$w = 6$ m

$A = 81 \text{ cm}^2$ $l = 9$ cm

$w = 9$ cm

Example 1

Find the approximate square root of 52.

Find $\sqrt{52}$

Solution

Since there is no whole number that when multiplied by itself gives you 52, you need to estimate.

You know that $\sqrt{49} = 7$ because $7 \times 7 = 49$, and you know that $\sqrt{64} = 8$ because $8 \times 8 = 64$.

Since 52 is in between 49 and 64, its square root is between 7 and 8. Since 52 is a little closer to 49 than 64, you know that the decimal number will be less than 5 (half), so you can estimate that the decimal number is around 2 or 3.

Therefore you can estimate that $\sqrt{52}$ = around 7.2 or 7.3

The actual square root of 52 given by a calculator is 7.211 102 551.

Example 2

Estimate $\sqrt{110}$.

Solution

110 is not a perfect square.

The closest perfect squares are 100 and 121, which have square roots of 10 and 11 respectively. Since 110 is almost exactly half way between each of these, you know that the square root of 110 will be almost exactly between 10 and 11. A good estimate for $\sqrt{110}$ is 10.5

The actual square root on a calculator is 10.488 088 48.

32

Each calculator is different, so you need to determine how yours works to calculate square roots. Generally, it will be in one of two ways.

1) Type the number, press the $\sqrt{}$ sign.

2) Press the $\sqrt{}$ sign, type the number, then press =.

NOTES

On some calculators, you will need to use the second function or the shift key to bring up the $\sqrt{}$.

Example 3

On your calculator, find $\sqrt{21}$.

Solution

Method 1: type 2, type 1, then press $\sqrt{}$

Method 2: press $\sqrt{}$, type 2, type 1, then press =

This will give you an answer of 4.582 575 695

The square root of a number with a decimal that does not terminate is an irrational number. The digits after the decimal place will go on forever even though your calculator usually shows 8 or 9 places. A question involving square roots will generally tell what decimal place to round to.

Example 4

Using a calculator, find $\sqrt{98}$ to the nearest tenth.

Solution

Using either method 1 or 2 (depending on your calculator), you find that $\sqrt{98}$ = 9.899 494 937. The tenths place is one after the decimal, so rounded to the nearest tenth, $\sqrt{98}$ is 9.9

Example 5

Find $\sqrt{175}$ to the nearest hundredth.

Solution

$\sqrt{175}$ = 13.23

To round numbers, look at the value of the digit after the one you want to round to. If the number is 0–4, the digit stays the same. If it is 5–9, it increases by 1.

Using your calculator, you can also find square roots of numbers that contain decimals.

For example $\sqrt{1.9}$ = 1.38 rounded to the nearest hundredth.

Square roots can often be used to find the dimensions of square objects.

NOTES

Example 6

The area of a square field is 169 m². How long is each side?

Solution

Because you know the field is square, you know each side must be the same length. Sometimes it is easiest to draw a diagram to help you see this.

$$A = l \times w$$

l

w

You know the formula for area is length times width ($A = l \times w$) and l and w must be the same number.

You need to determine what number multiplied by itself gives you 169. In other words, you need to take the square root of 169.

$\sqrt{169} = 13$ so you know that each side is 13 m long since $13 \times 13 = 169$.

Example 7

A square classroom is 49 m². What is its perimeter?

Solution

Just like in the previous example, you need to find $\sqrt{49}$ to see how long each side is. $\sqrt{49} = 7$ so, each side is 7 m long.

Perimeter is the distance around the outside of an object. Since each side is 7 m, and a square has 4 sides, the perimeter is 7 m + 7 m + 7 m + 7 m. The perimeter of the classroom is 28 m.

PRACTICE EXERCISE

1. Find the following square roots.

   a) $\sqrt{49}$ **b)** $\sqrt{0.16}$

   c) $\sqrt{1}$ **d)** $\sqrt{196}$

2. Using perfect squares, estimate the following square roots.

   a) $\sqrt{20}$ **b)** $\sqrt{104}$

   c) $\sqrt{66}$ **d)** $\sqrt{171}$

3. Use your calculator to find the following square roots. Round to the nearest hundredth.

   a) $\sqrt{11}$ **b)** $\sqrt{119}$

   c) $\sqrt{54}$ **d)** $\sqrt{213}$

4. A square wrestling mat is 64 m². What is its length?

5. Farmer Bill wants to split his square field into 9 identical smaller squares.

   If the 9 fields have a combined area of 144 km²,
   a) what is the area of each smaller section?

   b) what are the dimensions of each smaller section?

PRACTICE QUIZ 1

1. Write each number below in standard form.

   a) 3^4

   b) 8^0

   c) 10^{-3}

   d) 10^{-5}

   e) 2.79×10^6

   f) 5.8×10^{-2}

2. Write each number below in scientific notation.

   a) 4 420

   b) 0.000 000 723

3. Write an equivalent fraction for each number below.

   a) $\dfrac{5}{12}$

   b) $2\dfrac{2}{3}$

   c) 0.49

   d) 8

4. Fill in the blank with <, >, or = to make each statement true.

   a) $1\dfrac{7}{8}$ _____ $1\dfrac{5}{6}$

   b) -0.547 _____ -0.574

5. Use the following diagram to answer the questions below.

Write the ratio of:

a) ☆ to ♡

b) 😊 to all pictures

c) 😊 and ♡ to ☆

d) ⚡ to 😊

6. A volleyball team has a ratio of 2 setters to 12 other players.

    a) What is the ratio of setters to other players, in lowest form?

    b) If two players (not setters) got sick and had to sit out a game, what is the new ratio of setters to players?

    c) If the team doubled in size, how many setters would there be?

7. Fill in the chart below.

Fraction	Ratio	Decimal	Percent
			80%
$\frac{3}{2}$			
	3:8		
		0.44	

8. Arrange the numbers below in order from smallest to largest.

$\frac{2}{3}$ 0.42   18%   9:10

9. Estimate the square roots below.

a) $\sqrt{81}$

b) $\sqrt{1.44}$

c) $\sqrt{76}$

d) $\sqrt{129}$

10. Use a calculator to find each square root below, to the nearest tenth.

a) $\sqrt{225}$

b) $\sqrt{45}$

c) $\sqrt{98}$

d) $\sqrt{3}$

11. On Old MacDonald's farm, there are 28 chickens, 36 cows, 24 horses, and 12 pigs.

a) What is the ratio of cows to pigs?

b) What is the ratio of chickens and cows to horses and pigs?

c) What percentage of the animals are horses?

d) What percent of the animals are not chickens?

Lesson 7   OPERATIONS WITH FRACTIONS

Just like whole numbers or integers, fractions can be added, subtracted, multiplied, or divided.

TO ADD OR SUBTRACT FRACTIONS

Step 1

Change any mixed numbers to improper fractions.

Step 2

Find the lowest common denominator of the fractions and write new fractions with that denominator.

Step 3

Add or subtract the numerators of the fractions, depending on the operation given, while keeping the denominators the same.

Step 4

Put the fraction in lowest terms, changing any improper fractions to mixed numbers.

Example 1

$$\frac{4}{9} + \frac{2}{9} =$$

Solution

Step 1

There are no mixed numbers to change into improper fractions.

Step 2

Both fractions already have a common denominator of 9, so they do not need to be changed.

Step 3

$4 + 2 = 6$ will be the numerator; the denominator will stay 9. The new fraction is $\frac{6}{9}$

Step 4

$\frac{6}{9}$ can be reduced by dividing both the numerator and denominator by 3.

$$\frac{6 \div 3}{9 \div 3} = \frac{2}{3}$$

So $\dfrac{4}{9} + \dfrac{2}{9} = \dfrac{2}{3}$

This is easy to visualize because if you have $\dfrac{4}{9}$ of something and then add 2 more 9^{ths} of something, there will be six 9^{ths} all together.

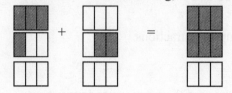

Example 2

$\dfrac{2}{3} + \dfrac{1}{4} =$

Solution

Step 1

There are no mixed numbers to change into improper fractions.

Step 2

The denominators are different. To find the lowest common denominator write the multiples of each denominator until you find the smallest that is in both lists.

3: 3, 6, 9, **12**, 15

4: 4, 8, **12**, 16

The common denominator is 12. Write equivalent fractions for each so both fractions have a denominator of 12.

$\dfrac{2 \times 4}{3 \times 4} + \dfrac{1 \times 3}{4 \times 3} = \dfrac{8}{12} + \dfrac{3}{12}$

Step 3

$8 + 3 = 11$ will be the numerator, the denominator will stay 12. The new fraction is

$\dfrac{11}{12}$

Step 4

$\dfrac{11}{12}$ can not be reduced. There is nothing that divides evenly into both the numerator and the denominator.

$\dfrac{2}{3} + \dfrac{1}{4} = \dfrac{11}{12}$

Example 3

$$2\frac{1}{6}+3\frac{3}{4}=$$

Solution

Step 1

Change the mixed numbers into improper fractions

$$2\frac{1}{6}=\frac{2\times6+1}{6}=\frac{13}{6} \qquad 3\frac{3}{4}=\frac{3\times4+3}{4}=\frac{15}{4}$$

Step 2

The denominators are different. To find the lowest common denominator write the multiples of each denominator until you find the smallest that is in both lists.

6: 6, **12**, 18, 24, 30
4: 4, 8, **12**, 16, 20, 24, 28

The common denominator is 12. Now write equivalent fractions for each so that both fractions have a denominator of 12.

$$\frac{13\times2}{6\times2}+\frac{15\times3}{4\times3}=\frac{26}{12}+\frac{45}{12}$$

Step 3

$26 + 45 = 71$ will be the numerator, the denominator will stay

12. The new fraction is $\frac{71}{12}$

Step 4

$\frac{71}{12}$ can be reduced, and made into a mixed number. To make a the

mixed number, find how many full times 12 goes into 71. 12 goes into 71 5 times, so that will be the whole number out in front.
Now $5 \times 12 = 60$, and $71 - 60 = 11$. So, 11 is the left over, which

becomes the new denominator. So $\frac{71}{12}=5\frac{11}{12}$.

So $2\frac{1}{6}+3\frac{3}{4}=5\frac{11}{12}$

To subtract fractions, you do the same thing except subtract the numerators in step 3 instead of adding them.

When putting mixed numbers into lowest terms, the whole number never changes.

NOTES

Example 4

$$\frac{3}{4} - \frac{1}{4} =$$

Solution

Step 1

There are no mixed numbers to change into improper fractions.

Step 2

Both fractions already have a common denominator of 4, so they do not need to be changed.

Step 3

$4 - 2 = 2$ will be the numerator, the denominator will stay 4. The new fraction is $\frac{2}{4}$.

Step 4

$\frac{2}{4}$ can be reduced by dividing both the numerator and denominator by 2.

$$\frac{2 \div 2}{4 \div 2} = \frac{1}{2}$$

So $\frac{3}{4} - \frac{1}{4} = \frac{1}{2}$

This is easy to see because if you have $\frac{3}{4}$ of something and take away $\frac{1}{4}$ of it, you are left with $\frac{2}{4}$ or $\frac{1}{2}$ of it.

 – =

Example 5

$$4\frac{3}{10} - 1\frac{1}{5} =$$

Solution

Step 1

Change the mixed numbers into improper fractions.

$$4\frac{3}{10} = \frac{43}{10} \qquad\qquad 1\frac{1}{5} = \frac{6}{5}$$

Step 2

The denominators are different. Find the lowest common denominator, which is 10. Write equivalent fractions for each so that both fractions have a denominator of 10.

$$\frac{43}{10} - \frac{6}{5} = \frac{43}{10} - \frac{12}{10}$$

Step 3

$43 - 12 = 31$ will be the numerator, the denominator will stay 10.

Step 4

$\frac{31}{10}$ can be reduced, and made into a mixed number.

$$\frac{31}{10} = 3\frac{1}{10}$$

So $4\frac{3}{10} - 1\frac{1}{5} = 3\frac{1}{10}$

TO MULTIPLY FRACTIONS

Step 1

Change any mixed numbers to improper fractions.

Step 2

Multiply numerator by numerator, and denominator by denominator.

Step 3

Put the fraction in lowest terms, change any improper fractions into mixed numbers.

You do not need common denominators to multiply fractions.

Example 1

$\frac{1}{2} \times \frac{3}{4} =$

Solution

Step 1

There are no mixed numbers to change into improper fractions.

Step 2

$\frac{1}{2} \times \frac{3}{4} = \frac{1 \times 3}{2 \times 4} = \frac{3}{8}$

NOTES

Step 3

$\frac{3}{8}$ is already in lowest terms.

$$\frac{1}{2} \times \frac{3}{4} = \frac{3}{8}$$

Example 2

$$4\frac{2}{3} \times 2\frac{4}{7} =$$

Solution

Step 1

Change the mixed numbers into improper fractions.

$$4\frac{2}{3} = \frac{14}{3} \qquad\qquad 2\frac{4}{7} = \frac{18}{7}$$

Step 2

$$\frac{14}{3} \times \frac{18}{7} = \frac{14 \times 18}{3 \times 7} = \frac{252}{21}$$

Step 3

$\frac{252}{21}$ can be reduced, and made into a mixed number.

$$\frac{252}{21} = 12\frac{0}{21} = 12$$

So $4\frac{2}{3} \times 2\frac{4}{7} = 12$

Remember "of" in math implies multiply.

Example 3

$\frac{1}{4}$ of 7

Solution

So $\frac{1}{4}$ of $7 = \frac{1}{4} \times 7$

To answer this question, you need two fractions to multiply. Make 7 into a fraction by putting it over 1.

You can make any whole number into a fraction by writing it with a denominator of 1.

So $\frac{1}{4} \times \frac{7}{1} = \frac{1 \times 7}{4 \times 1} = \frac{7}{4}$

$\frac{7}{4}$ converted into a mixed number is $1\frac{3}{4}$

So $\frac{1}{4}$ of $7 = 1\frac{3}{4}$

44

Example 4

i) $\dfrac{5}{7} \times \dfrac{7}{5} = \dfrac{35}{35} = \dfrac{1}{1} = 1$

ii) $\dfrac{1}{3} \times \dfrac{3}{1} = \dfrac{3}{3} = \dfrac{1}{1} = 1$

As shown example 4, when multiplying a fraction by a fraction where the numerator and denominator are switched, the answer is always equal to 1. These are called reciprocals. Reciprocals always have a product of 1.

The product of reciprocals = 1.

To write the reciprocal of a fraction, write a new fraction with the denominator becoming the numerator and the numerator becoming the denominator.

Example 5

i) The reciprocal of $\dfrac{2}{3}$ is $\dfrac{3}{2}$

ii) The reciprocal of $\dfrac{8}{5}$ is $\dfrac{5}{8}$

A mixed number must be written as an improper fraction before you can write the reciprocal.

Example 6

i) $1\dfrac{4}{7}$ becomes $\dfrac{11}{7}$ and the reciprocal is $\dfrac{7}{11}$.

ii) The reciprocal of $2\dfrac{5}{9}$ is $\dfrac{9}{23}$.

iii) The reciprocal of 2 is $\dfrac{1}{2}$ because 2 written as a fraction is $\dfrac{2}{1}$ and you

reverse numerator and denominator to get $\dfrac{1}{2}$.

TO DIVIDE FRACTIONS

Step 1

Change any mixed numbers to improper fractions.

Step 2

Find the reciprocal of the fraction to the right of the ÷ sign. Do this by reversing the numerator and the denominator.

NOTES

Step 3

Rewrite the question by changing the ÷ sign to a ×.

Step 4

Multiply the fractions, and then put the product in lowest terms. Change any improper fractions to mixed numbers.

Example 1

$$\frac{2}{5} \div \frac{1}{4} =$$

Solution
Step 1

There are no mixed numbers to change into improper fractions.

Step 2

The reciprocal of $\frac{1}{4}$ is $\frac{4}{1}$

Step 3

Change the question from $\frac{2}{5} \div \frac{1}{4}$ to $\frac{2}{5} \times \frac{4}{1}$.

Step 4

Multiply $\frac{2}{5} \times \frac{4}{1} = \frac{8}{5} = 1\frac{3}{5}$

So $\frac{2}{5} \div \frac{1}{4} = 1\frac{3}{5}$

Only find the reciprocal of the second fraction. The first always stays the same.

Example 2

$$\frac{7}{8} \div 1\frac{1}{6} =$$

Solution
Step 1

Change $1\frac{1}{6}$ to $\frac{7}{6}$.

Step 2

The reciprocal of $\frac{7}{6}$ is $\frac{6}{7}$

Step 3

Change the question from $\frac{7}{8} \div 1\frac{1}{6}$ to $\frac{7}{8} \times \frac{6}{7}$.

Step 4

Multiply $\dfrac{7}{8} \times \dfrac{6}{7} = \dfrac{42}{56} = \dfrac{3}{4}$

So $\dfrac{7}{8} \div 1\dfrac{1}{6} = \dfrac{3}{4}$

Example 3

$3\dfrac{4}{9} \div 2 =$

Solution

Step 1

Change $3\dfrac{4}{9}$ to $\dfrac{31}{9}$.

Step 2

The reciprocal of 2 is $\dfrac{1}{2}$ because 2 is equivalent to 2 over 1.

Step 3

Change the question from $3\dfrac{4}{9} \div 2$ to $\dfrac{31}{9} \times \dfrac{1}{2}$.

Step 4

Multiply $\dfrac{31}{9} \times \dfrac{1}{2} = \dfrac{31}{18} = 1\dfrac{13}{18}$

So $3\dfrac{4}{9} \div 2 = 1\dfrac{13}{18}$

When working with fractions, questions are often given as word problems. To solve the word problems, carefully read the question and underline the key words that will tell you what operation to perform.

KEY WORDS TO LOOK FOR

Add—sum, total, all together, more than
Subtract—difference, less than, take away, taken from
Multiply—"of," times, product
Divide—quotient, times greater or times less than, groups

NOTES

Example 1

Mandy is at the beach, making sandcastles. If each tower on the castle takes $\dfrac{2}{3}$ of a bucket of sand to make, how many buckets will Mandy need for 4 towers?

Solution

You know that each tower takes $\dfrac{2}{3}$ and there are 4 towers. To solve this question, use multiplication.

$$\frac{2}{3} \times 4 = \frac{2}{3} \times \frac{4}{1} = \frac{8}{3} = 2\frac{2}{3}$$

Mandy will use $2\dfrac{2}{3}$ buckets of sand to make the towers for her castle.

$\dfrac{2}{3}$ of means to multiply.

Example 2

Carmen is moving. On Monday, she packed $\dfrac{1}{8}$ of the dishes in her kitchen. On Tuesday she packed $\dfrac{1}{4}$ of the dishes. How many has she packed all together? How many does she have left to pack?

Solution

You know that Carmen has packed $\dfrac{1}{8}$ and $\dfrac{1}{4}$. Add these to see what she has packed all together.

$$\frac{1}{8} + \frac{1}{4} = \frac{1}{8} + \frac{2}{8} = \frac{3}{8}$$

Carmen has packed $\dfrac{3}{8}$ of the dishes.

To figure out how much she has left, subtract the $\dfrac{3}{8}$ from 1 because 1 would be all the dishes in the kitchen.

$$1 - \frac{3}{8} = \frac{1}{1} - \frac{3}{8} = \frac{8}{8} - \frac{3}{8} = \frac{5}{8}$$

Carmen still has $\dfrac{5}{8}$ of her dishes left to pack.

PRACTICE EXERCISE

1. Draw a diagram to show the following addition or subtraction statements.

   a) $\dfrac{2}{6} + \dfrac{3}{6} = \dfrac{5}{6}$

   b) $\dfrac{7}{9} - \dfrac{2}{9} = \dfrac{5}{9}$

2. Write the addition statement represented by the following diagram.

    $+$ $=$

3. Add the following fractions.

   a) $\dfrac{1}{2} + \dfrac{2}{2} =$ **b)** $\dfrac{9}{10} + \dfrac{3}{4} =$

   c) $6\dfrac{4}{5} + 2\dfrac{4}{3} =$ **d)** $3 + 4\dfrac{1}{2} =$

4. Subtract the following fractions.

   a) $\dfrac{6}{7} - \dfrac{2}{7} =$ **b)** $\dfrac{3}{5} - \dfrac{4}{10} =$

c) $7\dfrac{1}{6} - \dfrac{3}{8} =$

d) $3\dfrac{1}{3} - 2\dfrac{1}{8} =$

5. Multiply the following fractions.

a) $\dfrac{2}{3} \times \dfrac{1}{5} =$

b) $3\dfrac{1}{8} \times \dfrac{4}{6} =$

c) $\dfrac{1}{3}$ of $\dfrac{12}{15} =$

d) $\dfrac{11}{20}$ of $4 =$

6. Write the reciprocals of the following numbers.

a) $\dfrac{2}{5}$

b) $\dfrac{13}{25}$

c) $\dfrac{1}{6}$

d) $2\dfrac{7}{8}$

e) 5

7. Divide the following fractions.

a) $\dfrac{2}{7} \div \dfrac{5}{6} =$

b) $\dfrac{7}{10} \div 3 =$

c) $4 \div \dfrac{5}{8} =$

d) $8\dfrac{2}{3} \div 5\dfrac{1}{4} =$

8. Solve the following problems.

a) Elizabeth uses $2\frac{3}{4}$ cups of flour in waffle batter. If she wants to triple the recipe, how much flour will she need?

b) Melissa uses $\frac{1}{16}$ of a tank of gas to travel to and from her brother's house. If she sees him 7 times in a month, how much gas does she use? If the gas tank holds 40 L of gas, how many litres did she use?

c) Eric wants to split his garden into 5 equal sections. If his garden is $7\frac{5}{8}$ m^2, how big will each new section be?

d) Frank raked $\frac{2}{3}$ of the lawn yesterday and $\frac{1}{6}$ of it the day before. How much more does he have to do today to finish off the whole yard?

Lesson 8 OPERATIONS WITH RATIONAL NUMBERS

When working with positive and negative decimal numbers, the same integer rules from Grade 7 apply.

ADDING

Add the numbers using the rules for adding integers.
- If the signs are the same, add the numbers, keeping the sign of the original numbers.
- If the signs are different, ignore the signs, and subtract the small number from the large number.

Remember when adding or subtracting numbers with decimals, you must line up the decimals.

The sign of the answer will be as follows:
- If the numbers are both positive, the answer will be positive.
- If the numbers are both negative, the answer will be negative.
- If there is one positive and one negative number, the sign in the answer will be the same as the one with a higher magnitude (higher number).

Magnitude is the number with no sign.

Example 1

$-7 + 3 =$

Solution

Here, there is one positive number and one negative number. The magnitude of the negative number is larger (7 is greater than 3) so the answer will be negative.

Because the signs of the numbers are different, subtract the numbers. Take 3 away from 7 to get 4. The answer is –4.

To see this on a number line, start at 0 on a number line, and then go left to –7. From there go 3 places to the right and the result is –4.

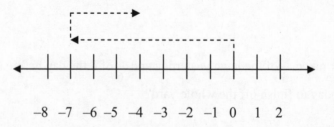

To solve any problems involving positive and negative decimal numbers, it is always a good idea to estimate your answer first and then solve. To do this, round each number to the nearest integer and perform the given operation.

Example 2

$-10.3 + 6.42 =$

Solution

Estimate:

$-10 + 6 = -4$

This works the same way as example 1. The signs are different with each integer. The larger magnitude belongs to the negative number, so the answer will be negative. Now subtract the numbers to get the result. Do not forget to line up the decimals when subtracting. You will need to add a 0 behind the 3 so you can subtract.

$$\begin{array}{r} 10.30 \\ -6.42 \\ \hline 3.88 \end{array}$$

The magnitude of the number is 3.88 and the sign will be negative, so the answer is −3.88.

Example 3

$-4.21 + (-6.9) =$

Solution

Estimate:

$-4 + (-7) = -11$

Here, both numbers are negative, so the answer will be a negative. Because both signs are the same, add the numbers together to get the answer.

$$\begin{array}{r} 4.21 \\ +6.90 \\ \hline 11.11 \end{array}$$

The magnitude of the numbers is 11.11 and the sign will be negative, so the answer is −11.11.

Opposite integers have the same magnitude, but different signs.

SUBTRACTING

Remember that you never actually subtract the numbers, but instead, always *add the opposite*. Remember this means change the minus sign to addition, then change the sign of the second number to its opposite, then add using the integer rules.

Remember to change only the sign of the second number.

Example 1

$-6.99 - 3.44 =$

$-6.99 + (-3.44) =$

Solution

Estimate

$-7 + (-3) = -10$

Now the signs are both negative, so add the number part and the answers will be negative.

6.99

+3.44

10.43

So $-6.99 - (3.44) = -10.43$

Example 2

$-1.13 - (-18.4) =$

$-1.13 + (^+18.4) =$

Solution

Estimate

$-1 + 18 = 17$

There are different signs, so subtract the numbers. The answer will be positive because 18.4 has a larger magnitude.

18.40

−1.13

17.27

So $-1.13 - (-18.4) = +17.27$

Example 3

$4.3 - 9.7 =$

$4.3 + (-9.7) =$

Solution

Estimate

$4 + -10 = -6$

There are different signs, so subtract the numbers. The answer will be negative because 9.7 has a larger magnitude.

9.7

−4.3

5.4

So $4.3 - 9.7 = -5.4$

MULTIPLYING

To solve questions involving multiplication, just multiply the numbers and give the answer the correct sign.

The sign of the answer will be as follows:

- If there are an ODD number of negative signs, the answer will be negative.
- If there are an EVEN number of negative signs, the answer will be positive.

If the number is positive, you do not need to write the + sign with the number.

Example 1

$(-4.6) \times (-3.2) =$

Solution

Estimate

$(-5) \times (-3) = 15$

The answer will be positive because there are an even number of negative signs.

$4.6 \times 3.2 = 14.72$

So $(-4.6) \times (-3.2) = (+14.72)$ or 14.72

Example 2

$5.83 \times (-1.9) =$

Solution

Estimate

$6 \times (-2) = -12$

The answer will be negative because there is one positive sign and one negative sign (can odd number of negative signs).

$5.83 \times 1.9 = 11.077$

So $5.83 \times (-1.9) = -11.077$

Example 3

$(-7.2) \times 0.4 =$

Solution

Estimate

$-7 \times 0.5 = -3.5$

The answer will be negative because there is one positive sign and one negative sign.

$7.2 \times 0.4 = 2.88$

So $-7.2 \times 0.4 = -2.88$

DIVIDING

To solve questions involving division, divide the numbers and give the answer the correct sign.

The sign of the answer will be as follows:

• If there are an ODD number of negative signs, the answer will be negative.

• If there are an EVEN number of negative signs, the answer will be positive.

Remember a line above a number indicates that it is a repeating number.

Example 1

$5.76 \div 9 =$

Solution

Estimate

$6 \div 9 = 0.\overline{6}$

Both signs are positive, so the answer will be positive.

$5.76 \div 9 = 0.64$

So $5.76 \div 9 = 0.64$

Example 2

$-18.2 \div (-0.7) =$

Solution

Estimate

$-18 \div (-1) = 18$

Both signs are negative (an even number) so the answer will be positive.

$18.2 \div 0.7 = 26$

So $-18.2 \div (-0.7) = 26$

Example 3

$-3.74 \div 0.22 =$

Solution

Estimate

$-4 \div 0.2 = -20$

Both signs are different (an odd number of negative signs) so the answer will be negative.

$3.74 \div 0.22 = 17$

So $-3.74 \div 0.22 = -17$

To solve all these types of problems on a calculator, use the operation buttons +, −, ×, and ÷. You also need to use the negative button. Depending on your specific calculator, there are many different ways this can be done. Generally you will either push the negative button first and then the number, or push the number first and then the negative button, then the operation and the next number. Consult your instructions on how to use your calculator if you are unsure.

Operations with rational numbers are frequently used in problem-solving questions.

Example 1

A submarine is put into the water and descends to a depth of –19.4 m. If it rises 7.2 m, what is its new depth?

Solution

The submarine is at a depth of –19.4 m. The word *rises* indicates to add a positive number to the depth that was given. Set up the addition statement and solve.

$-19.4 + 7.2 = -12.2$

The submarine is now at a depth of –12.2 m.

Example 2

The temperature outside is – 4°C. If it drops 1.2 degrees per hour, what is the new temperature after 7 hours?

Solution

This problem has two parts.

Part 1: Figure out how much the temperature is dropping. You know it is 1.2 degrees per hour, for 7 hours. Multiply to find the change.

$1.2 \times 7 = 8.4$. This is how many degrees it dropped in 7 hours.

Part 2: The word *drop* indicates to subtract 8.4 degrees from –4. Write the subtraction statement and solve.

$-4 - 8.4 =$

$-4 + (-8.4) = -12.4$

The temperature after 7 hours is – 12.4°C.

When solving questions with more than one operation, you must perform the operations in the proper order to get the correct answer. Use BEDMAS to remember this.

BEDMAS stands for bracket first, exponent second, division and multiplication in whatever order they appear in the question, and then addition and subtraction in whatever order they appear in the question. The rules for working with the positive and negative signs still apply.

BEDMAS:
- bracket
- exponent
- division
- multiplication
- addition
- subtraction

Example 1

$12.35 \div 1.3 \times (-2.6)$

Here, we have the operations division and multiplication. Do the division first and then the multiplication after that.

Solution

$12.35 \div 1.3 = 9.5$

After the division, you are left with

$9.5 \times (-2.6)$

-24.7

Do only one step at a time, each on a separate line.

NOTES

Example 2

$-4.7 \times (1.2 + (-7.5))$

Solution

Do the addition in the brackets first.

$-4.7 \times (-6.3) =$

Now multiply

$= 92.61$

PRACTICE EXERCISE

1. Estimate the answers to the following statements.

   a) $4.68 + (-1.2)$

   b) $-81.8 + (-33.47)$

   c) $2.19 - 5.92$

   d) $-0.74 - (-1.3)$

   e) $3.27 \times (-22.4)$

   f) $-10.6 \times (-7.99)$

   g) $-24.5 \div 6.2$

   h) $-9.57 \div (-5.1)$

2. Solve

   a) $3.13 + (-19.16)$

   b) $-4.13 + (-1.56)$

   c) $-1.2 + 3.16$

   d) $1.8 + (-4.3)$

3. Solve

   a) $-6.17 - (-21.4)$

   b) $5.21 - 3.28$

   c) $32.11 - (-4.2)$

   d) $1.719 - 3.287$

4. Solve

   a) $1.19 \times (-2.4)$

   b) $-71.7 \times (-1.1)$

   c) $-25.16 \times (-6.3)$

   d) $3.1 \times (-1.5)$

5. Solve

    a) $-33.58 \div (-4.6)$ **b)** $-19.32 \div 6$

    c) $5.992 \div (-0.7)$ **d)** $-18.5 \div (-0.5)$

6. Solve

    a) $-4.5 \div 0.5 + (-6.2)$ **b)** $7.33 + 2.1 \times (-8.4)$

    c) $(1.2)^2 + (-3.9)$ **d)** $(2.5 + (-9.1)) \times 4.4 - (-1.3)$

7. Solve the following problems.

    a) Matt builds a tower that is 15 building blocks high. If each block is 1.6 cm high, how tall is his tower?

    b) A hot-air balloon is 33.5 m above the ground. If it rises 2.8 m more and then falls 14.6 m, how far above the ground will it be?

Lesson 9 RATIO, RATE, PROPORTION, AND PERCENTAGE

Ratios, rates, proportions, and percentage are all related through equivalent fractions and can be used to solve various problems.

Ratios are comparisons of two or more numbers with the same units. For example, comparing the number of boys with girls in a class is comparing students. Ratios with two terms can also be written in fraction form.

Rates are comparisons of two things with different units. Typing speed is an example of a rate. It compares how many words you can type with the minutes it takes you to type them.

Proportions are two equivalent fractions separated by an equal sign. It shows how two ratios or rates are related.

Percentages are numbers with a denominator of 100.

When working with ratios, rates, proportions, and percentages to solve problems, it is easiest to set up proportions and solve for the missing parts.

Solve for x in the following proportion.

$$\frac{1}{2} = \frac{6}{x}$$

In this fraction, it is easy to see that x will be 12 because the numerator and denominator in the first fraction can be multiplied by 6. If it is not easy to see this by looking, you can always cross-multiply to find the answer.

To cross-multiply, multiply the two numbers that are diagonally across from each other in the fractions and divide by the other number.

So, to cross-multiply $\frac{1}{2} = \frac{6}{x}$

First multiply the two numbers that are diagonally across from each other (the 2 and the 6)

$2 \times 6 = 12$

Second, divide by the other number to find the missing value.

$12 \div 1 = 12$

The value of x is 12.

No matter where the missing part is, proportions can always be solved by cross-multiplying.

$$\frac{p}{12} = \frac{64}{96}$$

The two numbers that are diagonally across from each other are 12 and 64.

$12 \times 64 = 768$

$768 \div 96$ (the other number) $= 8$

So, the value of p is 8.

When working with problem-solving questions involving rates, ratios, and percentages, set up proportions and solve for the missing part.

Example 1

Marvin earns $18 for 3 hours of work. How much will he earn in 5 hours?

Solution

You can solve this two ways.

A unit rate is a rate where the second term has a value of 1.

First, you could find out how much Marvin makes each hour by dividing to find the unit rate. Then multiply that amount by 5 to see how much he makes in 5 hours.

$18 \div 3 = \$6$ per hour

$\$6 \times 5 = \$30$ for 5 hours.

The second way to solve this problem is to set up a proportion and cross-multiply. Always make sure you keep the similar parts in the same places. Here the money is in the numerator of both fractions, and the hours are in the denominator.

$$\frac{\$18}{3\,h} = \frac{x}{5\,h}$$

Multiply the two numbers across from each other, and divide by the other.

$18 \times 5 = 90 \div 3 = 30$

Both ways give the same answer: $30 for working 5 hours.

Example 2

To make 12 cupcakes, Alice needs 132 g of sugar. How much sugar does she need for 8 cupcakes?

Solution

To solve:

$132 \div 12 = 11$ g per cupcake

1 g $\times 8 = 88$ g for 8 cupcakes

or

$$\frac{12 \text{ cupcakes}}{132 \text{ g}} = \frac{8 \text{ cupcakes}}{x \text{ g}}$$

$132 \times 8 = 1\ 056$

$1\ 056 \div 12 = 88$

Alice needs 88 g of sugar for 8 cupcakes.

Example 3

A football team has a record of 5 wins to 4 losses. If their ratio of wins to losses stays the same, then out of 27 games, how many will they win?

Solution

Set up a proportion of numbers of wins (5) to games played ($5 + 4 = 9$).

$$\frac{5 \text{ wins}}{9 \text{ games}} = \frac{w}{27 \text{ games}}$$

$5 \times 27 = 135 \div 9 = 15$

If they play 27 games, the team will win 15.

Example 4

If 20% of a number is 60, what is the number?

Solution

Here you are given 20% of a number and want to find the entire number or 100% of the number. Set up proportions and cross-multiply.

$$\frac{20\%}{60} = \frac{100\%}{n}$$

To solve $100 \times 60 = 6\ 000 \div 20 = 300$

The number is 300.

PRACTICE EXERCISE

1. Write each ratio below in lowest terms.

   a) 25:20

   b) $\dfrac{26}{104}$

   c) 8 to 48

2. Complete each proportion below.

   a) $\dfrac{175}{x} = \dfrac{5}{3}$

   b) $\dfrac{6}{7} = \dfrac{a}{91}$

   c) $24:96 = r:24$

3. Find the missing values.

   a) $\dfrac{48}{j} = \dfrac{4}{1} = \dfrac{g}{7}$

   b) $5:9 = y:36$

4. Solve the problem below. (Make sure that all ratios are placed in lowest terms.)

   a) There are 15 girls and 18 boys in a play. What is the ratio of girls to total cast members?

   b) A dog walker earns $14.25 for 5 hours of work. How much will she earn if she works for 3 hours?

   c) If 6 tickets at Klondike Days cost $9, then how many tickets can you buy for $12?

   d) The ratio of gumballs in a machine is 25 red to 14 green. If there are 3 machines with the same proportions of gumballs, how many green ones are there all together?

64

e) A video store has a ratio of 4:1 for DVDs to VHS tapes. If there are 440 DVDs and VHS tapes in total in the store, how many VHS tapes are there?

f) Bobby is driving on the highway at a constant speed of 95 km per hour. How far will he drive in $6\frac{1}{2}$ hours?

g) In a particular school, 88% of girls in Grade 12 have their ears pierced. If 154 girls have their ears pierced, how many girls are in Grade 12?

h) The ratio of length to width of a picture frame is 3:5. If the actual length of the picture is 12 cm, what is the perimeter of the picture?

i) The human body is made up of 75% water. If the mass of water in Samantha's body is 45 kg, what is her total mass?

Lesson 10 CALCULATING PERCENTAGE

In math, "of" implies multiply.

Percentages can be used to calculate parts of numbers.

To find the percentage of a number, convert the percentage into a decimal by dividing the percentage by 100, then multiply by the given number.

Example 1

What is 20% of 300?

Solution

Find the decimal equivalent of 20%	$20\% \div 100 = 0.20$
Multiply by the given number	$0.20 \times 300 = 60$
Result	20% of 300 is 60

You can check to make sure that this answer is reasonable by doing the following. You know that 20 out of 100 is one-fifth. So, if you take the 300 and divide by 5 you get 60, which is one-fifth of 300.

Example 2

What is 124% of 488?

Solution

$124\% = 1.24$

$1.24 \times 488 = 605.12$

The answer is larger than the original number because the percentage is greater than 100%.

Percentages of numbers are often used to solve a variety of problems. To solve these, carefully read the questions and decide what you are asked to calculate: a percentage of two different numbers or the percentage of a number.

Example 3

A particular movie theatre holds 150 people. After it is renovated, it holds 225 people. By how much has the capacity of the theatre increased?

Solution

To solve this question, find a percentage. Set up a fraction with the new amount over the original. $\dfrac{225}{150}$ and calculate the percentage.

(numerator divided by denominator times 100)

$225 \div 150 = 1.5 \times 100 = 150\%$

The percentage increase for the theatre is 150%. This is because the old capacity (150) represents 100%, but with the addition of 75 seats,

(or 50% more) the new capacity is 150% of the old

(100 from before and 50% more).

Example 4

When Kevin was 4 years old, he was 110 cm tall. When he was 20 years old, he was 185 cm tall. By what percentage did his height increase? (Round to the nearest tenth.)

Solution

Set up a fraction $\dfrac{185}{110}$ and find the percentage.

$185 \div 110 \times 100 = 168.2\%$

Many percentage questions involve working with money involving discounts or sale prices, taxes, and commissions.

DISCOUNTS

When working with discounts, calculate the percentage of a number (the original price) to see how much cheaper something is.

Example 1

Calculate a 15% discount on a $29.00 DVD.

Solution

15% of $29 = 0.15 × $29 = $4.35

The discount on the DVD is $4.35.

To find the *sale or discounted price*, take the discount (that you already calculated) and SUBTRACT that number from the original price.

Calculate the sale price of the DVD.

Original price – discount = sale price

$29.00 – $4.35 = $24.65

The DVD would be $24.65 on sale.

Sometimes more than one increase or discount will be added together.

Example 2

A pair of shoes originally cost $49.95. If it is increased by 15% and then reduced by 15%, will the selling price be the same as the original price?

Solution

Calculate the increase first.

15% of $49.95

0.15 × 49.95 = $7.49

New price = $49.95 + $7.49 = $57.44

NOTES

Calculate the discount second.

15% of $57.44

$0.15 \times 57.44 = \$8.61$

Selling price $57.44 - \$8.61 = \$48.82$

The selling price is different from the original price because even though the price went up 15% and then down 15%, the 15% calculated for the discount is taken of a larger number (the increase) than the original price.

TAXES

To calculate the GST and PST of items, calculate the percentages of numbers using the given amounts.

GST (Goods and Services Tax)

The GST is currently 7% in all provinces in Canada.

Example 1

Calculate the GST on a $95 pair of running shoes, and the total cost after tax is added.

Solution

7% of $95.00 = $0.07 \times 95 = \$6.65$

$95.00 + \$6.65 = \$101.65$

PST (Provincial Sales Tax)

This tax varies in percentage from province to province. When given questions involving PST, the rate of tax will be given.

In most provinces, when you purchase and item, you pay BOTH GST and PST. So, when calculating/estimating the final price, you must add the cost of the GST and the PST to the original price.

Example 2

Calculate final price of a $750.00 couch including GST and PST (8%).

Solution

7% of $750.00 = $0.07 \times 750 = \$52.50$

8% of $750.00 = $0.08 \times 750 = \$60.00$

$750.000 + \$52.50 + \$60.00 = \$862.50$

The GST and PST are calculated from the final selling price, after any discounts have been applied.

COMMISSIONS

Commission is a percentage of money earned by salespeople based on their total amount of sales.

To calculate commission, take the percent of a number. This is the amount of money that the sales person will earn.

Example 1

Gary, a used-car salesman, receives 7.5% commission on all his sales. If Gary sells a truck for $9 000, how much does he get in commission?

Solution

7.5% of $9 000 = 0.075 × 9 000 = $675

Gary earns $675 for selling the truck.

PRACTICE EXERCISE

1. Calculate the percentage of the number. Round to the nearest whole number.
   a) 30% of 45

   b) 110% of 600

   c) 83% of 22

   d) 7.5% of 20

   e) $9\dfrac{1}{2}$% of 38

   f) 140% of 77

2. Fill in the blank with <, >, or = to make each statement true.
   a) 12% of 504 _____ 48% of 93

   b) 30% of 130 _____ 60% of 60

3. Al was at a restaurant and left a tip of 15% of his total bill. If his bill came to $24.32, how much was his tip?

4. Pete and Jeff were at a restaurant and had the exact same meal (including drinks), which cost $17.95 each. If Pete left a tip of 12% and Jeff left a tip of 15%, how much of a tip did they leave all together?

5. A new plasma TV originally cost $2 499. If the sale price is $2 200, what was the percentage of the discount?

6. A shirt costs $28.49. If it is marked 30% off, what is the shirt now selling for?

7. Karen bought a rocking chair for $150. How much GST will she have to pay?

8. A can of shaving cream costs $4.50. What is the total cost if the shaving cream in a province where you pay GST and PST is 6%?

9. Aaron gets 6.5% commission on all musical instruments that he sells. If he sells a violin for $3 400, how much money will Aaron make?

10. A particular house costs $195 000. If Wally, the real estate agent, earns $4 875 for selling this house, what is his rate of commission?

11. A particular computer costs $3 175.
    a) If it is discounted 15%, what is the sale price?
    b) If Lyndsey lives in a province where PST is 8% how much will she pay when all taxes are added to the sale price?
    c) Alex works in the store that sells this computer. If he earns 3% commission on what he sells (amount before taxes), how much money will he make if he sells Lyndsey the computer?

Lesson 11   RATIOS AND RATES

Ratios are comparisons of numbers with the same units; whereas rates are comparisons of numbers with different units.

An example of a problem involving ratios is the ratio of boys to girls in a class. Here, the units are the same because you are comparing students in both cases. Proportions are often used with rates to solve for the missing parts.

An example involving rates is the speed a race car driver can go. This is a rate because you are comparing the distance he drives in a certain amount of time.

Unit rates are special types of rates in which the second term always has a value of 1.

Examples of this would include:
i) Joy can type 35 words in 1 minute. Her rate is 35 words per minute (You do not usually write the 1 in the second term.)

ii) Anita bought one box of tissue for $3.49. The rate would be $3.49 per box.

To make any rate a unit rate, divide both terms by the value of the last term to make it 1.

For example, 8 freezees for 4 students is not a unit rate because the last number is 4 not 1. To write it as a unit rate, divide by the number of students to find the number of freezees per student. The unit rate is 2 freezees per student because both the 8 and the 4 were divided by 4.

Unit rates must always have units at the end.

Example 1

There are 240 crayons in 6 boxes. How many crayons are in one box?

Solution

Step 1

Write this as a rate.

240 crayons : 6 boxes

Step 2

Divide each term by 6 so the last term will be 1.

$(240 \div 6) : (6 \div 6) = 40:1$

Step 3

Write the rate.

There are 40 crayons in 1 box, or 40 crayons/box.

Example 2

Joel can bike 90 km in 5 hours. What is his rate of biking?

Solution

90 km : 5 h

$(90 \div 5):(5 \div 5) = 18:1$

Joel can bike 18 km/h.

Unit rates can also be used to compare prices and find out what is a better deal when buying something.

Example 3

Laundry soap comes in two sizes: $3.27 for 1.7 L or $1.49 for 0.8 L. Which is the better buy?

Solution

To solve this, write the unit rate for each box (price per L) and see which is cheaper.

$3.27:1.7 L

$1.49:0.8 L

$$\frac{3.27}{1.7L} = \frac{?}{1L}$$

$$\frac{1.49}{0.8} = \frac{?}{1L}$$

$1.92:1L (rounded to nearest cent)

$1.86:1L (rounded to nearest cent)

The second box is cheaper (a better buy) because it costs only $1.86/L, while the other box is $1.92/L

Money should always be rounded to the nearest cent.

The $ symbol is always placed in front of the numeric answer.

PRACTICE EXERCISE

1. Write each ratio in lowest terms.

   a) $\dfrac{15}{18}$

   b) $\dfrac{13}{52}$

   c) $\dfrac{66}{154}$

2. Solve the following proportions for the missing part.

   a) $\dfrac{3}{8} = \dfrac{f}{24}$

   b) $\dfrac{39}{k} = \dfrac{156}{144}$

3. Write whether each of the scenarios below describes a rate or a unit rate.
   a) Doug ran 18 laps in 15 minutes.

   b) Kate drove 105 km/h.

   c) There are 24 students in each Grade 8 class.

   d) Ricky scored 150 points in 7 games.

4. Write each scenario below a unit rate.
   a) Phillip can type 102 words in 3 min.

   b) A 10 kg bag of flour costs $4.95.

   c) Grace read 18 pages in 30 min.

5. Use proportions to solve the following rate questions.

a) A new truck can travel 400 km on 30 L of gas. How far can it travel on 1 L of gas? On 50 L of gas?

b) Pam makes $15 in 2 hours for cutting grass. How much does she make each hour? How much would she make in a week when she works 25 hours?

6. Which is a better buy and by how much?

a) 8 movie tickets for $90 or 6 for $75?

b) 5 pounds of apples for $4.99 or 3 pounds for $2.59?

PRACTICE QUIZ 2

1. Solve the following equations.

   a) $\dfrac{3}{5} + \dfrac{1}{4}$

   b) $2\dfrac{5}{6} - 1\dfrac{1}{3}$

   c) $\dfrac{1}{3} \times 2\dfrac{1}{7}$

   d) $1\dfrac{1}{5}$ of 12

   e) $9\dfrac{2}{4} \div \dfrac{5}{7}$

   f) $5\dfrac{3}{7} \div 6$

   g) $1.07 + (-12.9)$

   h) $-4.83 - (-5.96)$

   i) $3.4 \times (-2.6)$

   j) $-6.5 \div (-1.3)$

2. Solve for the missing value in each proportion below.

   a) $\dfrac{3}{4} = \dfrac{t}{72}$

   b) $\dfrac{h}{25} = \dfrac{40}{200}$

   c) $\dfrac{2}{3} = \dfrac{60}{c}$

   d) $\dfrac{86}{w} = \dfrac{15}{30}$

3. Write each fraction as a percent.

   a) $\dfrac{7}{20}$

   b) $\dfrac{10}{16}$

   c) $\dfrac{66}{50}$

   d) $2\dfrac{7}{25}$

4. Calculate the following equations.
   a) 20% of 60

   b) 6.5% of 182

   c) 144% of 13

5. Write the unit rate for each scenario below.

   a) A heart beats 292 times in 4 minutes.

   b) Carl sells 6 vacuums in 2.5 hours.

   c) Which is a better buy: 3 kg of coffee for $2.98 or 7 kg for $6.55? By how much?

   d) Alicia can bike 12 km in half an hour. How long will it take her to go 150 km?

   e) Scott's soccer team has a record of 3 wins to 5 losses to 1 tie. What is the ratio of wins to games played?

   f) One day, Jalene spent $6\frac{3}{8}$ hours painting a fence. The next day, Jalene painted for $2\frac{3}{4}$ hours. How long did Jaylene spend painting all together?

   g) A dresser is on sale for $159. If the original price was $199, what is the rate of discount to the nearest percentage?

   h) Marie works in a clothing store where she earns $3\frac{1}{2}$ % commission on her sales. What does she earn in a week if she sells $800 worth of clothes?

REVIEW SUMMARY

- Decimal numbers and fractions can be written as both positive and negative exponents. The value of the exponent determines how many times the base is multiplied by itself. Negative exponents always represent numbers that have a value less than 1.

- Scientific notation is used to write very large and very small numbers in a shortened form. In scientific notation, a number that is greater than 1 but less than 10 is multiplied by a power of 10.

- A rational number is any number that can be written as a fraction in the form of $\frac{a}{b}$, where the denominator is not zero. These include the whole numbers, integers, and terminating or repeating decimals. To compare rational numbers, write them in equivalent forms such as all decimals or all fractions with common denominators.

- Ratios are comparisons of two or more numbers using a colon or the word *to*. Each part of a ratio is called a term. The order that the terms are written in is important. Ratios can be written in equivalent forms through multiplication or division. They are usually left in lowest terms.

- A percentage is a number with a denominator of 100. It shows how much out of a whole is represented. Percents are an easy way to visualize fractions. Percents can be written from decimal numbers, ratios, or fractions.

- To calculate the percentage of a number, take the percentage, change it into a decimal by dividing by 100, and then multiply by the given value. This is often used to solve a variety of problem-solving questions.

- The square root of a number is a number that when multiplied by itself gives you the original number. You can estimate square roots using perfect squares, or use a calculator to get a good estimation. The square root sign looks like $\sqrt{}$.

- Fractions can be added, subtracted, multiplied, or divided. Adding or subtracting fractions requires common denominators. That way, you can add or subtract the numerators while keeping the denominators the same. Multiplying is numerator by numerator and denominator by denominator. To divide fractions, you take the reciprocal of the second fraction and multiply. Always leave answers in lowest terms, and change improper fractions to a mixed number.

- To add, subtract, multiply, and divide positive and negative decimal numbers, use the rules for working with integers. Remember to line up the decimals when adding or subtracting.

- Cross-multiplying can solve any proportion for a missing value. To do this, multiply the numbers that are diagonally across from each other, and divide by the other number.

- Rates are similar to ratios in that they are a comparison of two things, but rates have different units that must be included in the answer. A unit rate always has a second value of 1. Find a unit rate by dividing the value of the first term by the value of the second term.

PRACTICE TEST

1. Write each number below in standard form.

   a) 4^2 **b)** 7^0

   c) 10^3 **d)** 10^{-4}

   e) 10^{-1} **f)** $\dfrac{1}{10^5}$

   g) 3.45×10^1 **h)** 5.55×10^{-5}

2. Write the following numbers in scientific notation.

   a) 9 260 000   **b)** 0.000 000 24

3. Cross out the irrational numbers, then arrange the rational numbers from largest to smallest.

   $\dfrac{1}{5}$, $\sqrt{26}$, -2.2, $-\dfrac{1}{3}$, π, 0, 4.751, $\dfrac{4}{0}$, $1\dfrac{2}{8}$

4. Fill in the blanks with $<$, $>$, or $=$ to make each statement true.

   a) $\dfrac{-4}{1}$ _____ $\dfrac{-1}{4}$ **b)** $2\dfrac{5}{6}$ _____ 2.56

   c) -1.7 _____ -1.782 **d)** $4:6$ _____ $6:4$

   e) 0.66 _____ $\dfrac{2}{3}$ **f)** $\sqrt{144}$ _____ 12

5. Use the following diagram to write each of the following ratios in lowest terms.

   a) White diamonds to grey diamonds

   b) Grey diamonds to striped diamonds

   c) White diamonds to all diamonds

   d) Striped diamonds to spotted diamonds

6. Write each number below as a percent.

a) $\dfrac{73}{100}$

b) 0.475

c) 12:10

d) $\dfrac{20}{32}$

7. Write each number below as a decimal.

a) $\dfrac{2}{8}$

b) 18:12

c) 163%

d) 0.7%

8. Using perfect squares, estimate the value of each number below, and then calculate the actual value.

a) $\sqrt{36}$

b) $\sqrt{1.96}$

c) $\sqrt{97}$

d) $\sqrt{128}$

9. Solve for the missing values in the proportions below.

a) $\dfrac{j}{42} = \dfrac{5}{7}$

b) $\dfrac{4}{8} = \dfrac{x}{6}$

10. Use proportions to solve the following questions.

a) If your heart beats 7 times in 5 seconds, how may times will it beat in a minute?

b) Terri made 3 baskets for every 4 shots that she attempted in a basketball game. If the attempted 48 shots, how many did she miss?

c) Jian designs a bridge that is 11 times as long as it is wide. If the bridge is 467.5 m long, how wide is it?

d) The ratio of red gumballs to green gumballs to blue gumballs in a machine is 5:8:3. If there are 192 gumballs in the machine, how many are not blue?

11. Write each scenario below as a unit rate.

    a) 60 markers in 4 packs

    b) $84 earned in 8 hours

    c) A box of 12 chocolate bars costs $5.25. A box of 20 chocolate bars costs $7.50. Which is the better buy and by how much?

12. Solve the following number sentences.

    a) $\dfrac{1}{2}+\dfrac{7}{11}$ **b)** $5\dfrac{2}{3}-\dfrac{4}{9}$

    c) $\dfrac{3}{5}\times 3\dfrac{3}{4}$ **d)** $\dfrac{1}{2}\div 4$

    e) $-1.55+2.3$ **f)** $-6.5+(-13.4)$

    g) $25.7-(-15.9)$ **h)** $-30.08\div 9.4$

    i) $-63.64\div 7.4\times 1.285$ **j)** $-1.4\times(-18.5-(-27.93))$

13. Leslie can swim 24 laps in 30 min. Dave can swim 10 laps in 10 min. Who is the faster swimmer, and by how much?

14. Hugh and his wife, Karen, just had a baby. If Hugh changes 3 diapers a day and Karen changes 7, how many will they change in a week?

15. Jane and Clarence are playing their favourite card game. If Jane has a score of 1 895 and Clarence has –255, how many points is Jane winning by?

16. It is class election time, and Denise wins by a landslide with 85% of the votes. If 420 people voted, how many votes did Denise get? How many votes did her opponent get?

17. Emma is shopping for a new digital camera. She finds one that is regularly priced at $249.99. If she get a discount of 12% on the camera, how much will she pay for the camera before taxes? How much will she pay after the GST and a PST of 6% is added?

18. At the boat races, 75 people were organized into 15 teams. How many more people would be needed to make up 20 teams of the same size?

19. The area of particular postage stamp is 225 mm^2. How long would a row of 5 of these stamps be?

PATTERNS AND RELATIONS

When you are finished this unit, you should be able to . . .

- find patterns from problem-solving contexts and use expressions, equations, and substitutions to verify the solution (PLO 5, problem solving)
- substitute numbers for variables in expressions, and graph and analyze the relation (PLO 1, patterns)
- translate between oral and written expressions and algebraic expressions (PLO 2, patterns)
- solve various algebraic equations using concrete materials or diagrams (PLO 1, variables and equations)
- solve and verify various forms of first degree algebraic equations (PLO 2, variables and equations)
- create and solve problems, using first degree equations (PLO 3, variables and equations)

Lesson	Page	Completed on
1. Expressions and Equations	84	
2. Substituting Variables	91	
3. Relations	94	
4. Graphing Relations	103	
Practice Quiz 1	114	
5. Algebra Tiles	118	
6. One-step Equations	123	
7. Two-step Equations	130	
Practice Quiz 2	138	
Review Summary	142	
Practice Test	143	
Answers and Solutions	at the back of the book	

PREREQUISITE SKILLS AND KNOWLEDGE

Prior to beginning this unit, you should be able to. . .

- distinguish between expressions and equations
- understand how to apply orders of operations to solve expressions
- explain and understand tables of values and ordered pairs
- understand how to plot ordered pairs and draw simple graphs
- understand what it means to solve verify an equation
- understand how to perform operations with integers

Lesson 1   EXPRESSIONS AND EQUATIONS

Numbers and variables (letters or symbols that represent a number) are used to make up algebraic expressions and equations.

Equations and expressions are similar, with one main difference. Equations have an equal sign and can be solved; whereas, expressions do not have an equal sign and can have an infinite number of answers depending on the value of the variable.

For example,

$v - 4$ is an expression because it is not set equal to anything.

$v - 4 = 8$ is an equation because it is equal to 8.

Both expressions and equations can be written in word from. To do this, you need to know the common words that represent the operations addition, subtraction, multiplication, and division.

Here are some of the most common key words that indicate what operation is being performed.

Addition: add, increased by, sum, total, all together, more than

Subtraction: minus, decreased by, difference, less than, take away, taken from

Multiplication: of, times, product, by

Division: quotient, times greater or times less than, groups

When writing expressions in word form, numbers need to be written out as words, and "a number" represents the variable because a number is what the variable is replacing.

Examples

Write the following expression in words.

$x + 2$ →

Solution

a number increased by two

a number plus two

two more than a number

There is more than one way to write an expression in words. Any of the above sentences are correct.

$r - 5$ →

Solution

a number minus five

five less than a number

five taken away from a number

When working with subtraction, the order is important. Five taken away from a number is not the same as a number taken away from five. Whatever you are taking away FROM must come first.

84

$7p \rightarrow$

Solution

seven times a number

the product of seven and a number

If there is no operation sign between a number and a variable, the operation is multiplication.

$\dfrac{c}{9} \rightarrow$

Solution

a number divided by nine or one-ninth of a number

the quotient of nine and a number

Words used to represent an equal sign are: equal to, is, same, result.

$q - 6 = 14 \rightarrow$

Solution

a number minus six is fourteen

six taken from a number is equal to fourteen

fourteen is the same as a number decreased by six

$12a = 36 \rightarrow$

Solution

twelve times a number is thirty-six

a number multiplied by twelve is the same as thirty-six

thirty-six is equal to the product of twelve and a number

When more than one operation is shown in an expression or an equation, make sure that each part is included when it is written in words.

$8m + 5 = 45 \rightarrow$

Solution

the product of eight and a number, increased by five is equal to forty-five

Forty-five is the same as the sum of eight multiplied by a number and five

$\dfrac{k}{4} - 3 = 1 \rightarrow$

Solution

the quotient of a number and four is decreased by three and the result is one

one is the same as three taken away from the quotient of a number and four

If given a word sentence and asked to find the expression or equation, identify the operations, numbers and equal sign (if applicable) then write the expression or equation.

NOTES

Example 1

A number is increased by ten and the result is eighteen.

Solution

This is an equation because the word **result** is given. Set it up as follows and fill in the blanks.

_____ = _____

You know something is increased so you have addition.

_____ + _____ = _____

You can choose any letter or symbol as the variable. The most common letter used is x.

It's "a number" that is increased so that is your variable. Choose any letter to represent the number.

__x__ + _____ = _____

The number is increased by ten so that goes with the variable.

__x__ + __10__ = _____

The result is eighteen, so that finishes off the equation.

__x__ + __10__ = _____18_____

So, "a number is increased by ten and the result is eighteen" can be shown as $x + 10 = 18$.

Example 2

Twenty-four is the same as the product of six and a number.

Solution

This is an equation because of the word *same*, and it will be equal to twenty-four because that is what the expression is the same as.

24 = _____

The operation is multiplication as shown by the word *product*. So decide on a variable and multiply that by six.

$24 = 6j$

You could also write this as $6j = 24$. It does not matter which side of the equal sign the 24 is on, they both mean the same thing.

Example 3

The quotient of a number and seven is decreased by eleven.

Solution

There is nothing telling you what this is equal to, so this is an expression.

Quotient implies divide, and then decrease that by eleven.

$$\frac{z}{7} - 11$$

86

Sometimes word problems are given and you are asked to write an expression or an equation.

Example 4

Write an equation that shows when three bananas are added to a basket of bananas the result is seven.

Solution

Use the variable b to represent the bananas already in the basket. Three are added, so use the $+$ symbol. The result is seven.

$b + 3 = 7$

Example 5

Jellybeans are divided into five groups.

Solution

This is an expression because you do not know how many are in each group or if it is equal to anything. Let j be the variable, and show dividing by five since you know they are being put into groups.

$$\frac{j}{5}$$

Some equations will have more than one part to work with.

NOTES

Letters used to represent variables are sometimes chosen to reflect information presented in the problem.
E.g., j for jellybeans

Example 6

Connor is two years older than Kathy, and the sum of their ages is eighteen. Write the equation that represents this information.

Solution

So solve equations with more than one part, follow these general rules:

Step 1

Figure out the parts you are working with.

Here, it is Kathy and Connor

Step 2

Choose a variable for the part you know the least bit about.

In this question, it is Kathy because you know Connor is two years older than Kathy. So Kathy $= x$.

Step 3

Based on your variable, write the expression for the other part that you are working with. You know Kathy is x and Connor is two years older than Kathy, so Connor is $x + 2$

87

Step 4

Write the equation.

The **sum** of their ages is eighteen, so you need to add.

Kathy + Connor = 18

(Kathy is x) + (Connor is $x + 2$) = 18

$x + x + 2 = 18$

Because there are 2 x's, you can combine them ($1x + 1x = 2x$), so the equation is $2x + 2 = 18$.

Example 7

Austin's shoe size is twice Brooklyn's, and the difference in their shoe sizes is 10. Write the equation.

Solution

Step 1

The two things are Austin and Brooklyn.

Step 2

You know the least about Brooklyn so Brooklyn = x

Step 3

Austin's shoe size is twice Brooklyn's so Austin = $2x$

Step 4

Austin − (subtract because of the word *difference*) Brooklyn = 10

$2x - x = 10$

$2x$'s − $1x = 1x$, so the equation can be simplified to $x = 10$

Example 8

A number and six less than the number have a sum of 15. Write the equation.

Solution

Step 1

The two things are the first number and the second number.

Step 2

You know the least about the first number = x

Step 3

The second number is six less than the first = $x - 6$

Step 4

First number + second number = 15

$x + x - 6 = 15$

$2x - 6 = 15$

PRACTICE EXERCISE

1. Identify whether each statement is an expression or an equation.
   a) Two more than a number

   b) The difference between six and a number is twelve.

   c) Fourteen is the product of seven and a number.

   d) Eight more than the quotient of three and a number

   e) A number increased by seven and then multiplied by four is twenty-four.

2. Use the following information to answer the questions below.

   a) $10 - x = 5$ b) $2x = 12$

   c) $4x + 8$ d) $\dfrac{x}{6} - 7 = 15$

   e) $9x + 4$ f) $x - 10 = 5$
   g) $x + 2 = 12$ h) $4x = 8$

   i) $\dfrac{x}{7} - 6 = 15$ j) $9(x + 4)$

   Fill in the blank with the letter of the corresponding equation or expression.
   i)   _____   The product of two and a number is twelve.
   ii)   _____   Four times a number increased by eight
   iii) _____   Ten taken from a number is five.
   iv)   _____   The quotient of a number divided by six decreased by seven is fifteen.
   v)   _____   The sum of a number and four all multiplied by nine

3. Write the following equations in words.
   a) $4d + 6 = -18$

   b) $\dfrac{n}{2} - 3 = 8$

   c) $9 + c = 10$

   d) $5 - 3y = 7$

   e) $(2 + 6)m = 64$

4. Write the equation or expression.

a) The cost of eight bananas increased by four is two dollars.

b) The mass of Emma split into thirds is thirty-three kilograms.

c) Ben's age three years ago was twelve.

d) The sum of a number three times is twenty-seven.

e) A number and four times that number add up to ninety-five.

f) Matt is three times as tall as his two-year-old brother, and the sum of their heights is 160 cm.

g) Jenn has 15 more dollars in her pocket than Chad, and the sum in their money is $55.

Lesson 2 SUBSTITUTING VARIABLES

Variables are letters or symbols that represent numbers. If the number that the variable in an expression represents is given, it is possible to solve for the value of the expression.

NOTES

Example 1

$x + 4, x = 3$

Solution

Replace the x with 3 and use BEDMAS to solve.

$3 + 4 = 7$

So the value of $x + 4$ when $x = 3$ is 7.

For more complicated questions, put the value of the variable in brackets so you know what order to perform the operations in, and then solve.

BEDMAS tells you in what order to perform the given operations:

1. **Brackets**
2. **Exponent**
3. **Divide**
4. **Multiply**
5. **Addition**
6. **Subtraction**

Example 2

$5v - 5, v = 3$

Solution

$5(3) - 5$ (using BEDMAS, you know to do the multiplication first)

$5(3) = 15 - 5$

$15 - 5 = 10$

So, the value of $5v - 5$ when $v = 3$ is 10.

A common mistake that people make if they do not include the brackets is in the second line where the v is replaced with the 3.

 $53 - 5$

This looks like $53 - 5$, which is 48 because nothing indicates to multiply the 5 and the 3. So remember to put the brackets around the number that replaces the variable.

$5(3) - 5$. This way, you are less likely to make that mistake.

Example 3

$4(x - 7) + 2, x = 9$

Solution

$4[(9) - 7] + 2$ (do the 9 – 7 first because it is in brackets)

$4(2) + 2$ (multiply the 4 by 2)

$8 + 2$ (add)

10

The value of $4(x - 7) + 2$ when $x = 9$ is 10.

NOTES

Different variables in the same equation or expression are used to represent different numbers.

You can also substitute when you have more than one variable as long as you are given the values of each variable. Substitute for each variable (use brackets around each), and solve with BEDMAS.

Example 4

$x + y, x = 3, y = 2$

Solution

$(3) + (2) =$

5

Example 5

$2x - 4y, x = -1, y = 5$

Solution

$2(-1) - 4(5) =$

$-2 - 20 =$

-22

Substitution is used for many different types of problem-solving questions.

Example 6

The formula for finding perimeter of a rectangle is $P = 2l + 2w$. Find the perimeter of a rectangle whose length (l) is 10 cm and width (w) is 4 cm.

Solution

$P = 2l + 2w$

$\quad = 2(10) + 2(4)$

$\quad = 20 + 8$

$\quad = 28$

Example 7

The cost of going to the fair is $5 to get in and $1 for each ride. What is the total cost for Theresa if she goes on 9 rides?

Solution

Set this up with the $5, which never changes, and the $1 for each ride. You need to multiply the dollar by the number of rides (r) that each person goes on.

$C = 5 + 1r$

$\quad = 5 + 1(9)$

$\quad = 5 + 9$

$\quad = 14$

Theresa will spend $14 at the fair.

PRACTICE EXERCISE

1. Substitute 3 for x and solve.

   a) $x + 7$

   b) $5x - 10$

   c) $3(x + 4)$

   d) $-x - 8$

2. Solve each expression below, where $a = -2$ and $b = 1$.

   a) $4a + b$

   b) $(a + b)$

   c) $-9a - b$

   d) $\dfrac{a}{2} + b$

3. Write the expression, and then substitute 5 for the value of the variable.

   a) Three more than twice a number

   b) The product of a number and seven subtracted from one hundred

   c) A number increased by the same number all divided by two

   d) One-third of six times the number

Lesson 3 **RELATIONS**

Before you can graph an algebraic equation, you need to understand how the variables in the equation are related, or the **relation** between the variables. The relation is another term for the algebraic equation. The easiest way to do this is to write the variables from the equation in a table of values.

For the relation $x + 1 = y$, the table of values is shown below. This is correct because each y value is one more than the x value.

x	y
1	2
2	3
3	4
4	5
5	6

To make tables of values from equations,

1. Draw a T-chart.
2. Pick any values for x (usually 4 or 5 values).
3. Substitute each value of x into the equation.
4. Use BEDMAS to solve for y.
5. Complete the table.

Example 1

Make a table of values for the equation $2x - 3 = y$.

Solution

Step 1

x	y

Step 2

x	y
1	
2	
3	
4	
5	

Step 3

$2x - 3 = y$	$2x - 3 = y$	$2x - 3 = y$	$2x - 3 = y$	$2x - 3 = y$
$2(1) - 3 =$	$2(2) - 3 =$	$2(3) - 3 =$	$2(4) - 3 =$	$2(5) - 3 =$

Step 4

$2 - 3 =$	$4 - 3 =$	$6 - 3 =$	$8 - 3 =$	$10 - 3 =$
-1	1	3	5	7

Step 5

x	y
1	−1
2	1
3	3
4	5
5	7

Example 2

Make a table of values for the equation $x + y = 4$.

Solution

To make this table of values, the values of x and y added together must equal 4. Follow the same steps as above.

Steps 1 and 2

x	y
1	
2	
3	
4	
5	

Steps 3 and 4

$x + y = 4$	$x + y = 4$	$x + y = 4$	$x + y = 4$	$x + y = 4$
$(1) + (\ )$ $= 4$	$(2) + (\ )$ $= 4$	$(3) + (\ )$ $= 4$	$(4) + (\ )$ $= 4$	$(5) + (\ )$ $= 4$
$(1) + (3)$ $= 4$	$(2) + (2)$ $= 4$	$(3) + (1)$ $= 4$	$(4) + (0)$ $= 4$	$(5) + (-1)$ $= 4$

NOTES

Step 5

x	y
1	3
2	2
3	1
4	0
5	−1

When given a table of values and asked to write the relation, solve by the guess-and-check method. Make an educated guess as to what you think the relation is, then substitute the given values of x to see if you get the given value of y.

Here are some helpful hints to make the educated guesses at the relation.

There are generally 3 main types of equations:

You should always check more than one of the x values for the y value. Just because your equation works for one x value does not necessarily mean it will work for all of them.

- $x +$ or $-$ a number $= y$ (e.g., $x - 2 = y$)

  For this type of equation, as long as the values of x are changing by 1, the values of y also change by 1. You just have to compare x and y to see the difference.

The coefficient is the number in front of the variable.

- a number multiplied by x then $x +$ or $-$ a number $= y$ (e.g., $3x + 1 = y$)

  For this type of equation, as long as the values of x are changing by 1, the values of y also change by whatever the coefficient before the variable is. Once you figure out the coefficient, check to see if you need to add or subtract to get the value of y.

- $x +$ or $-$ y equals a number (e.g., $x - y = 5$)

  For this type of equation, one column in the table of values goes in increasing order and the other goes in decreasing order. You just need to find the difference between them.

  You may also see exponents in equations.
- $x^2 = y$

Find the equations for the following tables of values.

Example 1

x	y
1	3
2	5
3	7
4	9
5	11

Solution

- Look at the x values first to make sure they are all are changing by 1.
- Look at the y value to see what is happening. You see they are all going up by 2, so you know it is the second type of equation where it will be $2x +$ or $-$ a number.
- Check an x value: $2(1) = 2$, which is not your y value, so you need to add 1 to the $2x$
- Check another x value $2(2) + 1 = 5$.
- This equation is giving your y values, when you add 1 to the $2x$.
  The equation for the table is $2x + 1 = y$

Example 2

x	y
1	8
2	7
3	6
4	5
5	4

Solution

- Look at the x values first to make sure they are all are changing by 1.
- Look at the y value to see what is happening. You see they are all going down so you know it is the third type of equation where you will have $x +$ or $- y$ equals a number
- Check an x and y value by adding: $1 + 8 = 9$
- Check another set of values: $4 + 5 = 9$
- Because this is consistently giving you the same answer, you know x and y equal 9 when added.

  The equation for the table is $x + y = 9$

Example 3

x	y
5	2
6	3
7	4
8	5
9	6

Solution

- Look at the x values first to make sure they are all are changing by 1.
- Look at the y value to see what is happening. You see they are all going up by 1 so you know it is the first type of equation where it is $x +$ or $-$ a number equals y
- Check the first x value to see how you go from 5 to 2. Subtract 3.
- Check another value: $7 - 3 = 4$
- Because this is consistently giving you the same y value as in the table, you know the equation.

The equation for the table is $x - 3 = y$

Example 4

x	y
2	5
1	2
0	−1
−1	−4
−2	−7

Solution

- Look at the x values first to make sure they are all are changing by 1.
- Look at the y value to see what is happening. You see they are all going up by 3 so you know it is the second type of equation where it will be $3x +$ or $-$ a number.
- Check the first x value to see how you go from $3(2) = 6$. 6 is not the value of y, so subtract 1 to get the 5.
- Check another value. $3(1) - 1 = 3 - 1 = 2$, which is the value of y.
- Because this is consistently giving you the same y value as in the table, you know the equation.

The equation for the table is $3x - 1 = y$

If the x values in the table are not changing by 1, you can write in the missing values so they do change by 1, or just guess and check until you find the answer.

When finding the relation, make sure it is how x relates to y, not just how the values are changing in the x column or the y column.

Tables of values can also be used to write formulas when given diagrams.

Example 1

Diagram number

    1   2   3   4   5

Diagram

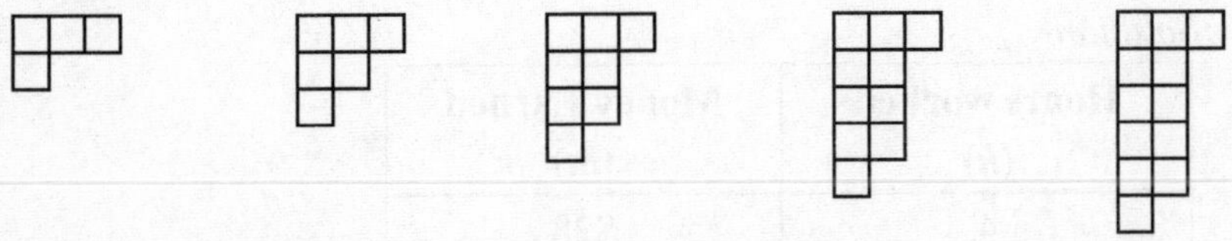

Write the relationship between the diagram number and the number of squares in each diagram.

Solution

Diagram number (*n*)	Number of squares (*s*)
1	4
2	6
3	8
4	10
5	12

Using what you know about tables of values, you can write the relation between diagram number and number of squares just like you can between x and y.

The relation is $2n + 2 = s$

In other words, the total number of squares is equal to the diagram number multiplied by 2 plus 2.

NOTES

Example 2

Money earned while working at a particular golf course is calculated as follows.

Hours worked	4	5	6	7	8
Money earned	$28	$35	$42	$49	$56

Write the relation between hours worked and money earned.

Solution

Hours worked (h)	Money Earned (m)
4	$28
5	$35
6	$42
7	$49
8	$56

The relation is 7 times the hours worked equals the money earned.

$m = 7h$

Example 3

Given the relation above, if Kim worked 2 hours, how much money would she make?

Solution

You know $m = 7h$, and you know Kim worked 2 hours so use $h = 2$ and substitute.

$m = 7h$

$m = 7(2) = 14$

In 2 hours, Kim would make $14.

Example 4

Given the relation above, if Ryan made $77, how many hours did he work?

Solution

$m = 7h$

$77 = 7h$

You know $7 \times 11 = 77$, so Ryan worked 11 hours to make $77.

PRACTICE EXERCISE

1. Write the relations for the following tables of values.

   a)

x	y
2	4
3	6
4	8
5	10
6	12

   b)

x	y
1	2
2	1
3	0
4	−1
5	−2

   c)

x	y
3	5
6	8
9	11
12	14
15	17

2. For each equation, make a table of values.

   a) $4x + 1 = y$ **b)** $x + 5 = y$ **c)** $x + y = 1$

3. Fill in the missing values in the table. Write the equation for each table.

a)

x	y
1	6
2	5
	4
4	
5	

b)

x	y
2	4
4	10
6	
	22
10	

4. Write the relationship between the diagram number and the number of circles in each diagram.

Diagram number	1	2	3	4	5

Diagram

5. Write the relationship between the length of a phone call and its cost.

Length of call (min)	1	2	3	4	5
Cost of call (cents)	40	70	100	130	160

6. Write the relationship between the week and total cars sold.

Week	2	4	6	8	10
Cars sold	11	21	31	41	51

7. Looking at the relationship above, how many cars could be expected to have sold by week 15? Week 20?

Lesson 4   GRAPHING RELATIONS

The graph of a relation is always a straight line. This is because there are an infinite number of points that will make the relation true, not just the few that are included in a table of values.

To graph a relation:

1. Make a table of values.
2. Write the ordered pairs from the table of values.
3. Plot the ordered pairs on the coordinate plane.
4. Join the points.
5. Label the graph.

Example 1

Draw a graph of $x + 2 = y$.

Solution

Step 1

x	y
1	3
2	4
3	5
4	6
5	7

Step 2

Remember ordered pairs always have brackets, a comma, and the coordinates in the order x then y.

(1, 3)

(2, 4)

(3, 5)

(4, 6)

(5, 7)

An easy way to remember the correct order of the variables x and y in an ordered pair is that x comes before y in the alphabet. Therefore (x, y)

If the x coordinate is positive, go right, and if it is negative, go left from the origin. If the y coordinate is positive, go up, and if it is negative, go down.

NOTES

Step 3

When plotting points, make sure you start at the origin (0, 0) and go horizontal first to the value of the *x*-coordinate, and then vertically second to the value of the *y*-coordinate.

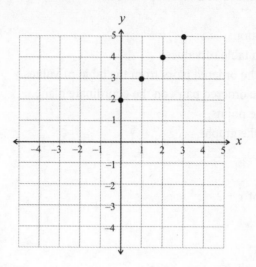

Step 4

With a ruler, join the points going **beyond** the two end points. Put arrows on the ends of the line to indicate that this line does not just stop at the end points, but could continue in both directions. This is because there are many other points that could be used in this relation other than just the ones in the table of values. Any *x* and *y* value on the line would make this equation true.

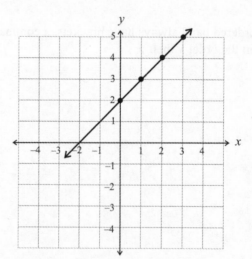

Step 5

Label the *x* and *y* axis of the graph, and write the equation beside the line.

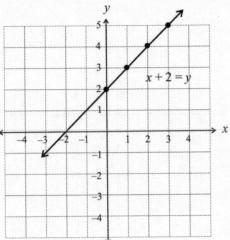

Example 2

Draw a graph of $x + y = 3$.

Solution

Step 1

x	*y*
1	2
2	1
3	0
4	−1
5	−2

Step 2

(1, 2)

(2, 1)

(3, 0)

(4, −1)

(5, −2)

Step 3

Remember if the y value is negative, it is going to be below the x-axis.

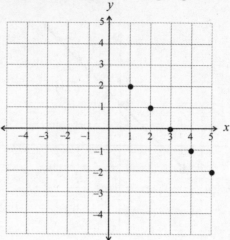

Step 4

Join the points.

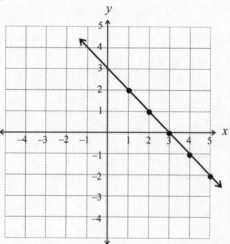

Step 5

Label the graph.

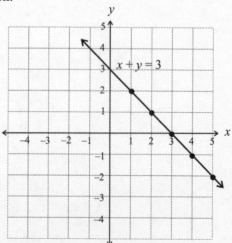

When you are given a relation, you are able to determine some information from it.

Example 3

Consider the following graph. Find the equation for the relation below.

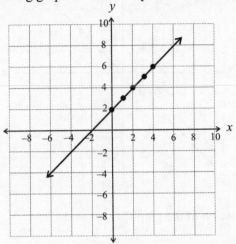

Solution

You can find the equation by writing the ordered pairs and then using guess and check to determine the equation.

Pick some of the main points on the graph.

(0, 2)
(1, 3)
(2, 4)
(3, 5)
(4, 6)

Using what you know about tables of values and relations, you can determine that the relation on the graph is $x + 2 = y$ because for every x value, the corresponding y value is two more.

Using the same graph, what is the y-coordinate at for $x = -4$? Look at the graph, find $x = -4$ and go down till you meet the line. This is at a y value of -2. So the y-coordinate when $x = -4$ is $y = -2$.

NOTES

Example 4

Use the following graph to answer the questions below.

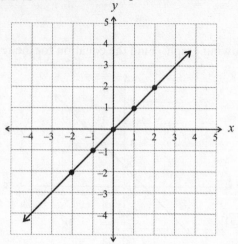

a) What is the relation of the graph?

Solution

The relation is $x = y$ because for every x value, the y value is exactly the same. For example $(2, 2)$, or $(-1, -1)$

b) What is the x-coordinate if $y = 3$?

Solution

Because you know the x value and the y value are the same, if the y coordinate is 3, the x coordinate is also 3. You could also look on the line where $y = 3$ and go down to see that that corresponds with $x = 3$.

c) Would the point $(5, 6)$ be on the line? Explain.

Solution

No $(5, 6)$ would not be on the line because only coordinates with the same x and y value are on the line. The point $(5, 6)$ would be found above the line.

Relations can also be used to solve problems.

Example 5

The boys' basketball team wants new jerseys. The cost to purchase them is $75 for the shipment and $25 for each jersey. Draw a graph of the cost to purchase jerseys and answer the following questions:

a) What is the cost of ordering 5 jerseys?

b) What would it cost to order 50 jerseys?

c) How many jerseys can you order for $250?

Solution

You know that one jersey costs $100 ($75 + $25) and 2 jerseys would cost $125 because there are 2 at $25 each plus $75 shipping. Do this to figure out a few points and draw the graph. The relation between the cost and number of jerseys is Cost = $25x + 75$. This shows that you multiply 25 by however many jerseys you have, then add the $75 shipping fee to get the total cost. The graph would look like this:

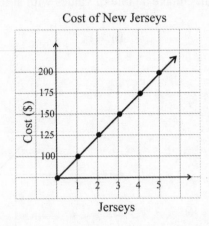

Cost of New Jerseys

On the graph, be sure to label what the *x*-axis and the *y*-axis represent.

a) The cost for 5 jerseys is $200. Look on the graph at $x = 5$, and go up until you reach the *y* value of 200.

b) For 50 jerseys, use the formula Cost = $25x + 75$ and substitute with $x = 50$.

25(50) +75 = 1 250 + 75 = $1 325.

c) If you extend the line on the graph to where the *y* value would equal 250, you find that the *x* value is 7, so you could buy 7 jerseys for $250.

PRACTICE EXERCISE

1. Using the relation $x + 6 = y$, fill in the missing coordinates in the ordered pairs.

   a) (2, ____)

   c) (10, ____)

   b) (____ , 0)

   d) (____ , 3)

2. For the following graphs, write three ordered pairs, make a table of values with at least five values, and find the equation.

   a)

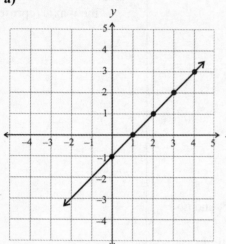

   b)

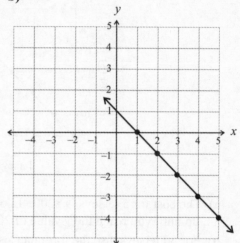

   c)

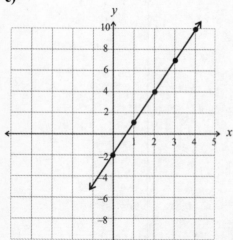

3. Make a table of values, then graph the following equations.

    a) $2x = y$ **b)** $x + y = 4$

    c) $x - 3 = y$

4. Use the following relation to answer the following questions.

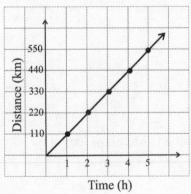

    a) Explain what is being graphed.

    b) What is the rate that the person is travelling?

    c) What is the relation?

    d) If the person travelled for 7 hours, how far would he go?

5. The graph below shows the relation between the length of a long distance call and the cost.

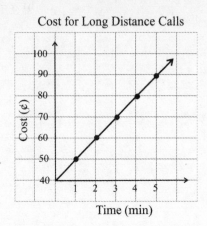

Cost for Long Distance Calls

a) If Becky talked for 2 minutes, how much would the call cost?

b) If she talked for 8 minutes how much would the call cost?

c) What is the base amount per call no matter how long it is?

d) Write the relation between length of call and cost.

6. Cindy's heart beats 70 times every minute. Graph this relation over 5 minutes.

7. The cost for a group of students on a field trip is $20 for transportation, plus $5 per student. Graph this relation, and calculate the cost for a group of 10 students to go on the field trip.

PRACTICE QUIZ 1

1. Write each equation below in words.
   a) $x + 5 = -8$

   b) $\dfrac{m}{3} - 2 = 12$

   c) $6t + 4 = -14$

2. Write the equation.
   a) Six more than three times a number is sixty-nine.

   b) Three less than half a number is twenty-two.

   c) The product of negative seven and a number is forty-nine.

3. Find the value of each expression below by substituting the given values.
   a) $w - 8$, $w = 5$

   b) $2r + 14$, $r = -7$

   c) $\dfrac{p}{7} - 9$, $p = 56$

4. Write the relation for each table of values.

a)

x	y
1	4
2	7
3	10
4	13
5	16

b)

x	y
4	6
5	5
6	4
7	3
8	2

c)

x	y
10	4
9	3
8	2
7	1
6	0

5. Make a table of values and write two ordered pairs for each of the following equations.

a) $x + 4 = y$ b) $x + y = 7$ c) $2x - 3 = y$

6. Fill in the missing coordinates using the equation $x + 2 = y$.

   a) (2, _____)

   b) (_____, 8)

   c) (0, _____)

7. Consider the following pattern.

Diagram number	1	2	3	4	5
Diagram					

   Write an equation that represents the

   a) diagram number to the total number of squares

   b) diagram number to number of shaded squares

8. Graph the following equations.

   a) $x + 1 = y$ **b)** $3x = y$

   c) $x + y = 5$

9. The following graph represents the rate at which Dave rows his boat across a lake.

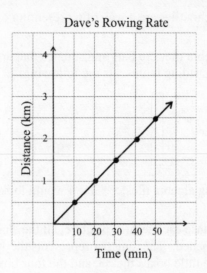

Dave's Rowing Rate

a) Write the relation representing Dave's rowing rate.

b) In an hour and a half, how far will Dave row?

Lesson 5   ALGEBRA TILES

Algebra tiles are a way of representing expressions or equations visually.

Algebra tiles are bars and squares that are shaded or unshaded. Each shape and shading represents the following:

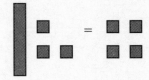

Shaded always represents positive values, and unshaded always represents negative values.

Using algebra tiles, $x + 3 = 4$ would look like

Because each term is positive, all the shapes must be shaded. The long bar represents the x, the three little boxes the +3, and the four boxes the +4.

When showing equations with algebra tiles, you never include the operation signs, only the equal sign.

Show $3x - 4 = 6$ with algebra tiles.

Because there is a 3 in front of the x, that shows that there are $3x$ bars. The –4 is represented with the four unshaded squares, and the 6 is represented by the six shaded boxes.

Example 1

Write the equation represented by the following algebra tiles.

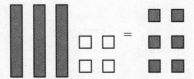

Solution

Look at the x rectangles first. There are 2 of them, so that is $2x$.
The squares to the right are positive, and there are 5, so that is +5.
After the equal sign, there are three negative blocks, so that is –3.
The equation is $2x + 5 = -3$.

Just like with integers, when you have opposite algebra tiles, the sum is 0.

Example 2

This shows that four positive tiles and four negative tiles added together equal zero because $+4 + (-4) = 0$

The same is true for the x blocks as well.

Knowing that opposites add to zero can help to simplify equations.

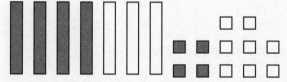

This shows that $2x + (-2x) = 0$

When you know that opposite algebra tiles give you 0, equations involving opposite tiles can be written in simpler form.

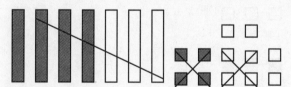

Look at the x's first. You have 4 positive, and 3 negative. Remove opposite tiles. This gives one positive x block left. Look at the ones blocks. You have 4 positive and 8 negative. This leaves 4 negative.

This simplifies to $x -4$.

Simplify the following:

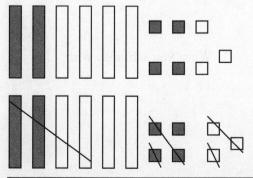

NOTES

The result is

$-2x + 1$

After simplifying an expression, you can substitute in for the variable.

Example 3

The equation above has been simplified to $-2x + 1$. Solve this expression for $x = 4$.

Solution

$-2x + 1 =$

$-2(4) + 1 =$

$-8 + 1 = 9$

Example 4

Simplify the following expression, and solve for $x = -2$.

Solution

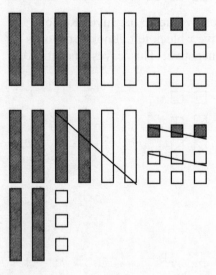

$2x - 3, x = -2$

$2(-2) - 3 =$

$-4 - 3 = -7$

The algebra tiles simplify to $2x - 3$. When you substitute with $x = -2$, the result is -7.

PRACTICE EXERCISE

1. Write the equation shown with each group of algebra tiles.

   a)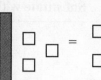

   b)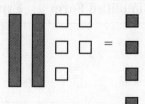

   c)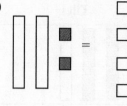

2. Show the following equations with algebra tiles.

   a) $x - 3 = 6$ **b)** $-2x = 10$ **c)** $5x + 4 = -2$

3. Simplify. Show the tiles and the expression.

   a)

   b)

4. Fill in the table.

	Tiles	Simplified Form	Expression	Substitute with $x = 2$
a)				
b)				
c)				

5. One less than the product of a number and three is eight. Write the equation, and show the algebra tiles.

Lesson 6 ONE-STEP EQUATIONS

One-step equations are algebra equations that can be solved by performing one operation to both sides of the equation to isolate the variable.

Remember from Grade 7 that "isolate the variable" means you need to get the variable on one side of the equation by itself and the numbers on the other side. The sides in the equation are separated by the equal sign.

To isolate variables, always perform the opposite operation of what is given.

Rules for isolating:
- Always perform the opposite operation
- Whatever you do to one side, you must do to the other side.

NOTES

Addition and subtraction are opposite operations, and multiplication and division are opposite operations.

Example 1

$x + 3 = 7$

Solution

To solve, -3 from both sides.

$x + 3 - 3 = 7 - 3$

($+3 - 3 = 0$ so you are left with just the x on the left side) and

($7 - 3 = 4$, which is what will be on the right side)

$x = 4$

This can also be shown with algebra tiles by adding 3 negatives to both sides of the equation to get the x by itself.

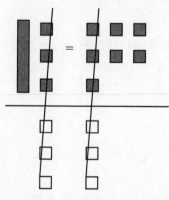

Show -3 from both sides.

You are left with $x = 4$

Example 2

$f - 7 = 12$

Solution

To solve, $+ 7$ to both sides.

$f - 7 + 7 = 12 + 7$

$f = 19$

Example 3

$u + 5 = -8$

Solution

$u + 5 - 5 = -8 - 5$

$u = -13$

Example 4

$p - 2 = -1$

Solution

$p - 2 + 2 = -1 + 2$

$p = 1$

Example 5

$12 - g = -8$

Solution

Here, you are still trying to get the variable g by itself. The g you want needs to be a positive one, so to get rid of the $-g$, you need to add g to both sides.

$12 - g + g = -8 + g$

This leaves you with $12 = -8 + g$.

Now, to get the g by itself on the right, add 8 to both sides to get rid of the -8

$12 + 8 = -8 + 8 + g$

$20 = g$

Example 6

$4m = 16$

Solution

$4m$ means 4 multiplied by m, so you need to do the opposite, which is divide by 4.

$$\frac{4m}{4} = \frac{16}{4}$$

$m = 4$

Example 7

$-8h = 56$

Solution

$$\frac{-8h}{-8} = \frac{56}{-8}$$

$$h = -7$$

Example 8

$\frac{t}{4} = 9$

Solution

This shows that t divided by 4 is 9. You need to do the opposite, which is multiply by 4.

$$\frac{t}{4} \times 4 = 9 \times 4$$

$$t = 36$$

Example 9

$\frac{r}{-3} = -5$

Solution

$$\frac{r}{-3} \times (-3) = -5 \times (-3)$$

$$r = +15$$

Example 10

Two more than a number is eighteen. What is the number?

Solution

To solve this, you need to translate the written expression into an algebraic equation and solve.

$x + 2 = 18$

$x + 2 - 2 = 18 - 2$

$x = 16$

The number is 16.

Example 11

The product of negative ten and a number is seventy. What is the number?

Solution

$-10x = 70$

$$\frac{-10x}{-10} = \frac{70}{-10}$$

$x = -7$

The number is –7.

Be sure to always substitute into the **original** equation when verifying an answer.

To verify or check algebraic equations, substitute the value of the variable into the original equation and solve. You need to show that the left side of the equation is equal to the right side.

Solve and check the following expressions:

Example 1

$x - 8 = 13$

Solution

$x - 8 + 8 = 13 + 8$

$x = 21$

Check

$x - 8 = 13$

$(21) - 8 = 13$

$13 = 13$

This shows that the left side equals the right side, so $x = 21$ is correct.

Example 2

$13j = -52$

Solution

$\dfrac{13j}{13} = \dfrac{-52}{13}$

$j = -4$

Check

$13j = -52$

$13(-4) = -52$

$-52 = -52$

Example 3

$\dfrac{12}{a} = 3$

Solution

To solve this, you need to get the a by itself. It can not be left in the denominator, so you need to multiply each side of the equation by a.

$\dfrac{12}{a} \times a = 3 \times a$

This gives you

$12 = 3a$

Now solve for a by dividing each side by 3.

$\dfrac{12}{3} = \dfrac{3a}{3}$

$4 = a$

PRACTICE EXERCISE

1. Show how to solve each equation below with algebra tiles.

    a) $x + 6 = 4$ **b)** $x - 3 = -2$

2. Solve for the variable.

    a) $3t = 18$ **b)** $\dfrac{m}{5} = 10$

    c) $2c = -22$ **d)** $j - 13 = 21$

    e) $\dfrac{h}{-5} = -6$ **f)** $-7n = -28$

    g) $v + 14 = -30$ **h)** $g - 12 = -8$

3. Solve and check the following equations.

    a) $s + 4 = 11$ **b)** $e - 6 = -10$

    c) $9t = -27$ **d)** $\dfrac{w}{-2} = 8$

    e) $-8p = -56$

4. Solve the following equations.

    a) $10 - w = 17$ **b)** $5 - y = -1$

    c) $\dfrac{18}{p} = 6$ **d)** $\dfrac{10}{t} = -5$

5. Write the equation and then solve.

  a) A number decreased by nine is negative five.

  b) Half a number is eleven.

  c) Twenty plus a number is forty-five.

  d) The product of negative six and a number is negative seventy-two.

  e) A number divided by negative nine is seven.

  f) In five years, Sharon will be seventeen. How old is Sharon now?

  g) Four times the height of a mouse is 36 cm. How tall is the mouse?

Lesson 7 TWO-STEP EQUATIONS

Think about solving two-step equations by doing BEDMAS backward.

Two-step equations are equations that require two operations to isolate the variable. Just as with one-step equations, the goal is to get the variable on one side of the equation and the numbers on the other.

To solve two-step equations:
- Do the opposite of the addition or subtraction first.
- Do the opposite of the multiplication or division second.
- Remember what ever you do to one side, you must do to the other.

Solve the following:

Example 1

$2x + 4 = 10$

Solution

Because you are trying to get the variable x by itself, you need to get rid of the 4 first. You do that just like you would have with a one-step equation: subtract 4 from each side.

$2x + 4 - 4 = 10 - 4$

$2x = 6$

Now, you have a one-step equation. Solve for the variable.

$$\frac{2x}{2} = \frac{6}{2}$$

$x = 3$

This can also be shown with algebra tiles by subtracting 4 from both sides and then splitting the tiles into two groups and getting rid of one group that shows the dividing by 2.

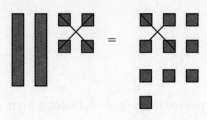

Show – 4 from both sides.

You are left with $2x = 6$.

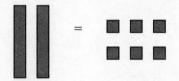

Split into two equal groups of $x = 3$

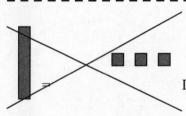

Delete one of these groups because that shows the dividing by 2.

The result is $x = 3$

Example 2

$-5w - 7 = 23$

Solution

$-5w - 7 + 7 = 23 + 7$

$-5w = 30$

$\dfrac{-5w}{-5} = \dfrac{30}{-5}$

$w = -6$

NOTES

Example 3

$$\frac{h}{8} + 6 = -11$$

Solution

To isolate the variable, you need to remove the 6 first. Subtract 6 from both sides.

$$\frac{h}{8} + 6 - 6 = -11 - 6$$

$$\frac{h}{8} = -17$$

$$\frac{h}{8} \times 8 = -17 \times 8$$

$$h = -136$$

To verify two-step equations,
- rewrite the question
- substitute the answer into the question
- solve with BEDMAS to check that the left side equals the right side

Example 4

Solve and check the following question.

$$\frac{r}{3} - 2 = -1$$

Solution

Solve

$$\frac{r}{3} - 2 + 2 = -1 + 2$$

$$\frac{r}{3} = 1$$

$$\frac{r}{3} \times 3 = 1 \times 3$$

$$r = 3$$

Check

$$\frac{r}{3} - 2 = -1$$

$$\frac{(3)}{3} - 2 = -1$$

$$1 - 2 = -1$$

$$-1 = -1$$

$$Ls = Rs$$

Because the left side equals the right side, you know that the solution $r = 3$ is correct.

Example 5

Three more than four times a number is twenty-three. What is the number? Verify your answer.

Solution

To solve this, write the algebraic equation first.

$$4p + 3 = 23 \qquad\qquad 4p + 3 = 23$$
$$4p + 3 - 3 = 23 - 3 \qquad 4(5) + 3 = 23$$
$$4p = 20 \qquad\qquad 20 + 3 = 23$$
$$\frac{4p}{4} = \frac{20}{4} \qquad\qquad 23 = 23$$
$$\qquad\qquad\qquad\qquad Ls = Rs$$
$$p = 5$$

Example 6

If Pam has 8 more movies than Ralph and together they have 30 movies, how many movies does each person have?

Solution

Write the equation, then solve.

Ralph $= x$

Pam $= x + 8$

Together they have 30.

Ralph + Pam $= 30$

$x + x + 8 = 30$

$2x + 8 = 30$

Solve the equation to see how many movies. Ralph has the value of x.

$2x + 8 = 30$

$2x + 8 - 8 = 30 - 8$

$2x = 22$

$x = 11$

If $x = 11$, this means Ralph has 11 movies because Ralph $= x$.

If $x + 8 = (11) + 8 = 19$, this means that Pam has 19 movies because Pam $= x + 8$.

Example 7

$3 - 2x = -15$

Solution

You are trying to solve to get the x by itself.

Do this by getting rid of the 3 first by subtracting 3 from both sides.

$3 - 3 - 2x = -15 - 3$

This gives you

$-2x = -18$

Divide both sides by -2 to isolate the variable.

$$\frac{-2x}{-2} = \frac{-18}{-2}$$

$x = 9$

Example 8

$$-5 = \frac{42}{f} + 9$$

Solution

To isolate the f, you need to subtract 9 from both sides first.

$$-5 - 9 = \frac{42}{f} + 9 - 9$$

$$-14 = \frac{42}{f}$$

Now, you multiply each side by f to get the f in the numerator.

$$-14 \times f = \frac{42}{f} \times f$$

$-14f = 42$

Divide each side by -14 to isolate the f

$$\frac{-14f}{-14} = \frac{42}{-14}$$

$f = -3$

PRACTICE EXERCISE

1. Solve the following equations.

   a) $3f + 4 = 10$ **b)** $4a - 16 = 0$

   c) $-4q - 8 = 20$ **d)** $3z - 3 = -3$

   e) $\dfrac{r}{3} + 6 = 13$ **f)** $\dfrac{d}{-4} - 7 = 5$

   g) $\dfrac{w}{2} + 11 = 16$ **h)** $\dfrac{k}{10} + 1 = -4$

2. Solve each equation and check.

   a) $3x - 6 = 9$ **b)** $4t - 8 = -10$

   c) $7 - 2b = 21$ **d)** $-3r - 4 = 5$

   e) $5 = 4y + 1$ **f)** $\dfrac{l}{3} - 1 = 2$

g) $\dfrac{g}{5} + 4 = 12$

h) $\dfrac{e}{9} - 2 = -4$

3. Solve the following equations.

a) $7 + \dfrac{15}{w} = 2$

b) $4 - \dfrac{24}{x} = -2$

c) $1 - 4k = 5$

d) $-11 - 3q = 43$

4. Write each equation then solve.

a) Four times Lauren's age increased by three is twenty-one.

b) Double a number decreased by four is eight.

c) The difference between one-third of a number and four is negative ten.

d) A number divided by negative four increased by one gives a result of two.

5. Darren is sixteen years older than Corey. The sum of their ages is forty-six. How old is each person?

6. The sum of two numbers is eighty-four. One number is ten more than the other number. What are the numbers?

PRACTICE QUIZ 2

1. Write the equation shown with each group of algebra tiles.

a)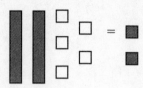

b)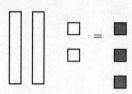

2. Fill in the table.

	Tiles	Simplified Form	Expression	Substitute with $x = -2$
a)				
b)				

3. Show how to solve the following equations with algebra tiles.

    a) $x + 3 = -6$ **b)** $2x + 3 = 7$

4. Solve each equation below. (You do not need to use algebra tiles.)

a) $x - 7 = 15$

b) $-3c = -27$

5. Solve and check each equation below.

a) $\dfrac{j}{5} = -8$

b) $x + 6 = 3$

6. Solve each equation below.

a) $3g - 9 = 33$

b) $-5u + 45 = 95$

c) $18 = \dfrac{n}{4} + 3$

d) $\dfrac{b}{-10} - 1 = -1$

7. Solve and check each equation below.

a) $2q - 2 = 16$

b) $-7d + 8 = 22$

c) $\dfrac{y}{3} - 10 = 15$

d) $\dfrac{l}{-1} + 4 = 9$

8. Solve each equation below.

a) $17 - 5y = -13$

b) $\dfrac{36}{z} + 4 = 10$

9. Write the equation, then solve.

a) The product of ten and a number decreased by seven gives a result of forty-three.

b) A quarter of a number increased by eight is twenty-one.

c) One-seventh of Jason's movies are comedies. If he has 6 comedies, how many movies does he have?

d) Cheri has seven more dollars in her pocket than Shawn. If together they have forty-one dollars, how much does each person have?

Review Summary

- An expression is a mathematical sentence with numbers and variables. Expressions are not set equal to anything and may have an infinite number of answers depending on the value of the variable. It is possible to substitute only for a given value of the variable to find the value of the expression. Equations are like expressions but they are equal to a number. With equations, it is possible to solve for the value of the variable.

- To translate between a written equation and an algebraic equation, understand what operation is given, then fill in the variable and numbers based on the problem. Remember that the order that the information is given in is important.

- When substituting into a given equation, put the value that you are substituting with in brackets to avoid confusion, then solve using BEDMAS.

- When given an equation, it is possible to make a table of values, or ordered pairs, by deciding on a value for x, and then solving for y. If given a table and asked to find the equation, use guess and check. Check more than one set of values for accuracy.

- The graph of a relation is always a straight line. This is because there is an infinite number of values that when substituted in for one variable, allow you to solve for the other. Use these values to make the ordered pairs, then graph the relation.

- Algebra tiles are a visual way to represent algebraic equations. When working with algebra tiles, the shaded values are positive and the unshaded values are negative. A long bar represents the x and a small square box represents one.

- When solving one-step equations, the goal is to get the variable by itself. Do this by using the opposite operation of the one given. Remember whatever you do to one side you have to do to the other.

- When solving two-step equations, the goal is to get the variable by itself. Just like with one-step equations, always do the opposite operations beginning with any adding or subtracting. The second step is the multiplication or division.

- To verify algebraic equations, substitute the value of the variable into the original equation and solve with BEDMAS. Show that the left side of the equation is equal to the right side. LS = RS

PRACTICE TEST

1. State whether each statement is an equation or an expression.
   a) The product of a number and eleven is increased by five.

   b) Six and a number decreased by the same number

   c) Thirteen and the quotient of a number and ten totals one.

2. Write the following equations in words.
   a) $3(x + 2) = 6$

   b) $-4 + x = 29$

3. Write the equation.
   a) A number times itself increased by four is twenty.

   b) Fourteen is the result of a number decreased by seven all multiplied by three.

4. Substitute for $a = -1$ and $b = 4$.
   a) $2a + b$ b) $-3a + 2b$

5. Complete the following ordered pairs using the relation $3x + 2 = y$.
   a) $(0, \underline{\quad})$

   b) $(\underline{\quad}, 8)$

   c) $(-3, \underline{\quad})$

6. Make a table of values and graph the following relations.

    a) $x - 4 = y$ **b)** $x + y = -2$

7. What equation is represented by the following ordered pairs?

    $(-1, -2)$ $(0, -1)$ $(1, 0)$

8. Solve each of the following equations.

    a) $17 - 5y = -13$ **b)** $\dfrac{36}{z} + 8 = 10$

9. Use the following graph to answer the questions below.

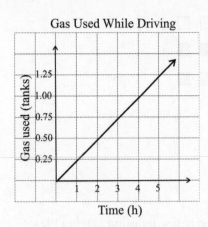

Gas Used While Driving

a) Describe in words what is being represented in the graph?

b) What equation represents the graph?

c) How much gas would be used in 8 hours?

d) What does the point (2, 1) mean in terms of the information presented in the graph?

10. Write the expression or equation represented by the following.

a)

b)

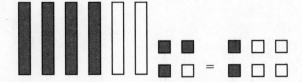

11. Simplify, then substitute for $x = 5$.

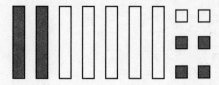

12. Show how to solve each equation below by using algebra tiles.

    a) $x + 3 = 5$

    b) $x - 1 = -7$

13. Solve and check the following equations.

    a) $m + 5 = -9$ **b)** $3s - 4 = 11$

c) $\dfrac{x}{5} - 8 = -4$

d) $4a - 8 = -12$

e) $\dfrac{e}{-3} - 11 = -13$

f) $3t + 60 = 108$

14. Solve each of the following equations.

a) $4w = -28$

b) $m - 3 = 17$

c) $\dfrac{x}{4} = 13$

d) $6 - y = 4$

e) $\dfrac{-50}{b} = 10$

f) $\dfrac{d}{8} + 19 = 26$

g) $13 - 4x = -3$

h) $\dfrac{96}{h} + 18 = 30$

15. Write an equation for each statement then solve.

a) The product of negative six and a number is seventy-two.

b) The sum of five multiplied by a number increased by four is fifty-nine.

c) The first book in a series has 152 more pages then the second book. If they have 554 pages all together, how many pages does each book have?

d) An ostrich egg is eight times heavier than a chicken's egg. If the difference in their masses is 280 g, what is the mass of each egg?

SHAPE AND SPACE

When you are finished this unit, you should be able to . . .

- use concrete materials and diagrams to develop the Pythagorean relationship (PLO 1, measurement)
- use the Pythagorean relationship to calculate the measure of the third side of a right triangle, given the other two sides. (PLO 1, measurement)
- describe patterns and generalize relationships by determining the areas and perimeters of quadrilaterals and the areas and circumference of circles (PLO 2, measurement)
- estimate, measure, and calculate the surface area and volume of any right prism or cylinder (PLO 2, measurement)
- estimate and calculate the area of composite figures (PLO 3, measurement)
- estimate, measure, and calculate the surface area of composite 3-D objects (PLO 1, 3-D objects and 2-D shapes)
- estimate, measure, and calculate the volume of composite 3-D objects (PLO 3, measurement)
- identify, investigate, and classify quadrilaterals, regular polygons, and circles, according to their properties (PLO 1, 3-D objects and 2-D shapes)
- build 3-D objects from a variety of representations (nets, skeletons) (PLO 2, transformations)
- represent, analyze, and describe enlargements and reductions (PLO 1, transformations)
- draw and interpret scale diagrams (PLO 2, transformations)

Lesson	Page	Completed on
1. Pythagorean Theorem	151	
2. Perimeter	160	
3. Area	168	
4. 2-D Composite Figures	180	
Practice Quiz 1	187	
5. 3-D Objects	194	
6. Surface Area	201	
7. Volume	211	
8. 3-D Composite Figures	217	
Practice Quiz 2	228	

9. Enlargements and Reductions	232	
10. Scale Diagrams	239	
11. Maps	244	
12. Networks	249	
Practice Quiz 3	259	
Review Summary	263	
Practice Test	265	
Answers and Solutions	at the back of the book	

PREREQUISITE SKILLS AND KNOWLEDGE

Prior to beginning this unit, you should be able to. . .

- perform calculations involving exponents
- explain the difference between right triangles and other types of triangles
- solve algebraic equations
- substitute into an expression and solve
- perform calculations with square roots
- use BEDMAS to solve equations
- calculate the perimeter and area of various shapes
- identify π as an irrational number with a rounded value of 3.14
- describe the differences between 2-D and 3-D objects
- distinguish between enlargements and reductions
- use ratios and proportions to solve problems

Lesson 1   PYTHAGOREAN THEOREM

The Pythagorean Theorem is used to find the length of one side of any **right** triangle when the other two sides are given.

This Theorem is called the "Pythagorean Theorem" because it was developed by Pythagoras, a Greek mathematician, in the 6th century BC. The Theorem states that $a^2 + b^2 = c^2$, where a and b are the sides adjacent to the right angle and c is the side across from the right angle. Side c, which is always the longest side of a right triangle, is called the hypotenuse, and sides a and b are called the legs.

The Pythagorean Theorem can only be used with right triangles.

Here are some examples of right triangles with the sides properly labelled.

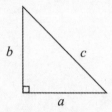

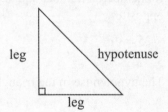

Notice that sides a and b are interchangeable. As long as they are the legs that make up the right angle, it does not matter which is labelled a and which is labelled b.

Here are two more examples of right triangles.

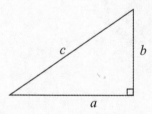

To find the missing side of a right triangle, use the Pythagorean Theorem, substitute in for the given values, and solve for the missing side.

Example 1

Find the missing side of the triangle below.

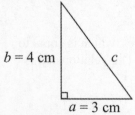

NOTES

Remember that a number squared and the square root of a number are opposites.

Solution

$a^2 + b^2 = c^2$

Substitute in for the values a and b because you are trying to find side c.

$(3)^2 + (4)^2 = c^2$

Work out the left side of the equation.

$3^2 = 3 \times 3 = 9$

$4^2 = 4 \times 4 = 16$

$9 + 16 = c^2$

$25 = c^2$

Because you are trying to solve for the value of c, you need to get rid of the exponent 2. You do this by taking the square root of both sides. Remember, a number squared and the square root of a number are opposites.

$\sqrt{25} = \sqrt{c^2}$

$5 = c$

The hypotenuse in the triangle is 5 cm.

In a diagram, this can be shown as follows:

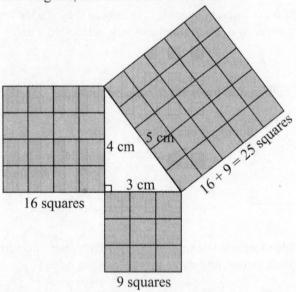

Making a square from side $a = 3$ gives 9 squares

Making a square from side $b = 4$ gives 16 squares.

Making the square from side $c = 5$ gives 25 squares, which is equal to the 9 squares and the 16 squares added together. This relationship is true for any right triangle.

Example 2

Solve for the missing side.

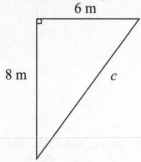

6 m

8 m c

Solution

$a^2 + b^2 = c^2$

Label one side a and the other side b.

$(6 \text{ m})^2 + (8 \text{ m})^2 = c^2$

$36 \text{ m} + 64 \text{ m} = c^2$

$100 \text{ m} = c^2$

Take the square root of both sides to solve for c.

$\sqrt{100} = \sqrt{c^2}$

$10 \text{ m} = c$

$c = 10 \text{ m}$

Remember to add the units of the triangle to the solution.

Example 3

Solve for the missing side. Round your answer to the tenths place value, if necessary.

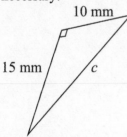

10 mm

15 mm c

Solution

$a^2 + b^2 = c^2$

$(15 \text{ mm})^2 + (10 \text{ mm})^2 = c^2$

$225 \text{ mm} + 100 \text{ mm} = c^2$

$325 \text{ mm} = c^2$

$\sqrt{325} = \sqrt{c^2}$

$18 \text{ mm} = c$

$c = 18 \text{ mm}$

Example 4

Solve for the missing side.

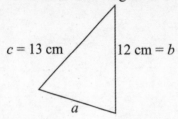

In this diagram, the missing side is one of the legs, side a, not side c, the hypotenuse, as in the previous examples.

Solution

$a^2 + b^2 = c^2$

Substitute in for the values b and c because you are trying to find side a.

$a^2 + (12)^2 = (13)^2$

Calculate the exponents.

$12^2 = 12 \times 12 = 144$
$13^2 = 13 \times 13 = 169$
$a^2 + 144 = 169$

Now, you must solve for a. To do this, you need to have a on one side of the equation and all the numbers on the other side of the equation. Using the opposite operation of $+ 144$, subtract 144 from both sides.

$a^2 + 144 - 144 = 169 - 144$
$a^2 = 25$

To solve for a, take the square root of both sides.

$\sqrt{a^2} = \sqrt{25}$

$a = 5$ cm

Side a is 5 cm.

Example 5

Find the missing length of the triangle below.

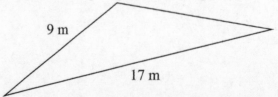

Label the sides given. The side across from the right angle is the hypotenuse or side c; therefore, $c = 17$ m. One of the legs is given, so label it a or b—it does not matter which because they are interchangeable. Solve for the other side.

$$a^2 + b^2 = c^2$$
$$(9)^2 + b^2 = (17)^2$$
$$81 + b^2 = 289$$
$$81 - 81 + b^2 = 289 - 81$$
$$b^2 = 208$$
$$\sqrt{b^2} = \sqrt{208}$$
$$b = 14.4 \text{ m}$$

The Pythagorean Theorem can also be used to solve problems involving a right triangle.

Example 6

The top end of a ladder is leaning against the side of a wall 1.5 m up from the ground. The base of the ladder is 2 m from the wall. How long is the ladder?

Solution

Draw and label a diagram that shows the problem.

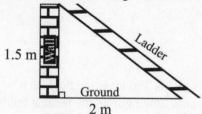

The diagram lets you See the right triangle, so it is easy to label the sides. The wall can be a and the ground b, (or vice versa) and the ladder will be side c because it is the side opposite the right angle.

Use the Pythagorean Theorem to solve for side c, the length of the ladder.

$$a^2 + b^2 = c^2$$
$$(1.5)^2 + (2)^2 = c^2$$
$$2.25 + 4 = c^2$$
$$6.25 = c^2$$
$$\sqrt{6.25} = \sqrt{c^2}$$
$$2.5 \text{ m} = c$$

The ladder is 2.5 m long.

Because most square roots are irrational numbers (decimal never ends) answers are usually left rounded to the nearest tenth.

NOTES

Example 7

A square field has a path running diagonally across it. If the field's sides are 4.2 m long, how long, to the nearest tenth of a metre, is the path?

Solution

Draw a diagram.

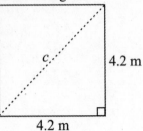

Label the sides *a* and *b* and, the diagonal path *c*.

Solve for the length of the path.

$a^2 + b^2 = c^2$

$(4.2)^2 + (4.2)^2 = c^2$

$17.64 + 17.64 = c^2$

$35.28 = c^2$

$\sqrt{35.28} = \sqrt{c^2}$

$5.9 \text{ m} = c$

The path across the field is 5.9 m.

Example 8

Joel is flying a kite. If the string of his kite is 7 m long and the kite is a horizontal distance of 4 m away from him, how high, to the nearest tenth of a metre, is the kite?

Solution

Draw a diagram.

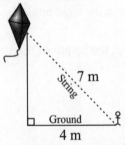

Label the leg that represents the horizontal distance *a* and the hypotenuse, which represents the string, *b*. Solve for the other side that makes up the right angle.

Solve for the missing side.

$$a^2 + b^2 = c^2$$
$$(4)^2 + b^2 = (7)^2$$
$$16 + b^2 = 49$$
$$16 - 16 + b^2 = 49 - 16$$
$$b^2 = 33$$

$$\sqrt{b^2} = \sqrt{33}$$

$b = 5.7$ m

The kite is 5.7 m up in the air.

PRACTICE EXERCISE

1. Label sides a, b, and c on the triangles below.

a)

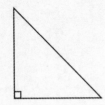

b)

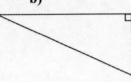

c)

2. Find the missing side in each right triangle shown below. Round your answer to the nearest tenth if necessary.

a)

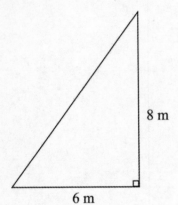

b)

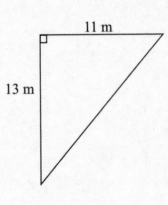

c)

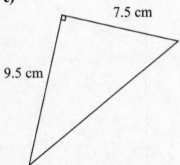

d)

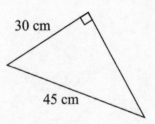

e)

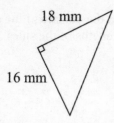

18 mm

16 mm

f)

14 m

4 m

3. Carolyn is making a triangular-shaped garden in her back yard. If the right corner of the garden is made from sides that are 2 m long and 3 m long, how long is the other side?

4. A 9 m ladder is leaning against a wall. If the base of the ladder is 4.5 m from the bottom of the wall, how far up the wall does the ladder reach?

5. A square park has sides that are 30 m. How long is the path that goes diagonally from one corner to the other?

6. A boat leaves a marina and travels west for 75 km, then south for 25 km to reach its destination. How much shorter would the trip have been if the boat could have travelled directly from the marina to its destination?

7. The bases of a ball diamond are 14 m apart. What is the distance between second base and home plate?

Lesson 2   PERIMETER

The perimeter of an object is the distance around the outside of the object. To find the perimeter of any object, add all the lengths of the sides together.

Example 1

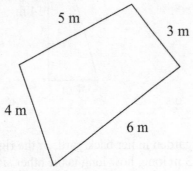

Solution
P = add all sides
$P = 5 \text{ m} + 3 \text{ m} + 6 \text{ m} + 4 \text{ m}$
$P = 18 \text{ m}$

Example 2

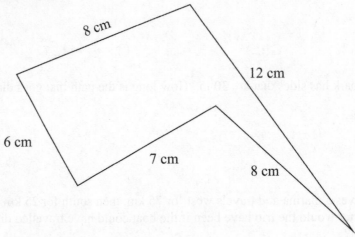

Solution
P = add all sides
$P = 8 \text{ cm} + 12 \text{ cm} + 8 \text{ cm} + 7 \text{ cm} + 6 \text{ cm}$
$P = 41 \text{ cm}$

If you are given the perimeter of an object and asked to find one missing side length, subtract all the given sides from the total perimeter.

Example 3

Find the length of side x on the diagram below.

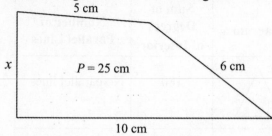

Solution
$P = 25$ cm
25 cm − 5 cm − 6 cm − 10 cm = missing side
4 cm = missing side
$x = 4$ cm

Example 4

Find the length of side x on the diagram below.

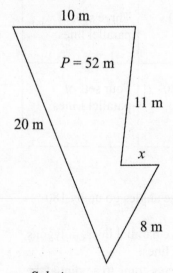

Solution
$P = 52$ m
52 m − 10 m − 11 m − 8 m − 20 m = missing side
3 m = missing side
$x = 3$ m

NOTES

To find the perimeter of regular polygons (polygons where all the sides are the same length) multiply the number of sides by the length of one of the sides.

The most common regular polygons are listed below.

Number of Sides	Name	Diagram	Sum of Degrees of Interior	Number of Parallel Lines
3	Triangle		180	No parallel lines
4	Square		360	Two sets of parallel lines, all angles right angles.
5	Pentagon		540	No parallel Lines
6	Hexagon		720	Three sets of parallel lines
8	Octagon		1 080	Four sets of parallel Lines

The formula $P = n \times s$, where n = the number of sides and s = side length, can be used to calculate the perimeter of any regular polygon.

The formula could also be written as $P = n \times l$ where the l represents side length instead of s.

General characteristics of polygons:
• from one polygon to the next, the sum of the angles go up by 180 degrees
• Polygons with an even number of sides have parallel lines, polygons with odd numbers of sides have no parallel lines.
• Polygons with an odd number of sides, always come to a point at the top.

Example 5

Find the perimeter of a square whose sides are 3 cm.

Solution

P = number of sides × side length (square has 4 sides)

$P = n \times l$

$P = 4 \times 3$ cm

$P = 12$ cm

Example 6

Find the perimeter of an octagon with side lengths of 6.2 cm.

Solution

P = number of sides × side length (octagon has 8 sides)

$P = n \times s$

$P = 8 \times 6.2$ cm

$P = 49.6$ cm

Example 7

If the perimeter of a pentagon is 100 m, how long is each side?

Solution

P = number of sides × side length (pentagon has 5 sides.)

$P = n \times s$

100 m = 5 × side length

Divide each side by 5 to solve for the side length alone.

$$\frac{100}{5} = \frac{5 \times \text{side length}}{5}$$

20 cm = side length

$s = 20$ cm

The perimeter of (or distance around) a circle is called circumference (C). It is calculated using the formula $C = \pi d$.

If no sign is given between variables, multiply.

The 16th letter of the Greek alphabet, π (called pi), represents the ratio of circumference to diameter of a circle. For most calculations involving π, the value 3.14 is used; however, pi is actually an irrational number whose decimal places never terminate or repeat.

In the formula the $C = \pi d$, d represents the diameter. This is the distance from one side of the circle to the other going straight through the middle. If you are only given the distance halfway across a circle (the radius), multiply that value by 2 to get the distance all the way across (the diameter).

Here is a circle with the diameter shown.

This circle has radius shown.

To calculate circumference, substitute known values into the equation $C = \pi d$, then solve.

Example 8

Calculate the perimeter of the following circles.

Solution

$C = \pi d$
$C = (3.14)(6)$
$C = 18.84$ m

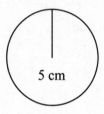

$C = \pi d$

Since the radius (halfway across the circle) is given, multiply by 2

to get the diameter. $5 \times 2 = 10$
$C = (3.14)(10)$
$C = 31.4$ cm

Example 9

Find the distance around a circular garden that has a 15 m path running from one side to the other through the centre.

Solution

Since the path goes from one side to the other, the diameter is 15 m.
$C = \pi d$
$C = (3.14)(15)$
$C = 47.1$ m

The distance around the garden is 47.1 m.

PRACTICE EXERCISE

1. Find the perimeter of the following diagrams.

   a)

   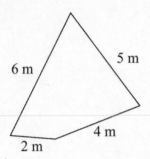

   6 m
   5 m
   4 m
   2 m

   b)

   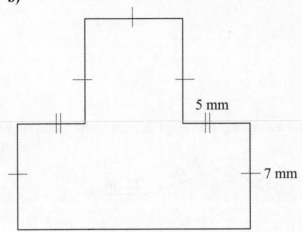

   5 mm

   7 mm

   c)

   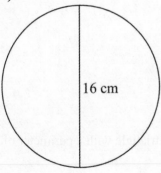

   16 cm

   d) A octagon with side length 10 mm

   e) A square with side length 12 cm

   f) A rectangle with a length of 7 cm and a width of 4 cm

g) A circle with a radius of 3.4 m

2. Find the missing side length in each of the following situations.

a)

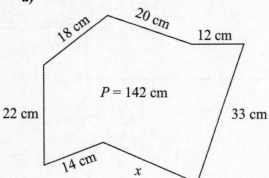

b)

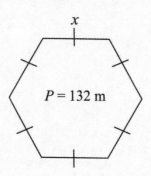

c) A pentagon with $P = 545$ mm

d) An equilateral triangle with a perimeter of 69 m

3. Find the radius of a circle that has a circumference of 47.1 cm.

4. A rectangular field has a perimeter of 46 m and a length of 14 m. What is its width?

5. In a rectangle, the length is twice the width. If the width is 13 mm, what is the perimeter of the rectangle?

6. A triangular garden has sides that are 12 m, 14 m, and 16 m. If each side is increased by 5 m, how much larger is the new perimeter of the garden?

Lesson 3 AREA

The area of an object is the number of square units that are enclosed within that object. The units for area are always squared (have an exponent of 2).

Different formulas are used to find the area of different shapes. Here are some common area formulas you should know.

Name of shape	Diagram of Shape	Formula for Area	Notes
Rectangle/ Square		$A = l \times w$	In a square, the length and the width are the same.
Parallelogram		$A = b \times h$	The h is the distance from the top to the base that forms a right angle with the base.
Triangle		$A = \dfrac{b \times h}{2}$	The h is the distance from the top to the base that forms a right angle with the base. It can be shown in many different places.
Trapezoid		$A = \dfrac{h(a+b)}{2}$	The sides a and b are the opposite sides (called the bases) that are parallel to each other.
Circle		$A = \pi r^2$	The r is the radius of the circle.

168

To solve for the area of the shapes, write the formula, substitute for the given values, and solve using BEDMAS. Do not forget the units in your answer.

Example 1

Find the area of the following shape.

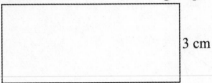

7 cm

Solution

Rectangle

$A = l \times w$

$A = (3) \times (7)$

$A = 21 \text{ cm}^2$

Example 2

Find the area of the triangle below.

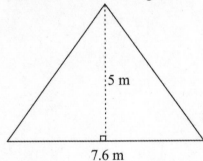

7.6 m

Solution

Triangle

$A = \dfrac{b \times h}{2}$

The height is the 5 m because that is the line that comes straight down from the top and makes a right angle with the base.

$A = \dfrac{(7.6) \times (5)}{2}$

$= \dfrac{38}{2}$

$A = 19 \text{ m}^2$

NOTES

Reminder:
BEDMAS tells you in what order to perform the given operations
1. Brackets
2. Exponents
3. Divide
3. Multiply
4. Addition
4. Subtraction

NOTES

The height is the line that goes from the top of the figure to the base and that forms a right angle with the base. In the example below, the base is extended with a dotted line to show where it would meet and form the right angle. Do not include the extended part in the area calculation, just the given length of the base.

Example 3

Find the area of the shape below.

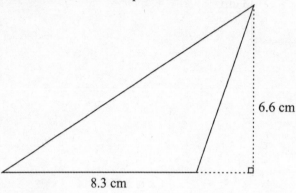

8.3 cm

6.6 cm

Solution

Triangle

$$A = \frac{b \times h}{2}$$

$$A = \frac{(8.3) \times (6.6)}{2}$$

$$= \frac{54.78}{2}$$

$$A = 27.39 \text{ cm}^2$$

Example 4

Find the area of the following parallelogram.

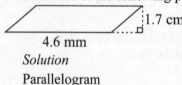

1.7 cm

4.6 mm

Solution

Parallelogram

$$A = b \times h$$

In this diagram, the units are different. The base is 4.6 mm and the height is 1.7 cm. Before solving, change measurements to the same unit. There are 10 mm in 1 cm, so multiply the 1.7 by 10 to get the number of millimetres.

1.7 cm × 10 = 17 mm

Now solve

$$A = (4.6) \times (17)$$

$$A = 78.2 \text{ mm}^2$$

Example 5

Find the area of the trapezoid below.

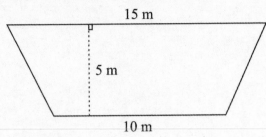

Solution

Trapezoid

$$A = \frac{h(a+b)}{2}$$

In a trapezoid, the *h* is the line that makes a right angle with the parallel bases, *a* and *b*. It does not matter which is *a* and which is *b*.

$$A = \frac{5(15+10)}{2}$$

$$A = \frac{5(25)}{2}$$

$$A = \frac{125}{2}$$

$$A = 62.5 \text{ m}^2$$

Always apply BEDMAS when solving equations

Example 6

Find the area of the circle below.

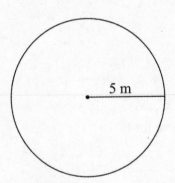

Solution

$$A = \pi r^2$$

$$A = (3.14)(5)^2$$

$$A = (3.14)(25)$$

$$A = 78.5 \text{ m}^2$$

Remember: $\pi = 3.14$

Remember a number squared is the number multiplied by itself, not multiplied by 2.

Remember:
Diameter ÷ 2 = Radius

Example 7

Find the area of the circle below.

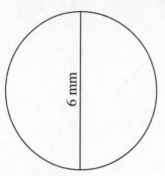

6 mm

Solution

$A = \pi r^2$

$A = (3.14)(3)^2$

$A = (3.14)(9)$

$A = 28.26$ mm^2

If you are given the area of an object and asked to find a missing side length, substitute in the values you know and solve for the missing side length.

Example 8

Find the length of side *l* on the rectangle below.

$A = 126$ m^2 *l*

12 m

Solution

$A = l \times w$

$126 = l \times 12$ — divide both sides by 12 to solve for *l*

$\dfrac{126}{12} = \dfrac{l \times 12}{12}$

$10.5 = l$

The missing length of the rectangle is 10.5 m.

    172

Example 9

Find the length of base b on the parallelogram shown below.

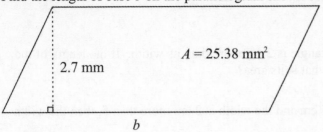

$A = 25.38 \text{ mm}^2$

2.7 mm

b

Solution

$A = b \times h$

$25.38 = b \times 2.7$

$\dfrac{25.38}{2.7} = \dfrac{b \times 2.7}{2.7}$

$9.4 = b$

The base of the parallelogram is 9.4 mm.

Example 10

Find the radius of the circle below.

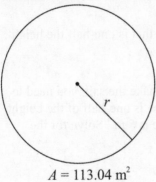

r

$A = 113.04 \text{ m}^2$

Solution

$A = \pi r^2$

$113.04 = (3.14)r^2$

$\dfrac{113.04}{3.14} = \dfrac{3.14r^2}{3.14}$

$36 = r^2$

The opposite of something squared is the square root, so take the square root of both sides to solve for r.

$\sqrt{36} = \sqrt{r^2}$

$6 = r$

The radius of the circle is 6 m.

To solve problems involving area, it is often helpful to draw a diagram and label the parts. This makes it easier to solve.

Example 11

The length of a rectangle is 2 cm more than its width. If the length of the rectangle is 5 cm, what is its area?

Solution

If the length is 5 cm and the width is 2 cm more than 5, then the width must be 7 cm.

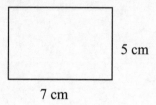

$A = l \times w$
$A = 5 \times 7$
$A = 35$ cm^2

Example 12

A triangular sail has a height of 10 m and a base that is one-half the height. How much material is needed to make the sail?

Solution

To find out how much material is needed to make the sail, you need to find the area. The height is 10 m, and the base is one-half of the height. One-half of 10 is 5, so the base of the triangle is 5 m. Solve for the area.

Triangle

$A = \dfrac{b \times h}{2}$

$A = \dfrac{(5) \times (10)}{2}$

$\quad = \dfrac{25}{2}$

$A = 12.5$ m^2

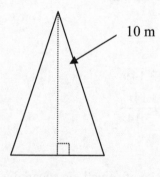

To make the sail, 12.5 m^2 of material is needed.

Example 13

A lawn sprinkler rotates in a complete circle, spraying water a distance of 3.5 m from the sprinkler head. With one complete revolution of the sprinkler, how much of the lawn will it cover?

Solution

This sprinkler is rotating in a circle. The water is sprayed a distance of 3.5 m from the centre, so 3.5 m is the radius of the circle. To see how much of the lawn it will cover, determine the area of this circle.

$A = \pi r^2$
$A = (3.14)(3.5)^2$
$A = (3.14)(12.25)$
$A = 38.465 \text{ m}^2$
    or 38.47 m^2

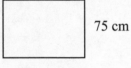

3.5 m

The sprinkler sprays water on 38.47m^2 of lawn.

Example 14

What is the area of the rectangle shown below?

75 cm

2 m

Solution

$A = l \times w$

Notice that the units are different. The length is 75 cm and the width is 2 m. Before solving, change to the same units. There are 100 cm in 1 m, so multiply 2 by 100 to get the centimetre measurement.

$2 \text{ m} \times 100 = 200 \text{ cm}$

Now solve.

$A = (75) \times (200)$
$A = 15\ 000 \text{ cm}^2$

PRACTICE EXERCISE

1. Calculate the area of each of the following shapes.

a)

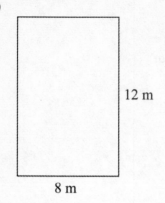

12 m

8 m

b)

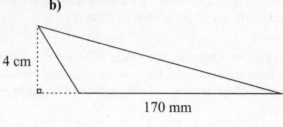

4 cm

170 mm

c)

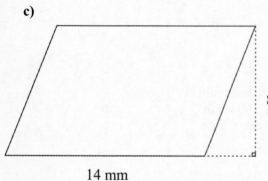

8 mm

14 mm

d)

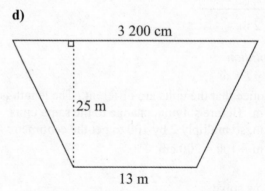

3 200 cm

25 m

13 m

e)

8.5 mm

2. How much carpet is needed to cover a floor that is 1.8 m by 1.4 m?

3. A particular rectangle measures 8 cm by 10 cm, and a particular trapezoid has bases of 16 cm and 20 cm, and a height of 5 cm. Which of these shapes has the greater area and by how much is it bigger?

4. The circumference of a circle is 50.24 mm. What is the area of the circle?

5. In a triangle, the base is three times greater than the height. If the base is 27 cm, what is the area of the triangle?

6. A rectangle measures 3 m by 7 m. What will the area be if each side length is doubled?

7. For each of the following diagrams, find the missing measurement.

   a)

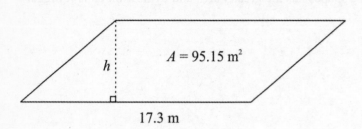

$A = 95.15$ m^2

h

17.3 m

   b)

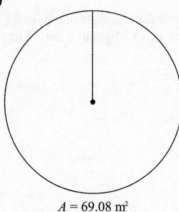

$A = 69.08$ m^2

   c)

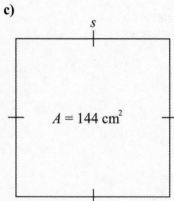

s

$A = 144$ cm^2

8. The area of a rectangular garden is 400 m^2. If one side is 40 m, what is the length of the other side?

178

9. If the perimeter of a square is 80 mm, what is its area?

10. The area of a parallelogram is 72 cm^2. If the base is one-half the height, what are the dimensions of the parallelogram?

11. If the radius of a circular garden doubles, how many times larger will the area be?

Lesson 4   2-D COMPOSITE FIGURES

Composite figures are made of two or more shapes put together. To find the area of a composite figure, calculate the area of each shape, and then add the areas together.

Example 1

Find the area of the composite figure shown below.

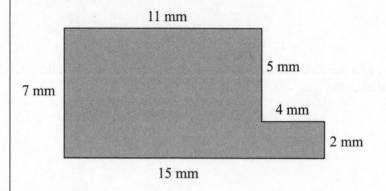

Solution

This shape is made up of two rectangles put together: a large one on the left and a smaller one on the right.

To find the area of the composite shape, find the area of each rectangle and add them together.

$A_{large} = l \times w$
$\phantom{A_{large}} = 7 \times 11$
$\phantom{A_{large}} = 77 \text{ mm}^2$

$A_{small} = l \times w$
$\phantom{A_{small}} = 2 \times 4$
$\phantom{A_{small}} = 8 \text{ mm}^2$

$A_{total} = A_{large} + A_{small}$
$\phantom{A_{total}} = 77 \text{ mm}^2 + 8 \text{ mm}^2$
$\phantom{A_{total}} = 85 \text{ mm}^2$

Example 2

Find the area of the composite figure shown here.

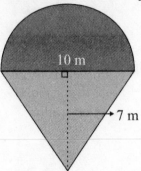

Solution

This composite figure is made up of half a circle and a triangle. Find the area of each part and add.

$$A_{triangle} = \frac{b \times h}{2}$$
$$= \frac{10 \times 7}{2}$$
$$= \frac{70}{2}$$
$$= 35 \text{ m}^2$$

$A_{circle} = \pi r^2$ (make sure you use radius, not diameter)
$$= (3.14)(5)^2$$
$$= (3.14)(25)$$
$$= 78.5 \text{ m}^2$$

There is only half a circle in the diagram, so divide by 2 for half the area.
$$= 78.5 \div 2 = 39.25 \text{ m}^2$$

$$A_{total} = A_{triangle} + A_{half\ circle}$$
$$= 35 \text{ m}^2 + 39.25 \text{ m}^2$$
$$= 74.25 \text{ m}^2$$

To find the area of a composite figure that has one or more pieces missing, subtract the area of the missing piece or pieces from the total area of the figure.

Example 3

Find the area of the shaded part of the composite figure shown below.

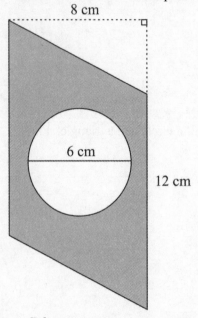

Solution

This composite figure is made up of a parallelogram and a circle. The circle in the middle is white, which indicates that a piece is missing out of the parallelogram. To find the area of the shaded part, find the area of the circle and subtract that from the area of the parallelogram.

$$A_{\text{parallelogram}} = b \times h \qquad A_{\text{circle}} = \pi r^2 \text{ (use radius, not diameter)}$$
$$= 12 \times 8 \qquad\qquad = (3.14)(3)^2$$
$$= 96 \text{ cm}^2 \qquad\qquad = (3.14)(9)$$
$$\qquad\qquad\qquad = 28.26 \text{ cm}^2$$

$$A_{\text{shaded}} = A_{\text{parallelogram}} - A_{\text{circle}}$$
$$= 96 \text{ cm}^2 - 28.26 \text{ cm}^2$$
$$= 67.74 \text{ cm}^2$$

Example 4

Find the area of the shaded part of the composite figure below.

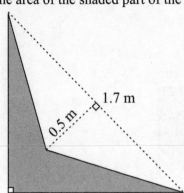

1.2 m

0.5 m

1.7 m

1.2 m

Solution

This composite figure has missing pieces, so you will need to subtract the area of the smaller triangle from the area of the large right triangle.

$$A_{\text{right triangle}} = \frac{b \times h}{2} \qquad A_{\text{triangle}} = \frac{b \times h}{2}$$

$$= \frac{1.2 \times 1.2}{2} \qquad = \frac{1.7 \times 0.5}{2}$$

$$= \frac{1.44}{2} \qquad = \frac{0.85}{2}$$

$$= 0.72 \text{ m}^2 \qquad = 0.425 \text{ m}^2$$

$$A_{\text{total}} = A_{\text{right triangle}} - A_{\text{triangle}}$$
$$= 0.72 \text{ m}^2 - 0.425 \text{ m}^2$$
$$= 0.295 \text{ m}^2$$

Remember that sides with the same number of ticks on them are equal in length.

Example 5

Find the perimeter and area of the following composite figure.

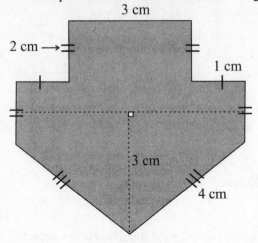

Solution

Perimeter = add all sides together

Start one place and work your way around adding.

Starting at the top:

P = 3 cm + 2 cm + 1 cm + 2 cm + 4 cm + 4 cm + 2 cm + 1 cm + 2 cm

P = 21 cm

Area = find the area of each shape and add them together because the entire figure is shaded in.

$A_{\text{total}} = A_{\text{top rectangle}} + A_{\text{bottom rectangle}} + A_{\text{triangle}}$

$$\begin{aligned} A_{\text{top rectangle}} &= l \times w \\ &= 3 \times 2 \\ &= 6 \text{ cm}^2 \end{aligned} \qquad \begin{aligned} A_{\text{bottom rectangle}} &= l \times w \\ &= 5 \times 2 \end{aligned}$$

(the 5 comes from adding 1 + 3 + 1 for the length)

$$= 14 \text{ cm}^2$$

$$A_{\text{right triangle}} = \frac{b \times h}{2}$$

$$= \frac{5 \times 3}{2}$$

$$= \frac{15}{2}$$

$$= 7.5 \text{ cm}^2$$

$$\begin{aligned} A_{\text{total}} &= A_{\text{top rectangle}} + A_{\text{bottom rectangle}} + A_{\text{triangle}} \\ &= 6 \text{ cm}^2 + 14 \text{ cm}^2 + 7.5 \text{ cm}^2 \\ &= 27.5 \text{ cm}^2 \end{aligned}$$

PRACTICE QUIZ 1

1. Find the missing length on each right triangle below. Round your answer to the nearest tenth if necessary.

    a)

    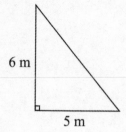

    6 m

    5 m

    b)

    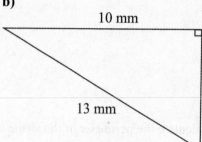

    10 mm

    13 mm

    c)

    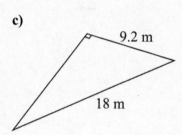

    9.2 m

    18 m

2. A computer screen is 30 cm by 20 cm. What is the length of its diagonal?

3. A flag pole is 4 m high. There is a wire attached from the tip of the pole to the ground. If the wire is 8.2 m long, at what distance from the bottom of the pole is the wire attached to the ground?

4. Calculate the perimeter of the shape below.

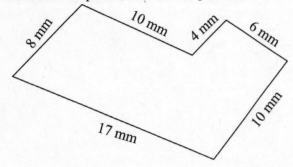

5. If a circle has a radius of 8 mm, what is its circumference?

6. Find the length of the missing side on the shape below.

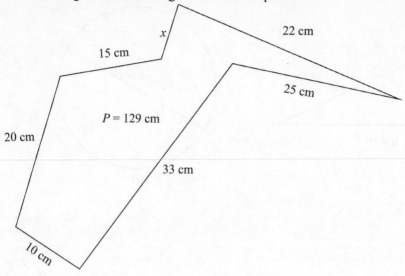

15 cm

x

22 cm

P = 129 cm

20 cm

25 cm

33 cm

10 cm

7. A hexagon has a perimeter of 84 cm. What is the length of each side?

8. Calculate the area of each figure below. Round your answer to the nearest tenth if necessary.

a)

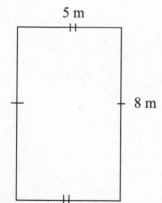

5 m

8 m

b)

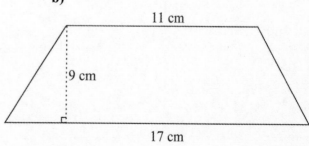

11 cm

9 cm

17 cm

c)

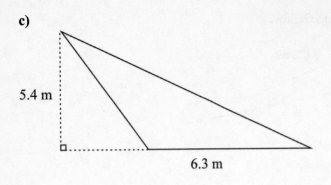

5.4 m

6.3 m

d)

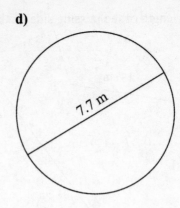

7.7 m

9. The base of a parallelogram is 4 cm. The height of this parallelogram is twice the base. What is its area?

10. Find the length of the missing side on each of the shapes below.

a)

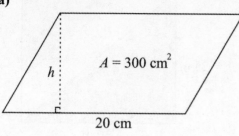

$A = 300 \text{ cm}^2$

h

20 cm

b)

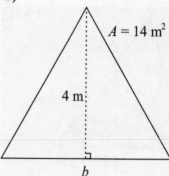

$A = 14 \text{ m}^2$

4 m

b

11. Find the area of the shaded part of each diagram below.

a)

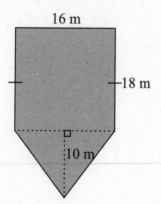

16 m

18 m

10 m

b)

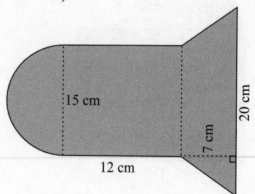

15 cm

12 cm

7 cm

20 cm

c)

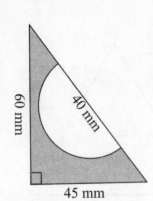

d)

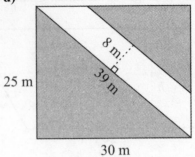

13. Find the perimeter and area of the following diagram.

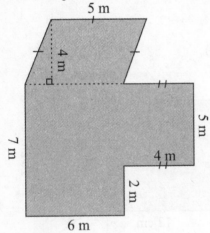

14. The perimeter of a square is 52 cm. What is its area?

15. The base of triangle is 6 m. The height of the triangle is 2 m less than the base. What is the area of the triangle?

16. The circumference of a circle is 25.12 m. What is its area?

Lesson 5   3-D OBJECTS

Three-dimensional (3-D) shapes can generally be classified into three main groups: prisms, pyramids, and circular shapes.

Prisms are solids that are made up of rectangles and various end pieces. The names for the solids come from the end pieces. A rectangular prism has a rectangular face on each end and 4 rectangles that join the ends together.

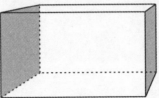

A triangular prism has a triangle face on each end, and 3 rectangles that join them.

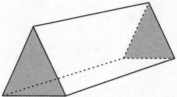

A pentagonal prism has 2 pentagonal faces and 5 rectangles that join them.

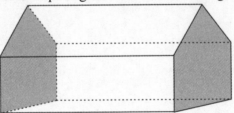

The number of sides on each prism end piece determines the number of rectangles in a prism.

Pyramids are made up of a base, and triangles that meet at a single point at the top. The names for the pyramids come from the shape of the base. A square pyramid has a square on the bottom and 4 equal triangles that meet at a single vertex.

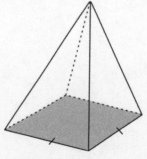

A pentagonal pyramid has a pentagon on the bottom and 5 equal triangles that meet at a single vertex.

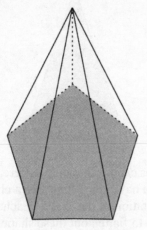

The most common three-dimensional shapes that involve circles are cylinders, spheres, and cones.

Cylinders are made up of two circles and a rectangle around the middle.

A sphere is a round, ball-shaped, object.

NOTES

A cone has a circular base and a rounded shape that meets at a single point.

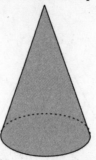

Three-dimensional shapes can be shown in different ways. The solid shape is what you see when you have something like a child's building block. This is the solid representation of the shape. Each of the outside edges are called faces. If you were to flatten out these shapes, the two-dimensional (2-D) drawing you would see is called the **net**. The net is a 2-D representation of a 3-D object. You can use nets to calculate the surface area of different objects.

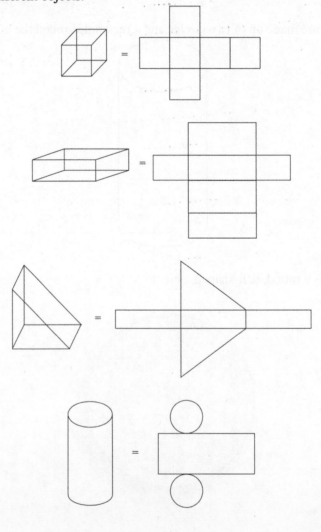

When just the edges and vertices of a shape are shown, it is called a skeleton. The skeleton is the basic shape of the figure without any solid faces. Building a shape out of toothpick edges and marshmallow vertices to hold the edges together would give you the skeleton of the shape.

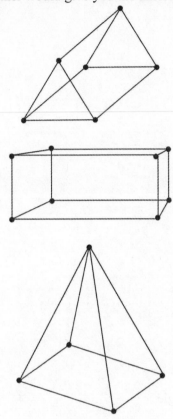

To group the various shapes, consider specific characteristics and group them accordingly.

Example 1

List the solids with eight vertices.

Solution

Look at the shapes from the beginning of this lesson and count the vertices. A rectangular prism and a cube each have eight vertices. A heptagonal pyramid also has eight vertices. It has 7 vertices around the bottom in the heptagon, and the one at the point where all the triangles meet.

Reminder:
heptagon has 7 sides

Example 2

Name all the solids that have at least one rectangle.

Solution

Any type of prism, a square pyramid (because a square is a rectangle, just a special one), and a cylinder (has a rectangle around the middle)

PRACTICE EXERCISE

1. List the 2-D shapes that make up the 3-D object named below.
   a) pentagonal pyramid

   b) octagonal prism

   c) cylinder

2. List three 3-D shapes with no parallel sides

3. List all the shapes with at least one rounded edge

4. Name all the shapes that contain at least one rectangle

5. Name the shapes that have fewer than four edges

6. Name a shape with six vertices

7. For each shape named below,
  i. draw the diagram
  ii. draw the skeleton
  iii. draw the net
  iv. state the number of edges
  v. state the number of vertices

  a) Rectangular prism

  b) Square pyramid

c) cube

d) triangular pyramid

Lesson 6 SURFACE AREA

The surface area of a three-dimensional solid is the sum of the areas of the faces of the shape. To calculate the surface area, draw the net of the shape, figure out the area of each part, and add them together.

Example 1

Calculate the surface area of the following shape.

Rectangular Prism

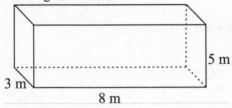

3 m   5 m   8 m

Solution

The net for the rectangular prism is

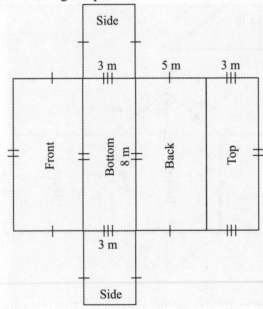

When you look at this net, you realize that there are some sides that are the same size. The front and the back are the same. The top and the bottom are the same, and the sides are the same. When calculating the area, you can just find it for one side and then multiply by two because there are two parts the same.

Front and Back
(2 equal rectangles)

$A = l \times w$

$A = 5 \times 8$

$A = 40 \times 2$ (front and back)

$A = 80 \text{ m}^2$

Top and Bottom
(2 equal rectangles)

$A = l \times w$

$A = 3 \times 8$

$A = 24 \times 2$ (top and bottom)

$A = 48 \text{ m}^2$

Sides (2 equal rectangles)

$A = l \times w$
$A = 5 \times 3$
$A = 15 \times 2$ (2 sides)
$A = 30 \text{ m}^2$

Surface Area $(SA) = 80 \text{ m}^2 + 48 \text{ m}^2 + 30 \text{ m}^2 = 158 \text{ m}^2$

Example 2

Calculate the surface area of the triangular prism shown.
Triangular Prism

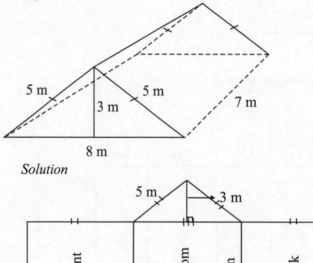

Solution

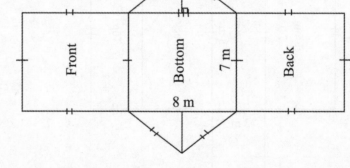

In this net, all the rectangles are the same size. This is because the triangle is an equilateral triangle (all the sides are the same), so the rectangles joining all the sides will be the same. Calculate the area of one rectangle and multiply by 3 because there are three equal rectangles.

Front, back (2 equal rectangles)

$A = l \times w$
$A = 7 \times 5$
$A = 35 \times 2$ (2 equal rectangles)
$A = 70 \text{ m}^2$

Bottom rectangle

$A = l \times w$
$A = 7 \times 8$
$A = 56$

Sides (2 equal triangles)

$$A = \frac{b \times h}{2}$$

$$A = \frac{(8) \times (3)}{2}$$

$$= \frac{24}{2}$$

$$= 12$$

$A = 12 \times 2$ (2 equal triangles)

$A = 24$ m^2

$SA = 70$ m^2 + 56 m^2 = 150 m^2

Example 3

Find the surface area of the square pyramid shown below.

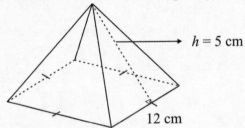

$h = 5$ cm

12 cm

Solution

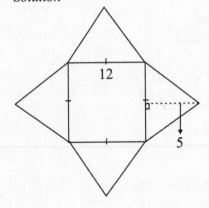

12

5

Be careful when working with triangular prisms. Check to see if the rectangles are all the same size or different sizes. Only equilateral triangles have rectangles that are all the same size.

NOTES

Bottom (square)

$A = l \times w$

$A = 12 \times 12$

$A = 144$

$A = 144 \text{ cm}^2$

Sides (4 equal triangles)

$A = \dfrac{b \times h}{2}$

$A = \dfrac{(12) \times (5)}{2}$

$= \dfrac{60}{2}$

$A = 30 \times 4$ (4 equal triangles)

$A = 120 \text{ cm}^2$

$SA = 144 \text{ cm}^2 + 120 \text{ cm}^2 = 264 \text{ cm}^2$

Example 4

What is the surface area of the cube shown below?

Cube

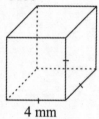

4 mm

Solution

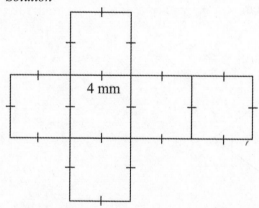

4 mm

A cube has six equal sides, so just find the area of one, and then multiply by 6.

$A = l \times w$

$A = 4 \times 4$

$A = 16 \times 6$ (6 equal squares)

$A = 96 \text{ mm}^2$

$SA = 96 \text{ mm}^2$

Example 5

Find the surface area of the following cylinder.

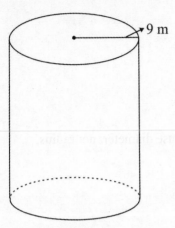

9 m

A cylinder is made up of two equal circles and one rectangle that goes around the middle.

Solution

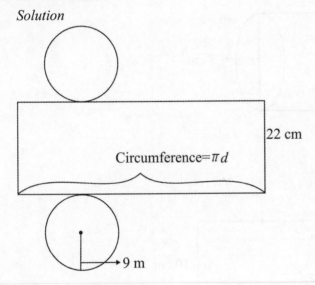

22 cm

Circumference=πd

9 m

Circles (2 equal circles)

$A = \pi r^2$

$A = (3.14)(9)^2$

$A = (3.14)(81)$

$A = 254.34 \times 2$

$A = 508.68$ m^2

The formula for area of a rectangle is given by the formula $A = l \times w$. In the rectangular part of the cylinder, the l is equal to the height, but you need to calculate the width. When you unroll the middle, the width is the same distance as what goes around the circle. The width of the rectangle is equal to the circumference of the circle.

So, for the rectangle, rewrite the area formula as follows:

$A = l \times w$

$A = h \times$ circumference

$A = h \times \pi d$

Rectangle

Solution

$A = h \times \pi d$

$r = 9, d = 9 \times 2 = 18$

$A = 22 \times (3.14)(18)$ — make sure that you use diameter, not radius, which was given

$A = 1\ 243.44\ \text{m}^2$

$SA = 508.68\ \text{m}^2 + 1\ 243.44\ \text{m}^2 = 1\ 752.12\ \text{m}^2$

Example 6

What is the surface area of the cylinder shown below?

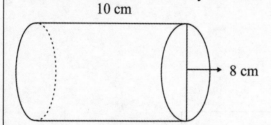

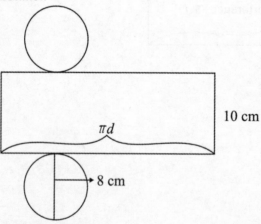

Solution

Circles (2 equal circles)	Rectangle
$A = \pi r^2$	$A = h \times \pi d$
$A = (3.14)(4)^2$	$A = 10 \times (3.14)(8)$
$A = (3.14)(16)$	$A = 251.2\ \text{cm}^2$
$A = 50.24 \times 2$	
$A = 100.48\ \text{cm}^2$	

$SA = 100.48\ \text{cm}^2 + 251.2\ \text{cm}^2 = 351.68\ \text{cm}^2$

Example 7

Anne wants to paint the walls of her bedroom. If the room is 3.5 m long, 3 m wide, and 2.5 m high, how much paint will she need to cover the walls. If paint costs $1.49/m^2, how much will the paint cost?

Solution

Because Anne is only painting the walls, you only need to worry about the front, back, and sides of the rectangular prism, **not** the top and the bottom.

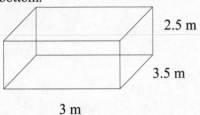

2.5 m

3.5 m

3 m

Front and Back (2 equal rectangles)

$A = l \times w$

$A = 3 \times 2.5$

$A = 7.5 \times 2$

$A = 15 \text{ m}^2$

Sides (2 equal rectangles)

$A = l \times w$

$A = 3.5 \times 2.5$

$A = 8.75 \times 2$

$A = 17.5 \text{ m}^2$

$SA = 15 \text{ m}^2 + 17.5 \text{ m}^2 = 32.5 \text{ m}^2$

Anne will need 32.5 m^2 of paint to cover the walls.

Because paint costs $1.49/m^2, multiply to find its cost.

$32.5 \text{ m}^2 \times \$1.49/\text{m}^2 = \$48.43$

It will cost Anne $48.43 to paint her room.

Remember with money to round to the nearest penny.

PRACTICE EXERCISE

1. Find the surface area of the following shapes.

   a)

   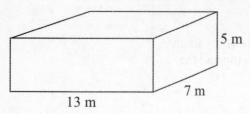

   5 m

   13 m   7 m

   b)

   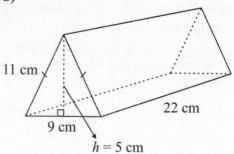

   11 cm

   22 cm

   9 cm

   $h = 5$ cm

   c)

   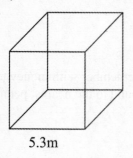

   5.3m

   d)

   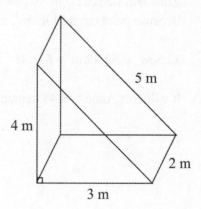

   5 m

   4 m

   2 m

   3 m

e)

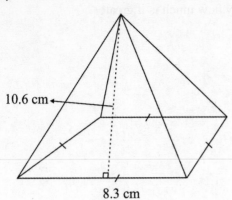

10.6 cm

8.3 cm

f)

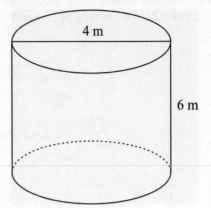

4 m

6 m

g)

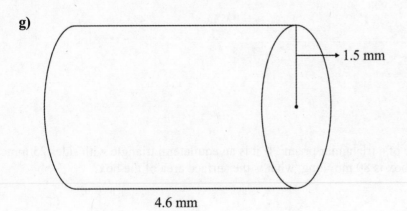

1.5 mm

4.6 mm

2. A cylinder has a diameter of 15 cm and a height of 35 cm. A rectangular prism has dimensions 10 cm by 8 cm by 25 cm. Which has a greater surface area, and by how much is it greater?

3. A soup can has a radius of 3.5 cm and the height of 11 cm. What is the area of the **label** that goes around the can?

4. A chocolate bar box is the shape of a triangular prism. If it is an equilateral triangle with sides 25 mm and a height of 18 mm, and the box is 80 mm long, what is the surface area of the box?

Lesson 7   VOLUME

The volume of a three-dimensional solid is the amount of space that the object takes up. To calculate the volume of any three-dimensional shape, use the formula: area of the base times the height of the object.

V = Area of Base × Height

Example 1

Calculate the volume of the rectangular prism shown below

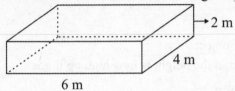

6 m

Solution

V = area of the base × height of object

For a rectangular prism, the base is a rectangle and the height is how high up it goes.

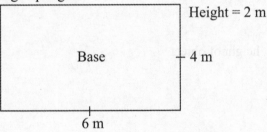

Height = 2 m

4 m

Base

6 m

V = area of the base × height of object

$V = (l \times w) \times$ height

$V = (6 \times 4) \times 2$

$V = 24 \times 2$

$V = 48 \text{ m}^3$

The units for volume are always cubed because you are multiplying three dimensions together. The exponent that indicates cubed units is a 3.

NOTES

Example 2

Find the volume of the cube shown below.

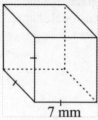

7 mm

Solution

V = area of the base × height of object

For a cube, the base is a square and the height is how high up it goes.

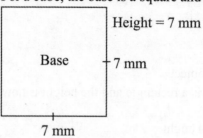

Base

Height = 7 mm

7 mm

7 mm

V = area of the base × height of object

$V = (l \times w) \times$ height

$V = (7 \times 7) \times 7$

$V = 49 \times 7$

$V = 343$ mm^3

Example 3

What is the volume of the triangular prism shown below?

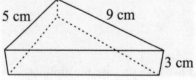

5 cm   9 cm   3 cm

Solution

V = area of the base × height of object

For a triangular prism, the base is a triangle and the height is how high up it goes.

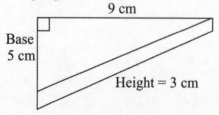

9 cm

Base
5 cm

Height = 3 cm

V = area of the base × height of object

$V = \dfrac{b \times h}{2} \times$ height

The height you are multiplying by needs to be the height of the entire prism, not just the height of a triangle

If a triangular prism is sitting on a rectangular piece, you need to turn it over so it is sitting on its base. The base always needs to be an end piece of a prism, not a rectangular part.

$$V = \frac{5 \times 9}{2} \times 3$$

$$V = \frac{45}{2} \times 3$$

$$V = 22.5 \times 3$$

$$V = 67.5 \text{ cm}^3$$

Example 4

What is the volume of the cylinder shown below?

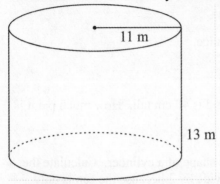

Solution

V = area of the base × height of object

For a cylinder, the base is a circle and the height is how high up it goes.

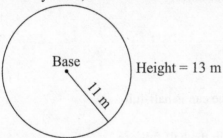

V = area of the base × height of object

$V = \pi r^2 \times$ height

$V = (3.14)(11)^2 \times 13$

$V = (3.14)(121) \times 13$

$V = 379.94 \times 13$

$V = 4\,939.22 \text{ m}^3$

Example 5

A juice box has dimensions of 3 cm × 2 cm × 7 cm. How much juice can it hold?

You know that a juice box is in the shape of a rectangular prism. Find the volume to see how much juice it can hold.

Solution

V = area of the base × height of object

$V = (l \times w) \times$ height

$V = (3 \times 2) \times 7$

$V = 6 \times 7$

$V = 42$ cm^3

The juice box can hold 42 cm^3 of juice.

Example 6

A paint can has a diameter of 25 cm and is 40 cm tall. How much paint is there in the can if it is half-full.

Solution

You know that a paint can is in the shape of a cylinder. Calculate the volume of the cylinder and then divide by 2 because the can is only half-full.

V = area of the base × height of object

$V = \pi r^2 \times$ height

$V = (3.14)(12.5)^2 \times 40$

$V = (3.14)(156.25) \times 40$

$V = 490.625 \times 40$

$V = 1\ 9625$ cm^3 ÷ 2 because the can is half-full

$V = 9\ 812.5$ cm^3

There is 9 812.5 cm^3 of paint in the half full-can.

PRACTICE EXERCISE

1. Find the volume of the following object.

a)

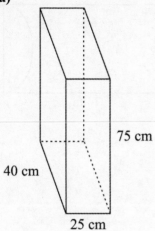

75 cm

40 cm

25 cm

b)

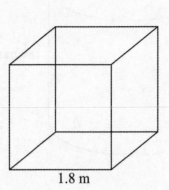

1.8 m

c)

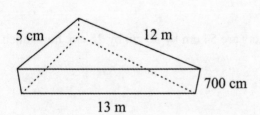

5 cm   12 m

700 cm

13 m

d)

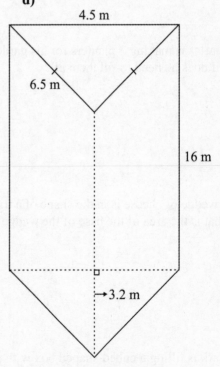

4.5 m

6.5 m

16 m

3.2 m

e)

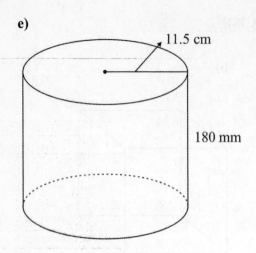

11.5 cm

180 mm

f)

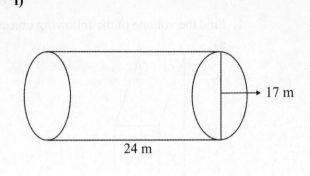

17 m

24 m

2. If a fish tank has dimensions of 90 cm by 75 cm by 60 cm, how much water can it hold?

3. Charles is making 3 planters for his garden. If the planters are 54 cm by 30 cm by 25 cm, how much soil does he need to fill them all?

4. A wedge of cheese is in the shape of a triangular prism. If its volume is 35 cm^3 and its height is 5 cm, what is the area of the base of the wedge of cheese?

5. Mark is filling a cubed-shaped box with packing peanuts. If he measured one side of the box to be 55 cm, how many cubic centimetres cm^3 of peanuts does he need to fill the box?

Lesson 8   3-D COMPOSITE FIGURES

Three-dimensional composite figures are made of two or more shapes put together. To calculate the surface area of a 3-D composite figure, find the surface area of each shape, and then add the surface areas together. To calculate the volume of a 3-D composite figure, find the volume of each shape, and then add the volumes together.

Example 1

Find the surface area of the following composite figure.

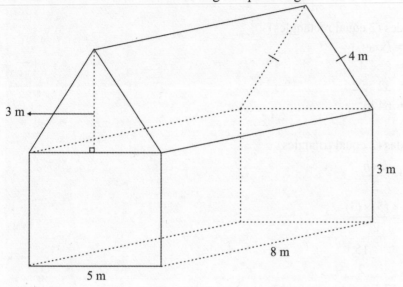

Solution

To find the surface area of this shape, calculate the outside surfaces. Because this is a solid shape, find the surface area of each face and then add them together.

Break the figure into two shapes: the rectangular prism and the triangular prism.

Rectangular prism: there is no top because the triangular prism sits on top of the prism.

Front and Back (2 equal rectangles)   Bottom (no top)

$A = l \times w$ $A = l \times w$

$A = 5 \times 3$ $A = 5 \times 8$

$A = 15 \times 2$ $A = 40$

$A = 30 \text{ m}^2$ $A = 40 \text{ m}^2$

Sides (2 equal rectangles)

$A = l \times w$

$A = 8 \times 3$

$A = 24 \times 2$

$A = 48 \text{ m}^2$

Surface area of rectangular prism $= 30 \text{ m}^2 + 40 \text{ m}^2 + 48 \text{ m}^2 = 118 \text{ m}^2$

Triangular prism: There is no bottom to this figure because it sits on the rectangular prism.

Sides (2 equal rectangles)

$A = l \times w$

$A = 8 \times 4$

$A = 32 \times 2$

$A = 64 \text{ m}^2$

Sides (2 equal triangles)

$A = \dfrac{b \times h}{2}$

$A = \dfrac{(5) \times (3)}{2}$

$\quad = \dfrac{15}{2}$

$A = 7.5 \times 2$ because there are 2 triangles that are equal

$A = 15 \text{ m}^2$

Surface area of triangular prism $= 64 \text{ m}^2 + 15 \text{ m}^2 = 79 \text{ m}^2$

Surface area of composite figure = rectangular prism + triangular prism $= 118 \text{ m}^2 + 79 \text{ m}^2 = 197 \text{ m}^2$

Example 2

Find the surface area of the composite figure shown below.

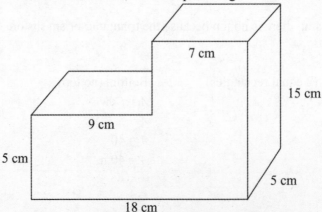

To solve for the surface area of this composite figure, break the shape into two parts. The rectangular prism on the left, and the one on the right. (You could also break it up and down.)

Solution

Left Rectangular Prism:

For this prism, there are five surfaces: a front and back, a top and bottom, and a left side. There is no right side because that is attached to the other prism.

Front and Back
(2 equal rectangles)
$A = l \times w$
$A = 5 \times 9$
$A = 45 \times 2$
$A = 90 \text{ cm}^2$

Bottom and top
(2 equal rectangles)
$A = l \times w$
$A = 5 \times 9$
$A = 45 \times 2$
$A = 90 \text{ cm}^2$

Left side
$A = l \times w$
$A = 5 \times 5$
$A = 25$
$A = 25 \text{ cm}^2$

Surface area of left rectangular prism = $90 \text{ cm}^2 + 90 \text{ cm}^2 + 25 \text{ cm}^2 = 205 \text{ cm}^2$

Right Rectangular Prism:

For this prism, there are six surfaces: a front and back piece, a top and bottom piece, a full right side, and a smaller left side. For the left side of this prism, use a length of 10 cm. This length is calculated by subtracting the height of the left rectangular prism (5 cm) from the total height of the right rectangular prism (15 cm).

Front and Back
(2 equal rectangles)
$A = l \times w$
$A = 15 \times 7$
$A = 105 \times 2$
$A = 210 \text{ cm}^2$

Bottom and top
(2 rectangles)
$A = l \times w$
$A = 5 \times 7$
$A = 35 \times 2$
$A = 70 \text{ cm}^2$

Right side
$A = l \times w$
$A = 15 \times 5$
$A = 75$
$A = 75 \text{ cm}^2$

Left Side
$A = l \times w$
$A = 10 \times 5$
$A = 50$
$A = 50 \text{ cm}^2$

Surface area of right rectangular prism = $210 \text{ cm}^2 + 70 \text{ cm}^2 + 75 \text{ cm}^2 + 50 \text{ cm}^2 = 405 \text{ cm}^2$

Surface area of composite figure = Left Prism + Right Prism
$$= 205 \text{ cm}^2 + 405 \text{ cm}^2 = 610 \text{ cm}^2$$

Example 3

Calculate the surface area of the composite figure below.

To find the surface area of a composite figure that has one or more pieces missing find the surface area of the total large shape then subtract the area of the end pieces of the smaller shape, and add the area of the inside surface. Surface area can be thought of as anything that air could touch. Air could go right though the centre of an object, so all that centre surface must be included in the surface area.

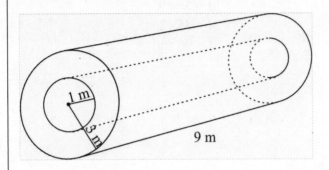

Solution

Large Cylinder
Circles (2 equal)

$A = \pi r^2$

$A = (3.14)(3)^2$

$A = (3.14)(9)$

$A = 28.26 \times 2$

$A = 56.52 \text{ cm}^2$

Rectangle

$A = h \times \pi d$

$A = 9 \times (3.14)(6)$

$A = 169.56 \text{ cm}^2$

SA of large cylinder = 56.52 cm² +169.56 cm² = 226.08 cm²

Small cylinder
Circles (2 end pieces that will be subtracted)

$A = \pi r^2$

$A = (3.14)(1)^2$

$A = (3.14)(1)$

$A = 3.14 \times 2$

$A = 6.28 \text{ cm}^2$

Rectangle (middle that will be added)

$A = h \times \pi d$

$A = 9 \times (3.14)(2)$

$A = 56.52 \text{ cm}^2$

Total surface area = large cylinder – end pieces of small + middle of small

$SA = 226.08 \text{ cm}^2 - 6.28 \text{ cm}^2 + 56.52 \text{ cm}^2 = 276.05 \text{ cm}^2$

Example 4

Find the surface area of the composite figure shown below.

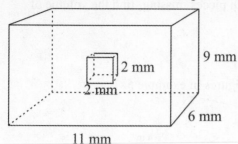

As in the previous example, there is a piece missing out of the middle of this figure, calculate the surface area of the large prism, then subtract the end pieces of the smaller one, and add the rectangular insides.

Solution

Large Prism

Front and Back	Top and Bottom
(2 equal rectangles)	(2 equal rectangles)

$A = l \times w$ $A = l \times w$

$A = 9 \times 11$ $A = 6 \times 11$

$A = 99 \times 2$ $A = 66 \times 2$

$A = 198 \text{ mm}^2$ $A = 132 \text{ mm}^2$

Sides (2 equal rectangles)

$A = l \times w$

$A = 9 \times 6$

$A = 54 \times 2$

$A = 108 \text{ mm}^2$

Surface Area of large prism =
$198 \text{ mm}^2 + 132 \text{ mm}^2 + 108 \text{ mm}^2 = 438 \text{ m}^2$

Smaller Prism

Front and Back	Top and Bottom
(end pieces to be subtracted)	(middle piece to be added)

$A = l \times w$ $A = l \times w$

$A = 2 \times 2$ $A = 2 \times 6$

$A = 4 \times 2$ $A = 12 \times 2$

$A = 8 \text{ mm}^2$ $A = 24 \text{ mm}^2$

Sides (middle to be added)

$A = l \times w$

$A = 2 \times 6$

$A = 12 \times 2$

$A = 24 \text{ mm}^2$

Total surface area = large prism − end pieces of small + middle of small
$SA = 438 \text{ mm}^2 - 8 \text{ mm}^2 + 24 \text{ mm}^2 + 24 \text{ mm}^2 = 478 \text{ mm}^2$

NOTES

Finding the volume of 3-D composite figures is much easier than finding the surface area. For figures with no missing parts, just find the volume of each part, then add. For figures with pieces missing, find the volume of each part and subtract.

Example 5

Find the volume of the composite figures in example 5.

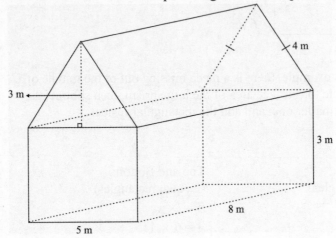

Solution

V = Volume of rectangular prism + Volume of triangular prism

Rectangular prism

V = area of the base × height of object

V = (l × w) × height

V = (8 × 5) × 3

V = 40 × 3

V = 120 m^3

Volume of triangular prism (remember to think of this shape as sitting on the base)

V = area of the base × height of object

$V = \dfrac{b \times h}{2} \times$ height

$V = \dfrac{8 \times 3}{2} \times 5$

$V = \dfrac{24}{2} \times 5$

V = 12 × 5

V = 60 m^3

V = Volume of rectangular prism + Volume of triangular prism

V = 120 m^3 + 60 m^3 = 180 m^3

Example 6

Find the volume of the composite figure in example 2.

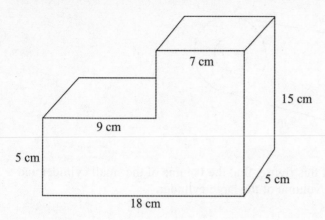

Solution

V = Volume of left rectangular prism + Volume of right rectangular prism

Left prism
V = area of the base × height of object
$V = (l \times w) \times$ height
$V = (9 \times 5) \times 5$
$V = 45 \times 5$
$V = 225$ cm^3

Right prism
V = area of the base × height of object
$V = (l \times w) \times$ height
$V = (7 \times 5) \times 15$
$V = 35 \times 15$
$V = 525$ cm^3

V = Volume of left rectangular prism + Volume of right rectangular prism
$V = 225$ cm$^3 + 525$ cm$^3 = 750$ cm^3

Example 7

Find the volume of the composite figure in example 3.

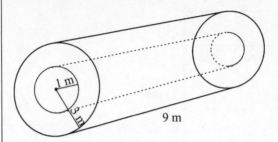

To find the volume of this figure, find the volume of the small cylinder and subtract that from the volume of the large cylinder.

Solution

V = Volume of large cylinder – Volume of small cylinder

Large Cylinder

V = area of the base × height of object

$V = \pi r^2 \times$ height

$V = (3.14)\,(3)^2 \times 9$

$V = (3.14)\,(9) \times 9$

$V = 28.26 \times 9$

$V = 254.34$ cm^3

Small Cylinder

V = area of the base × height of object

$V = \pi r^2 \times$ height

$V = (3.14)\,(1)^2 \times 9$

$V = (3.14)\,(1) \times 9$

$V = 3.14 \times 9$

$V = 28.26$ cm^3

V = Volume of large cylinder – Volume of small cylinder

$V = 254.34$ cm^3 – 28.26 cm^3

$V = 226.08$ cm^3

Example 8

Find the volume of the composite figure in example 4.

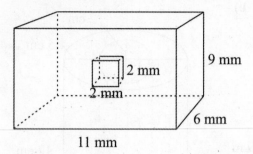

To find the volume of this figure, find the volume of the small rectangular prism and subtract that from the volume of the large rectangular.

Solution

V = Volume of large prism – Volume of small prism

Large Prism

V = area of the base × height of object

$V = (l \times w) \times$ height

$V = (6 \times 11) \times 9$

$V = 66 \times 9$

$V = 594$ mm^3

Small Prism

V = area of the base × height of object

$V = (l \times w) \times$ height

$V = (6 \times 2) \times 2$

$V = 12 \times 2$

$V = 24$ mm^3

V = Volume of large prism – Volume of small prism

$V = 594$ mm^3 – 24 mm^3 = 570 mm^3

PRACTICE EXERCISE

1. Find the surface area and volume of the following composite figures.

a)

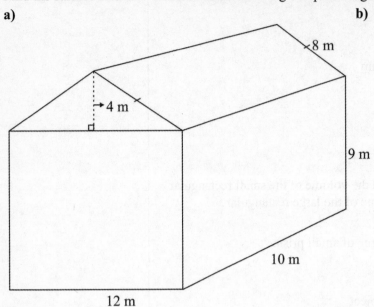

b)

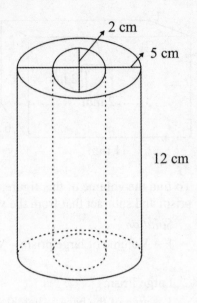

c)

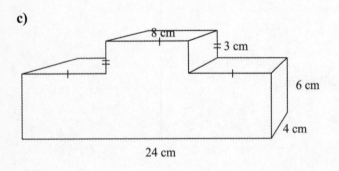

d)

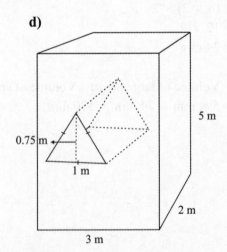

e)

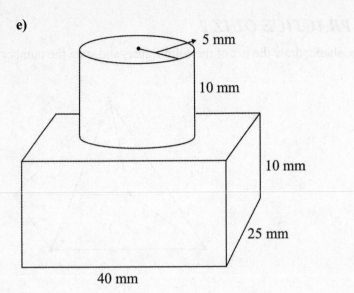

5 mm

10 mm

10 mm

25 mm

40 mm

PRACTICE QUIZ 2

1. For each skeleton shown below, name the shape, draw the net of the solid figure, and state the number of edges and vertices.

a)

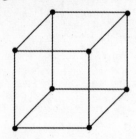

b)

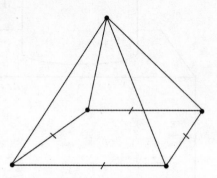

c)

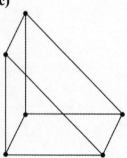

2. Find the surface area of each figure below.

a)

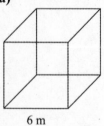

6 m

b)

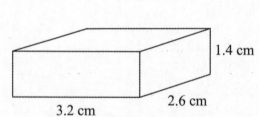

1.4 cm

2.6 cm

3.2 cm

c)

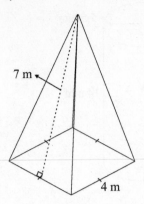

7 m

4 m

d)

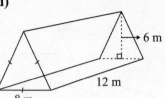

6 m

12 m

8 m

e)

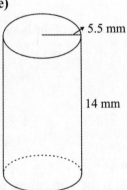

5.5 mm

14 mm

3. Find the volume of each of the following figures.

a)

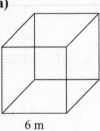

6 m

b)

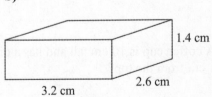

1.4 cm

2.6 cm

3.2 cm

c)

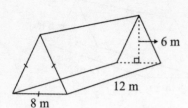

d)

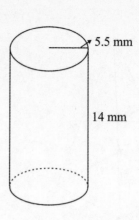

4. A textbook has dimensions of 20 cm by 23 cm by 3 cm thick. What is the surface area of the book?

5. A cylindrical-shaped tank has a diameter of 1.5 m and a height of 7.5 m. What is the surface area of the tank if it is sitting on the ground and the bottom is not included in the area?

6. A coffee cup is 10 cm tall and has a diameter of 7 cm. How much coffee would it hold if it is filled 1 cm from the top?

7. A fridge is 1.25 m tall, 0.75 m wide, and 1 m deep. How many cubic centimetres of food can it hold?

8. Find the surface area and volume of each composite figure below.

a)

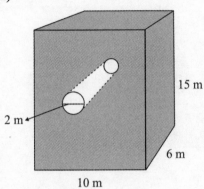

15 m

2 m

6 m

10 m

b)

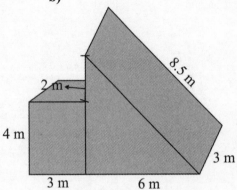

8.5 m

2 m

4 m

3 m

3 m

6 m

Lesson 9 ENLARGEMENTS AND REDUCTIONS

NOTES

An enlargement or a reduction involves taking an object and making it larger or smaller respectively. The scale factor between the original object and the new larger or smaller, object (called the image) is a number that tells you how much larger or smaller the object was made. If the scale factor is a number greater than one, the object was made larger. If the scale factor is a number smaller than one, the object was made smaller.

Consider the following diagram of a triangle that has been enlarged.

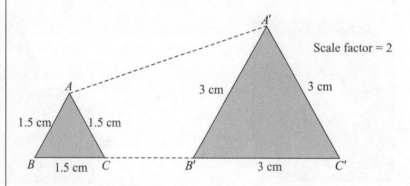

The image of the triangle is larger than the original, so the scale factor must be a number greater than 1.

In the original triangle, line AB is 1.5 cm. In the image, line $A'B'$ (said A prime, B prime) is 3 cm. The size of the triangle has been doubled, so the scale factor of the diagram is 2.

To find the scale factor of any enlargement or reduction:
- pick one length in the image
- find the corresponding length in the original
- divide the length of image by the length in the original to give you the scale factor

The ' symbol is called the prime symbol. It is used to show the vertex on an image that corresponds with a vertex on the original diagram.

Vertex A on a diagram would be labelled as A' (said A prime) on the image after an enlargement or reduction.

Scale factor =

$$\frac{\text{Image length}}{\text{Original length}}$$

Consider the following diagram.

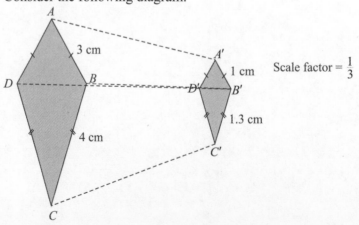

232

Notice in this diagram, the image (labelled with the ' symbols) is smaller than the original, so the scale factor is going to be less then one.

- Pick one length in the image
  Line $A'B'$ is 1 cm long.
- Find the corresponding length in the original
  Line AB is 3 cm long.
- Divide the length of image by the length in the original to find the scale factor.

$1 \div 3 = \dfrac{1}{3} = 0.\overline{3}$

The scale factor for the diagram is $\dfrac{1}{3}$, which means the image is three times smaller then the original diagram.

If the scale factor of a diagram is given and you are asked to find the length of a missing side, take the length of the original side and multiply by the scale factor to find the length of the missing side on the image.

Example 1

What is the length of side $\overline{C'B'}$ in the image below?

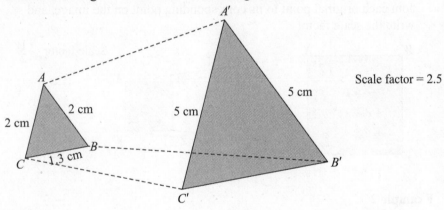

Scale factor = 2.5

Solution

The length of $\overline{CB}$ is 1.3 cm, and the a scale factor of the image is 2.5. Multiply to find new length:
1.3 cm × 2.5 = 3.25 cm.
The length of side $C'B'$ in the image is 3.25 cm.

Example 2

Draw a square with 3 cm sides and label it WXYZ. Using a scale factor of one-half, draw an image of the square.

Solution

The scale factor is $\dfrac{1}{2}$ so the image will be smaller than the original.

This is a reduction.

Draw and label the original square.

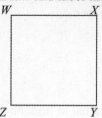

Calculate how long each new side will be.

$3 \times \dfrac{1}{2} = 1\dfrac{1}{2}$ or 1.5 Each new side will be 1.5 cm long.

Draw the image and label with the ' symbol for each letter.

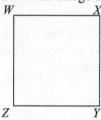

Join each original point to its corresponding point on the image, and write the scale factor.

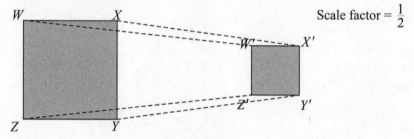

Scale factor = $\dfrac{1}{2}$

Scale factors should be left as fractions, ratios or whole numbers, unless otherwise indicated.

Example 2

Complete the following table.

	Original Length (cm)	New Length (cm)	Scale Factor
1.	7	14	
2.		27	$4\dfrac{1}{2}$
3.	11		$\dfrac{1}{2}$
4.		2.25	3
5.	24	6	

Given two of the three relevant numbers, you can find the other by manipulating the general formula: original length × scale factor = new length.

Solution

1. To find scale factor, divide new length divided by original length

$14 \div 7 = 2$

2. To find original length, divide new length by scale factor

$27 \div 4\frac{1}{2} = 6$

3. To find new length, multiply original length by scale factor

$11 \times \frac{1}{2} = 5.5$

4. To find original length, divide new length by scale factor

$3 \div 2.25 = 0.75$

5. To find scale factor, divide new length divided by original length

$6 \div 24 = \frac{1}{4}$

	Original Length (cm)	New Length (cm)	Scale Factor
1.	7	14	2
2.	6	27	$4\frac{1}{2}$
3.	11	5.5	$\frac{1}{2}$
4.	0.75	2.25	3
5.	24	6	$\frac{1}{4}$

According to scale factors, 1, 2 and 4 would be enlargements because the scale factor is greater than one, and 3 and 5 would be reductions because the scale factor is less than one.

PRACTICE EXERCISE

1. Fro each of the following scale factors, determine if the image would be larger or smaller than the original.

   a) 7

   b) $3\frac{1}{2}$

   c) $\frac{1}{4}$

2. Complete the table below.

Original Length (cm)	New Length (cm)	Scale Factor
7		32
75	15	
	8.1	2.7
14.2		0.4
0.93	93	

3. If a point is labelled F in an original diagram, how will it be labelled on the image?

4. If a point is labelled H in an image, how is it labelled in the original diagram?

5. What is the scale factor of the diagram below?

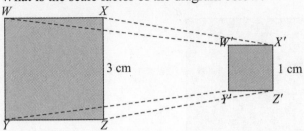

3 cm

1 cm

6. In an image of the triangle shown what would the lengths of $\overline{L'M'}, \overline{M'N'}$ and $\overline{N'L'}$ be given the information below?

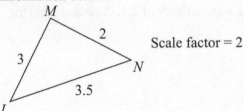

Scale factor = 2

7. For the diagram below, state the scale factor and write the lengths of the sides of the image.

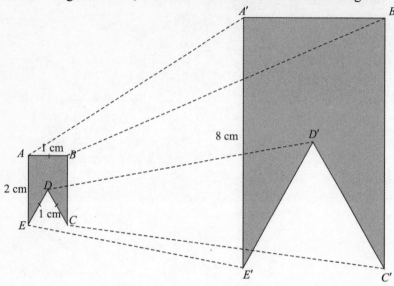

8. Draw a rectangle 1 cm by 2 cm and label is *JKLM*. Using a scale factor of 2.5, draw and label the image.

9. If a calf is 0.75 m tall and its mother is 1.5 m tall, what is the scale factor of the height of the calf to the height of the mother?

Lesson 10 SCALE DIAGRAMS

Scale drawings are used when objects are too large or small to be drawn on a piece of paper. Something drawn to scale means the original object has been reduced or enlarged by a specified amount (the scale factor) to fit onto a piece of paper.

To solve problems involving scale drawings, set up proportions and cross-multiply to calculate the new lengths.

Example 1

Find the actual length of a car that is shown on a piece of paper as 6 cm long with a scale factor of 1:35.

Solution

Write the scale as a fraction: $\frac{1}{35}$

Set up a proportion with the scale being the first fraction and the second fraction being size of the object on the paper over the actual size of the object. Since the drawing of the car is 6 cm, that is the number that goes in the numerator of the fraction. Now, solve for the actual length.

$$\frac{1}{35} = \frac{6}{a}$$

Solve for the variable by cross-multiplying.

$6 \times 35 = 210 \div 1 = 210$

This tells you the car is 210 cm in real life, which is equivalent to 2.1 m.

The second fraction must be set up as **D**rawing **O**ver **A**ctual, which can be remembered by using the acronym **D. O. A.**

Example 2

A building that is 37 m tall is to be drawn on a paper. If the scale factor is 1:2 000, how tall is drawing of the building?

Solution

Scale $= \frac{1}{2\,000}$

The proportion will have 37 m on the bottom of a fraction because it is the actual size and you are looking for the drawing size.

$$\frac{1}{2\,000} = \frac{d}{37}$$

$1 \times 37 = 37 \div 2\,000 = 0.018\,5$ m

The drawing is 0.0185 m tall, which is equivalent to 1.85 cm.

To cross multiply, multiply the numbers that are diagonally across from each other, and divide by the lone number.

The drawing size is usually given in centimetres or millimetres. If it is not, convert to those units.

When solving for scale, the fraction must have the same units in the numerator and denominator.

Example 3

A field mouse is 5.5 cm long. It is shown on a poster as 66 cm long. What is the scale factor of the drawing?

Solution

Here, you are solving for the scale. Write the fraction of the drawing size over the actual size and reduce it to find the scale.

$$\frac{\text{drawing}}{\text{actual}} = \frac{66}{5.5} = \frac{66 \div 5.5}{5.5 \div 5.5} = \frac{12}{1}$$

The scale for this diagram is 12:1. Because it is greater than 1, you know that the image is larger then the original. This makes sense because the poster is much larger than the actual mouse.

Scale drawings can also be used to help you determine actual distances between two places on a map.

Example 4

Vancouver is about 1 500 km from Fort Nelson. How far apart are these cities on a map with a scale of 1:20 000 000?

Solution

Set up proportions with the scale factor on the left and the map distance over the actual distance on the right, and solve with cross-multiplying.

$$\frac{1}{20\,000\,000} = \frac{m}{1\,500}$$

$1 \times 1\,500 = 1\,500 \div 20\,000\,000 = 0.000\,075$ km

The cities would be 0.000 075 km apart on a map. Convert the distance to centimetres because that is a standard measure on reading maps: 0.000 075 km = 7.5 cm. The cities would be 7.5 cm apart on a map.

Remember, there are 100 000 cm in 1 km.

Example 5

Williams Lake and Vancouver are 2.6 cm apart on a map with a scale factor of
1:22 000 000. How far apart are they actually?

Solution

$$\frac{1}{22\,000\,000} = \frac{2.6}{a}$$

$2.6 \times 22\,000\,000 = 57\,200\,000 \div 1 = 57\,200\,000$. They are 57 200 000 cm apart. Convert the distance to kilometres.
572 000 000 cm = 572 km.

Williams Lake and Vancouver are actually 572 km apart in real life.

Example 6

Kamloops and Drumheller are 6 cm apart on a map. If they are actually 654 km apart, what is the scale factor of the map?

Solution

Make a fraction with the map distance over the actual distance, and reduce it until there is a numerator of 1; this is the scale.

$$\frac{map}{actual} = \frac{6 \text{ cm}}{654 \text{ km}}$$

Convert both distances to centimetres so both are in the same units for the ratio.

650 km = 65 000 000 cm

$$\frac{6 \text{ cm}}{65\ 400\ 000 \text{ cm}}$$

Reduce the fraction so the numerator is 1.

$$\frac{6}{65\ 400\ 000} = \frac{6 \div 6}{65\ 400\ 000 \div 6} = \frac{1}{10\ 900\ 000}$$

The scale factor of the map is 1:10 900 000. This means that every 1 cm on the map is equal to 10 900 000 cm (109 km) in real life.

PRACTICE EXERCISE

1. In a drawing, a lamp is 2 cm tall. If the scale factor is 1:125, what is the actual height of the lamp in metres?

2. A tulip is 75 cm tall in real life. What is the size of the tulip in a drawing that has a scale factor of 1:25?

3. Joe's ruler is 15 cm long. The teacher's ruler is 100 cm long. What is the scale factor of the teacher's ruler compared with Joe's ruler?

4. A building is 7 cm tall on a drawing. Gives a scale factor of 360, what is the actual height of the building in metres?

5. The scale factor of a drawing of a mosquito is 4:1. If the mosquito is actually 0.75 cm long, how long is it on the drawing?

6. Before being burned, a candle was 40 cm tall. After burning, it was 6 cm tall. What is the scale of the reduction in the height of the candle?

7. Ottawa and Toronto are 363 km apart. If a map has a scale of 1:7 000 000, how far apart are they on the map?

8. Halifax and Montreal are almost 800 km apart. If they are 2 cm apart on the map, what is the scale factor of the map?

9. Winnipeg and Calgary are 7.45 cm apart on a map. If the scale is 1: 16 000 000, how far apart are the cities?

10. Regina and Toronto are 2 626 km apart. On a map with a scale of 1:25 000 000, how far apart are they?

Lesson 11 MAPS

Mathematically, a map is any two-dimensional diagram with different regions on it. A map is not necessarily something that shows roads and cities.

Here is an example of a simple map

Adjacent regions are regions that share a common border.

This is a simple map with eight regions. Each region has a border around it that separates it from adjacent regions. Even though there are only two colours on the map, no two regions that share a common border are the same color. It is necessary with all maps to make each region distinct.

Consider the following map.

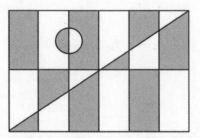

No matter what the shapes are used in a map, when the map is coloured, no adjacent regions can be the same colour. Here, you will notice that there are only two colours on this map.

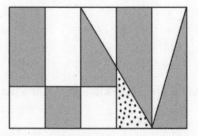

This map has three colours on it. Start colouring on the left using two colours. When you get to the dotted triangle you relize that it cannot be white or black because there already are adjacent regions that are black and white so a third colour must be added.

While trying to colour a map of England in 1853, Francis Guthrie came up with a Theorem. He realized he never needed more than four colours. Guthrie's Theorem states: any map can be coloured using at most four colours so that no adjacent regions (those sharing a common boundary, not just a point at the end) are the same colour.

Consider this map.

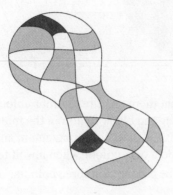

To colour it, start at one side and work with two colours until you have no choice but to add a third colour. In this map, it happens when you have the two main colours on either side of a region and must put a different colour in the middle. A fourth colour is not necessary here because there is no region where there are three colours surrounding it.

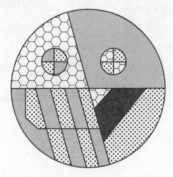

This map requires four different colours. By starting with the grey, spotted, and hexagon regions, you can fill in everything except for the little bar on the bottom right. That bar is already touching a hexagon region on the left, a gray region at the top, and a spotted region on the left as well as below. You have no choice but to use a fourth colour.

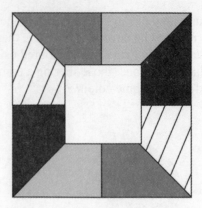

You will notice here that there are already four colours in the map, and all four colours are touching the blank region in the middle. To solve this problem, you would have to start colouring again, and use fewer colours at the beginning. Only add a new colour when absolutely necessary.

This map can actually be coloured in three colours. It would look something like this.

PRACTICE EXERCISE

1. How many regions are in each of the following maps?

   a)

   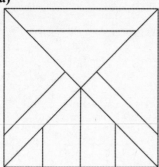

   b)

   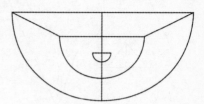

   c)

   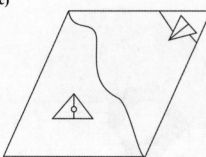

2. What is the minimum number of colours necessary to colour each of the maps below?

   a)

   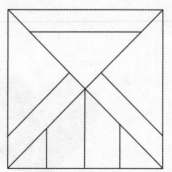

   b)

   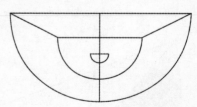

c)

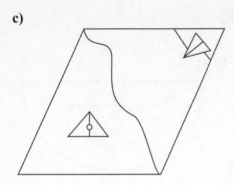

3. For each of the maps below, determine what pattern (grey, black, checked, or spiral) the white region could be coloured?

a)

b)

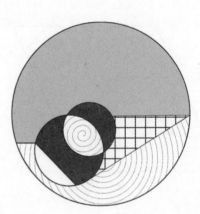

c)

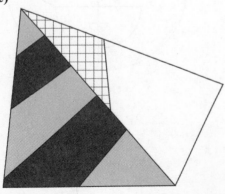

d)

Lesson 12   NETWORKS

Networks are a collection of lines (edges) and dots (vertices) that are all connected. Networks can provide a simple way to represent various problems.

Examples of networks include:

A traceable network is a network in which you can begin at one vertex and travel across each edge only once. It does not matter how many times you pass through a vertex or where you end up.

To determine if a network is traceable or not, you need to determine the "degree" of each vertex. The degree of a vertex is the number of edges connected to that vertex.

Examples

This vertex has a degree of 1 because there is one edge coming out from it.

This vertex has a degree of 2 because there are two edges coming out from it.

This vertex has a degree of 5 because there are five edges coming out from it.

Look at the following network, and determine the degree of each vertex.

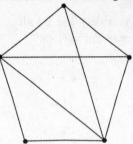

Count the number of edges coming out from each vertex and label the vertices appropriately.

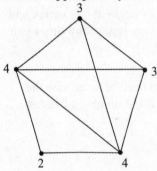

Count the number of odd and even vertices in the network. An odd vertex is one with an odd number of edges (that has an odd-number of degrees), and an even vertex has an even number of edges (that has an even number of degrees).

Odd vertices – 2 (the 3 and 3)
Even vertices – 3 (the 2, 4, and 4)

Any network is traceable if it has 2 or fewer odd vertices. Because the above network has 2 odd vertices, it is traceable, which means you can start at a vertex, and cross **every** edge once and only once.

This network could be traced at follows. Start at the top odd vertex and follow the arrows as follows. Note that at the second 4 that you come to, go next to the available 2, not the available 3.

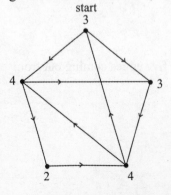

When tracing networks, always start at an odd vertex, if possible.

Example 1

Determine if the following network is traceable.

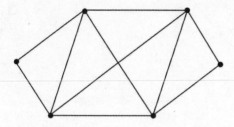

Solution

Label the degree of the vertices, and determine the number of odd and even ones.

Odd vertices – 0

Even vertices – 6

Because there are fewer than 2 odd vertices (0 in this case), this network is traceable. One possible way is as follows.

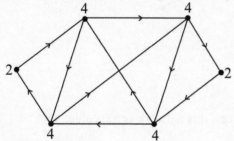

Start anywhere because there are no odd vertices

Example 2

Determine of the following network is traceable.

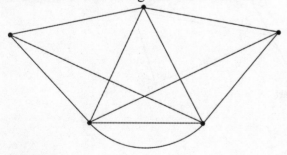

Solution

Odd vertices – 4

Even vertices – 1

Here, there is only 1 even vertex and 4 odd ones. Because there are more than 2 odd vertices, this network is not traceable.

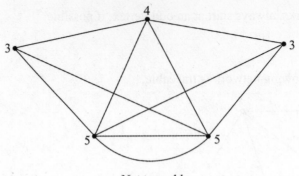

Not traceable

Example 3

Determine of the following network is traceable

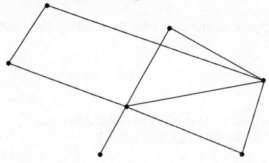

Solution
Odd vertices – 2
Even vertices – 5

Because there are 2 odd vertices, this network is traceable. One possible way is as follows:

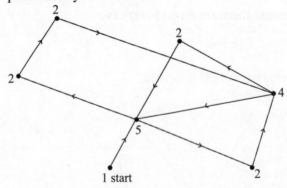

Example 4

Networks can be used to solve problems.

Mary has a map marked with four towns (A, B, C, D) and all of the roads connecting them. If Mary starts at town B, what is the shortest distance that she can travel to go to each town once?

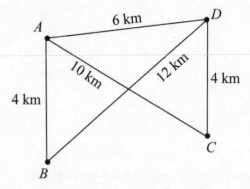

Solution

Here each town is a vertex, and each road is an edge. First, determine if the network is traceable to see if Mary can make it to each stop. Then, guess and check a few different ways to see which is the shortest.

Odd vertices – 2
Even vertices – 2

Yes, the network is traceable.

The distance between towns A and B, and between towns C and D is only 4 km, so it is likely that Mary will want to use those.

Guess $B \rightarrow D \rightarrow A \rightarrow C = 12 + 6 + 10 = 28$ km
Guess $B \rightarrow A \rightarrow C \rightarrow D = 4 + 10 + 4 = 18$ km
Guess $B \rightarrow A \rightarrow D \rightarrow C = 4 + 6 + 4 = 14$ km

The last route given the shortest distance that Mary could go to travel to each town once.

NOTES

Example 5

Consider the following network of people's houses and connecting roads.

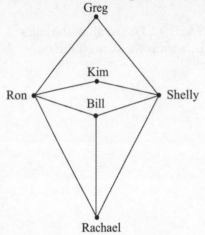

Shelly can go directly to Greg's house without going by any other houses because there is an edge joining these vertices. To get to Ron's house, Shelley would have to walk by someone else's house because there is no direct road between them.

Who is connected to the most people?

Solution

Both Shelly and Ron because their vertices each have a degree of 4.

Who is connected to the fewest houses?

Solution

Both Kim and Greg because their vertices each have degree 2.

What is the fastest way for Greg to get to Rachael's house?

Solution

Walking by either Shelly's house or Ron's house and then straight to Rachael's house.

If Greg had to drop off a package at Kim's house first, could he go directly to Bill's after?

Solution

No, he would have to pass by Ron's or Shelly's house first because Kim and Bill are not directly connected.

NOTES

Example 6

Consider the following network showing approximate distances of air travel between some western cities.

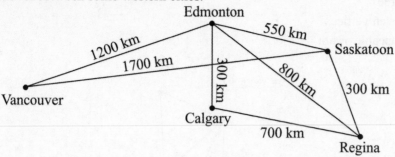

How far is it from Vancouver to Saskatoon?

Solution

1 700 km

How far is it from Vancouver to Saskatoon if you must stop in Edmonton first?

Solution

1 750 km

What is the shortest distance from Calgary to Saskatoon? Through which city must you travel?

Solution

850 km, through Edmonton

How much shorter is it to go from Regina to Vancouver if you do not need to stop in Calgary than if you do?

Solution

It is 2 000 km if you do not go to Calgary and 2 200 km if you do go to Calgary, so it is 200 km shorter.

PRACTICE EXERCISE

1. For each of the following networks:
   i.   label each vertex with its degree
   ii. state the number of odd and even vertices
   iii. tell whether the network is traceable or not

a)

b)

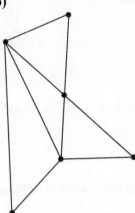

c)

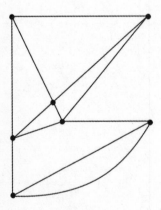

d)

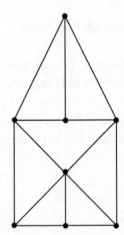

e)

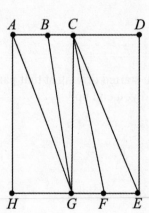

2. To each of the following networks, add either 1 or 2 lines to make the network traceable.

a)

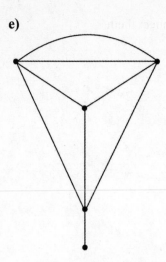

b)

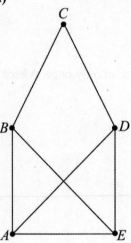

3. Consider the following network of places in a city and the roads that connect them.

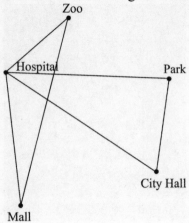

a) What place in the city can you travel directly to from anywhere else?

b) If you wanted to go from the zoo to city hall by the shortest route, what would you have to pass by?

c) If you started driving at that park, drove to every place and crossed each road only once, where would you end up?

PRACTICE QUIZ 3

1. Complete the table below.

	Original Length (cm)	New Length (cm)	Scale Factor
a)	10	30	
b)	15		$\frac{1}{2}$
c)		15	$2\frac{1}{2}$

2. What is the scale factor of the following diagram?

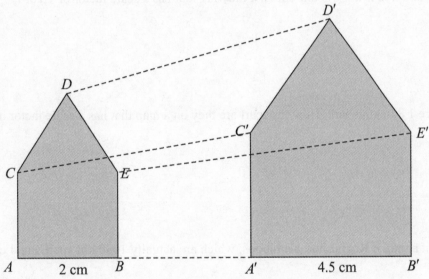

3. Triangle *CAT* has sides that are 6 cm long each. Draw the image of the triangle after a reduction of $\frac{1}{3}$.

4. A picture is 4.5 cm by 18 cm. If it is enlarged to a size of 27 cm by 108 cm, what is the scale factor of the enlargement?

5. What is the height of a person who is 162 cm tall in real life in a picture that has a scale factor of 1:9?

6. What is the actual height of a tree if it is 3.5 cm tall on a drawing that has a scale factor of 1:255?

7. Victoria and Winnipeg are 1 840 km apart. How far apart are they on a map that has a scale factor of 1:50 000 000?

8. What is the scale factor of a map if Regina and Kamloops, which are actually 1080 km apart, are 4 cm apart on the map?

9. What is the minimum number of colours needed to colour each map below?

a)
                                                                     b)

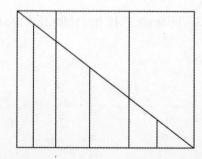

c)

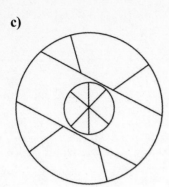

10. Determine if each of the following networks is traceable.

a)

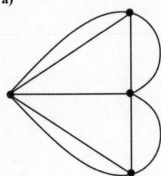

b)

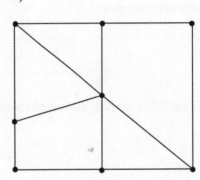

c)

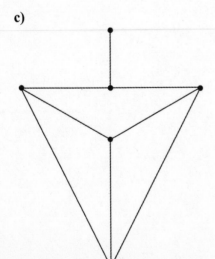

11. Consider the following network and answer the questions below.

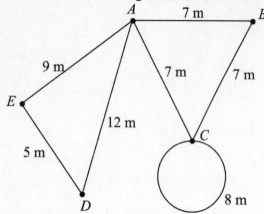

a) Determine the degree of each vertex, then state the number of odd and even vertices. Is the network traceable?

b) What is the shortest distance between points *B* and *D*?

c) What vertex is directly connected to every other vertex? How do you know?

d) What is happening at vertex *C*?

Review Summary

- The Pythagorean Theorem was developed by a mathematician named Pythagoras to find the missing sides of a right triangle. The Theorem is $a^2 + b^2 = c^2$, where a and be are the sides that make up the right angle, and c is the hypotenuse which is the longest side found across from the right angle. To find the length of any side when given the other two, substitute into the formula for what you know and solve for the unknown. Remember to take the square root at the end of the problem because that is the opposite operation of something squared. When asked to solve problems involving right triangles, it is often helpful to draw a picture and then solve.

- Distance around a figure is called perimeter. To calculate the perimeter of an object, add up the lengths of all the sides. To find the perimeter of a regular polygon (where all the sides are the same length), multiply the number of sides by the side length. The perimeter of a circle is called circumference. Use the formula $C = \pi d$ to calculate it. If you are given the perimeter of an object and asked to find a missing side length, substitute into a formula you know for perimeter and solve for the unknown side.

- Area is the amount of space something takes up. To calculate the area of any 2-D shape, use the given formulas for area, substitute in for what you know, and solve. The units for area are always squared (exponent 2).

- Composite figures are two or more shapes that are put together to make one figure. To calculate the area of 2-D composite figures, calculate the area of each part. If the figure has two or more pieces joined, add the areas of each part together. If there are pieces missing from a figure, subtract the area of the missing shape from the shape that is given.

- There are three main types of 3-D object, prisms, pyramids and shapes involving circles. Each type of 3-D object can be represented in the following ways: the solid shape, the net which is what the solid shape would like folded out on a 2-D plane, or as a skeleton which is a diagram of just the edges and vertices.

- Surface area is the sum of the areas of all the faces of a three dimensional object. To calculate surface area, find the area of each face of the shape and add all the areas together. The units for surface area are squared. Sometimes it is helpful to draw a net of the shape to see all the faces that you are working with.

- Volume of a 3-D object is how much space the object takes up. Volume is always calculated using the general formula $V = $ area of the base $\times$ height. The base is the face that the object is sitting on, and the height is the height of the entire object. The units for volume are cubed (exponent 3).

- To find out the surface area of any 3-D composite figure, you need to find the area of all the outside faces. If two objects are joined together, you need to calculate the area of each face of the object and add them all together. If it is a figure with a piece missing, you need to subtract the small end pieces, and add the middle which has become part of the surface.

- To find the volume of a composite figure, find the volume of each shape. Then add if there are two more pieces together, and subtract if there are pieces missing from a figure.

- An enlargement or a reduction is when something is drawn larger or smaller by a specific amount called a scale factor. The enlargement of reduction drawn is called the image. An image has the same proportions as the original drawing, and looks the same only a different size. For each labeled vertex in a drawing, the corresponding one in the image is labeled with the same letter and a ' (prime) symbol.

- When an enlargement or a reduction has taken place, a scale drawing can be used to show the change. The scale factor is used in the ratio d:a (drawing size to actual size) to show the change between the drawing and the actual sizes of an object. If the scale factor is greater than 1 the drawing is an enlargement, and if the scale factor is less than 1, the drawing is a reduction. On maps, actual distances and map (or drawing) distance can be calculated in the same way using d:a.

- A 2-D diagram divided into regions is called a map. Any map can be coloured with a maximum of four colours so that no regions with a common boarder are the same colour. If two regions meet at a tip, they can be the same colour because a tip is not a common boarder. To colour a map, start with two colors and only add more as necessary.

- A network is a set of connected vertices and edges. It is said to be traceable if you can travel over each edge without ever crossing over one more than once, it does not matter how many times you go through each vertex. To determine if a network is traceable calculate the degree of each vertex. The degree of a vertex is the number of edges attached to that vertex. If a network has two or less odd vertices (vertices with an odd number of edges attached to it), it is traceable.

PRACTICE TEST

1. For each of the triangles below, find the missing side length. Round answer to the nearest tenth if necessary.

   a)

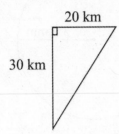

   b)

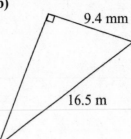

2. Jim and Rick are fishing together and decide to move to different parts of the lake. Jim travels 50 km west and Rick travels 65 km south. How far apart (diagonally) are they when they reach their destinations?

3. Find the perimeter of a regular decagon with side lengths of 7 mm.

4. What is the missing side length in the following diagram?

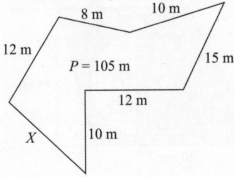

5. Calculate the area of the following shapes.

a)

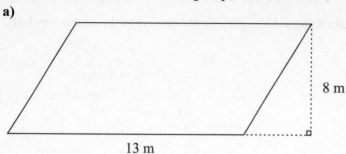

b)

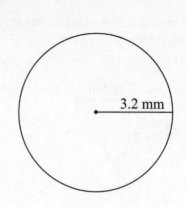

c) A triangle that has a base of 7 m and a height of 15 m.

d) A rectangle that has sides of 3 cm and 4 cm and whose lengths are tripled?

6. For each of the diagram below, calculate the area of the shaded part.

a)

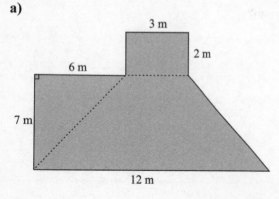

b)

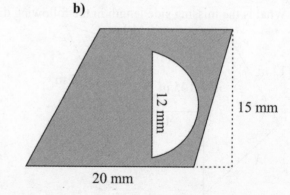

7. For each net below, name the shape and draw the skeleton.

a)

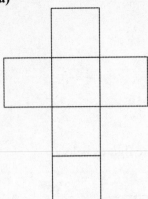

b)

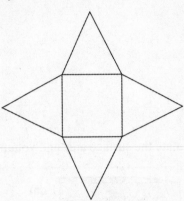

8. Calculate the surface area and volume of the following 3-D shapes

a)

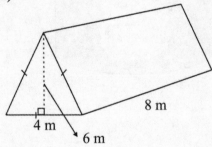

8 m

4 m

6 m

b)

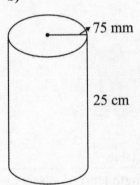

75 mm

25 cm

c)

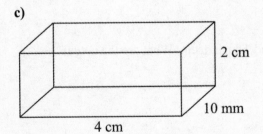

2 cm

10 mm

4 cm

9. A bathtub is half-full of water. How much water is in it if the dimensions of the tub are 1.5 m by 0.8 m by 80 cm?

10. Calculate the surface area and volume of the shaded parts of the composite figures below.

a)

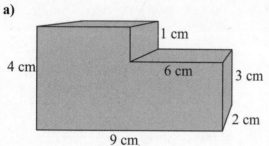

b)

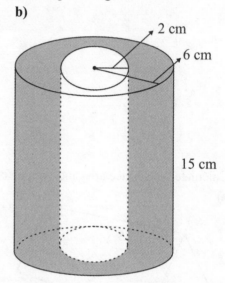

11. Complete the table.

Original Length (cm)	New Length (cm)	Scale Factor
	32.5	6.5
18		$\frac{1}{3}$
	7	1

12. A drawing of a piano is 6 inches high, 8 inches long, and 1 inch deep. What are the actual dimensions of the piano if it has a scale factor of 7?

13. A drawing of a fly is 10 cm across. What is the scale factor if the actual size of the fly is 2 cm across?

14. Vancouver and Merritt are 280 km apart. How far are they apart on a map that has a scale factor of 1:5 000 000?

15. What is the minimum number of colours needed to colour the regions of the following maps?

a)

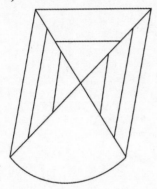

b)

16. What is the shortest path on this network from point *A* to *B*?

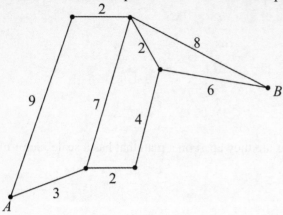

17. Consider the following network.

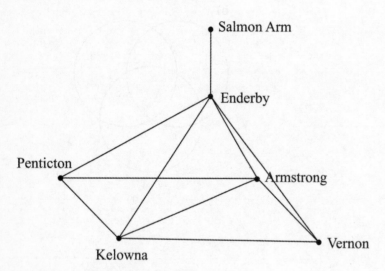

a) What is being represented?

b) Is it possible to start at Salmon Arm and travel every route shown without travelling the same road twice? Explain your answer.

STATISTICS AND PROBABILITY

When you are finished this unit, you should be able to . . .

- formulate questions for investigation by using existing data (PLO 1, Data Analysis)
- select, defend, and use appropriate methods of collecting data including surveys, research, and technology (PLO 2, Data Analysis)
- display data by hand or by computer in a variety of ways including box-and-whisker plots (PLO 3, Data Analysis)
- determine and use the most appropriate measure of central tendency in a given context (PLO 4 Data Analysis)
- construct sets of data when given measures of central tendency and variability (PLO 4 Data Analysis)
- use computer or other simulations to solve probability and data-collection problems (PLO 1, Chance and Uncertainty)
- recognize the probability of equally likely outcomes when given an event (PLO 2, Chance and Uncertainty)
- determine the probability of two independent events with a sample space of 52 or fewer events (PLO 3, Chance and Uncertainty)
- make population predictions from characteristics of a given sample (PLO 4, Chance and Uncertainty)

Lesson	Page	Completed on
1. Surveys	273	
2. Survey Results	280	
3. Graphing	286	
4. Data Sets	293	
5. Stem-and-Leaf Plots and Box-and-Whisker Plots	301	
Practice Quiz 1	310	
6. Probability	316	
7. Independent Events	322	
Practice Quiz 2	333	
Review Summary	337	
Practice Test	338	
Answers and Solutions	at the back of the book	

PREREQUISITE SKILLS AND KNOWLEDGE

Prior to beginning this unit, you should be able to. . .

- describe what a survey is
- distinguish between a random and a biased sample
- do basic graphing
- cross-multiply
- calculate percentage from a fraction
- calculate the percentage of a number
- describe what a tally represents
- distinguish between mean, median, and mode
- calculate quartiles and range, given a set of data
- describe basic probability
- put a fraction into lowest terms

Lesson 1 SURVEYS

A survey is a way of collecting information about a given topic. Surveys can be taken in a variety of ways. Some common methods of collecting information are through interviews, questionnaires, and experiments conducted face-to-face, by phone or e-mail, or on the Internet.

The many different methods of collecting information are used for a variety of reasons. For example, a survey done on computer with choices for each question will be easy to take and the data from this will be easy to put together, but it will not give you a lot of detailed information. A questionnaire will give you a lot of detailed information, but will take a long time to administer and go through to check all the responses.

In a survey, the people who provide the information are called the sample. There are two main sample types: a random sample and a biased sample. A random sample is a sample in which everyone has an equal chance of being selected and the survey is fair. A biased sample is a sample in which only specific groups of people are surveyed and the results of the survey are unfair.

For example, if you wanted to take a survey to find out people's favourite sport, asking every tenth person coming out of a mall would give you a random sample. Asking every tenth person leaving a hockey game would give you a biased sample because there is a better chance that those people like hockey more than other sports.

Example 1

Given the following information, explain why the survey is biased, and how you could change the question to make it unbiased?

In a survey to see how often people go to the dentist, a group of people were asked how many times they had been to the dentist in the last month. The results were:

0 – 87%

1 – 6%

2 – 4%

3 – 2%

More than 3 – 1%

Solution

Most people go to the dentist only once or twice a year; therefore, this is a biased survey because you are only asking about the last month. According to the information, it looks like 87% of people never go to the dentist, but in reality they have likely gone in the past year, not the last month. A better survey question would be: How many times in the past three years have you been to the dentist? This would give you a better indication about how many times per year people go.

Example 2

Consider the following set of data about people's favourite pets.

Dog – 24

Cat – 18

Rodent – 9

Bird – 4

Reptile – 6

Give two other possible survey questions that this data could represent.

Solution

What type of pet do you currently have in your house?

How many of each type of animal is found in the pet store?

Do you think this a random or a biased survey?

Solution

The results look like they are from a random survey because there is a good distribution of the most common pets and smaller numbers to go with the least common animals that people keep as pets.

How could you make this survey biased?

Solution

Go to the reptile store and ask customers what their favourite pets are.

Who might the information from this survey be useful to?

Solution

A pet store owner determining what to stock.

A pet food maker to determine how much of each type of food to produce.

The number of people sampled in a survey is important. The more people surveyed, the more accurate the results will be.

Example 3

If you wanted to take a survey to see what is the average amount of money people spend on back-to-school clothes in August, the more people you survey, the more accurate the results will be.

Number of people surveyed	Average amount spent
1	$120
2	$278
3	$194
25	$215
75	$219
150	$224
300	$225
500	$225

Solution

With more and more people, the money is averaging closer to $225. With only a few people surveyed at the beginning, the numbers jump around quite a bit before they begin to even out close to the $225. These results indicate that on average, people spend $225 on back-to-school clothes each August.

Example 4

Consider the following questions if you want to find information on the most common type of vehicle people drive.

Who would you survey?

Solution

You would need a random sample of people who drive, not just every tenth person at the mall or something like that because some of the sampled people could be children who are not old enough to drive.

How would you collect the data?

Solution

A good way to collect this data would be to mail out a questionnaire to the head of each household because they are likely of driving age. You could also do a phone survey and ask for someone who drives in the household.

How many people should you survey?

Solution

A good survey should have at least 25 people so there are a variety of answers and patterns can be identified.

How could you word the survey question?

Solution

What type of vehicle do you drive most often?

Example 5

Jody took a survey of children in kindergarten and Grade 1 to determine their favourite TV show. What would happen to the results if she had surveyed students in Grade 7 and 8 instead?

Solution

Jody's results would have been completely different because the kids in Grade 7 and 8 are much older and they watch different shows on TV. If she was to survey senior citizens with the same question, the results would likely be completely different again because of the variety of shows they watch.

PRACTICE EXERCISE

1. Tim Hortons wants to open a new drive-through-only franchise. Give two ways they could collect information on where a good location to build would be.

2. What is the least time-consuming method of collecting information for a survey?

3. What method of collecting information for a survey would give you the most detailed results?

4. Grade 12 students need to determine a theme for their graduation. The committee decided to take a random sample of all students in the school. They questioned every tenth person on an alphabetical list of all students in the school. Is this survey going to give accurate results on picking a theme for the graduation? Explain.

5. CBC took a survey to see how many people regularly watch Hockey Night in Canada. The results they got were as follows:

Never – 22

Occasionally – 26

Often – 34

Always – 18

a) How many people were surveyed?

b) In what way might these numbers change if the people were asked how often they watched hockey during playoff time?

c) To whom would this information be useful?

6. Consider the following information.

Cola – 42%, Sprite – 23%, Orange – 18%, Ginger ale – 6%, Root beer – 11%

a) What is a possible question that could have been asked to obtain the results above?

b) Who could this information be used for?

c) Tell how a random sample could have been chosen for this survey?

d) Write a biased question that would give you the results above.

7. A car dealership surveyed people to see how many own a truck. They mailed out a questionnaire to 50 farmers and 50 city residents. Explain why the results would be biased and what could be done to change them.

8. Louise surveyed 45 parents about their opinion on the best restaurant to eat in. How would the results change if Louise had surveyed 45 children?

9. Explain how the following questions would lead to biased results. How would you change them so you would get unbiased results?

a) Do you agree that people convicted of stealing should all go to jail?

b) Would you rather watch a boring newscast or a funny sitcom on TV?

Lesson 2 SURVEY RESULTS

When taking a survey, the most common way of displaying the data is on a tally sheet or tally chart.

A chart should have the following sections:

- The title—describing the question
- The choices
- The tally—vertical ticks that are crossed diagonally to show groups of five
- The frequency—the number represented by the tally
- The fraction—the frequency of the response as a fraction of the total people surveyed
- The percentage—the value of the fraction as a percent

Example 1

Jamie took a survey of what colour of socks his classmates were wearing. The results were as follows:
Black – 4, White – 6, Coloured – 3, Striped – 2, No socks – 5.

Solution

This information displayed on a tally sheet would look like this:

Colour of Socks in Jamie's Class				
Sock Type	**Tally**	**Frequency**	**Fraction**	**Percent**
Black	I I I I	4	$\frac{4}{20}$	20%
White	H H H I	6	$\frac{6}{20}$	30%
Coloured	I I I	3	$\frac{3}{20}$	15%
Striped	I I	2	$\frac{2}{20}$	10%
No Socks	H H H	5	$\frac{5}{20}$	25%

Information in tally sheets can be used to make predictions for an entire population.

Solution

Number of Siblings				
Siblings	**Tally**	**Frequency**	**Fraction**	**Percent**
None	IIII	4	$\frac{4}{25}$	16%
One	HHH	5	$\frac{5}{25}$	20%
Two	HHH HHH I	11	$\frac{11}{25}$	44%
Three	II	2	$\frac{2}{25}$	8%
More than three	III	3	$\frac{3}{25}$	12%

a) What is the most common number of children in a family? The data does not include the person surveyed.

Solution

3—the child and his or her two siblings.

b) How many kids are an only child?

Solution

4

c) Approximately how many kids out of 225 would you expect to have three or more brothers or sisters?

Solution

Because the question is asking for three **or** more, you need to add the number with three siblings (2) and the number with more than three siblings (3). This gives you 5 out of 25 have three or more brothers and sisters. Set up the proportion and cross-multiply.

$$\frac{5}{25} = \frac{x}{225} \quad x = 45$$

Therefore, 45 children out of the 225 have three or more brothers and sisters.

PRACTICE EXERCISE

1. Fill in the missing parts in the tally sheet below.

	Flower	Tally	Frequency	Fraction	Percent
	Types of Flowers in a Garden				
a)	Rose		9		
b)	Petunia	⊮⊮ ‖ ⊮⊮			
c)	Tulip				16%
d)	Marigold			$\frac{19}{50}$	
e)	Other	‖			

2. **a)** What is the most common flower in the garden?

   b) How many more marigolds are there than roses?

   c) What percentage less tulips are there than petunias?

3. Use the following data about favourite breakfast foods to answer the following questions.

   Eggs – 19, Bacon – 12, Hash browns – 9, Toast – 6, Cereal – 4

   a) Make a complete tally sheet to represent these data.

   b) How many people prefer bacon and eggs?

   c) What percentage of people like hash browns over cereal?

d) How many people prefer eggs over toast?

e) There are 30 people in a restaurant. How many would you expect to like bacon?

f) There are 850 people in a cafeteria. If there in the equivalent of 6 bowls of cereal in one box, how many boxes would be needed each day for breakfast?

4. Use the following data to answer the questions below.

   Favourite day of the week:

   Mon – 1, Tues – 3, Wed – 3, Thurs – 5, Fri – 7, Sat – 12, Sun – 9

   a) Make a complete tally chart representing these data.

   b) What two days are the most popular? Why do you think that is?

   c) If 160 people were surveyed, how many people would be expected to say that they prefer a weekday?

   d) If 60 000 people were surveyed, how many would be expected to say that they prefer Fridays?

   e) Using the same choices, write a new question that could represent the given data.

Lesson 3 GRAPHING

Survey results can be visually displayed using a variety of graphs. Bar graphs are best for displaying data with distinct categories that you want to compare with each other. Line graphs are used to graph something that shows trends over time. Pictographs use pictures to compare two or more similar things. Circle graphs use percentage to show how much out of a whole circle is represented by each category.

BAR GRAPH

These can be drawn either horizontally or vertically. In a bar graph, all the bars need to be the same width and equally spaced. You must label each axis and tell what they are representing including the units. Always title the graph at the end. Here is an example of a bar graph showing the numbers of different types of animals found in a zoo.

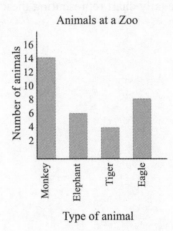

LINE GRAPH

These are used to show something continuous over a certain period of time. With line graphs, it is standard to put the time on the *x*-axis and what you are showing on the *y*-axis. Again, you must label each axis and tell what they represent including the units. Always title the graph at the end. Here is an example of a line graph showing how many lawns can be mowed over a certain amount of time.

Remember the *x*-axis on a graph is the horizontal one and the *y*-axis is the vertical one.

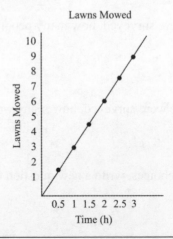

PICTOGRAPH

This graph has pictures that represent what is being displayed. It does not always give you an exact number, but an estimate for what you are surveying. Remember to always include a legend showing what each picture represents. You may use only one picture in each graph. This graph shows the approximate number of each type of book found in a library.

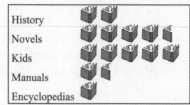

Types of Books in the Library

Each represents 150 books

CIRCLE GRAPH

Circle graphs represent things using percentage. To make a circle graph, find the portion of 360 (the number of degrees in a circle) that each section takes up. Do this by taking the percentage of the number. Once you have the angles, draw them using a protractor and label the sections by percentage on the graph. Give the graph a title. Here is a circle graph of the favourite sports of Grade 8 students.

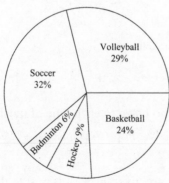

Favourite Sports

When given information and asked to display it on a graph, you need to be able to determine which graph would best represent it and be able to justify your answer. Use bar graphs for distinct categories with numbers, use line graphs for trends over time, use pictographs for approximate values, and use circle graphs when given percentage.

Given the following information, determine the best type of graph to display it on, justify your answer, and then draw the graph.

Example 1

How junior high school students spend their day.

Sleeping – 9, Eating – 2.5, School – 6, TV/Computer – 3, Recreation – 2, Other – 1.5

Solution

Because this is given with the categories and the hours spent on each, it is best to display it on a bar graph. Each category will be one bar, and the height of each bar will represent the hours spent on each activity.

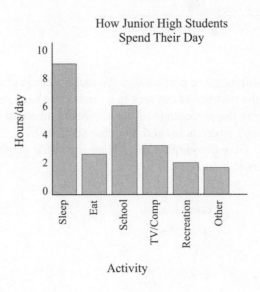

Example 2

Percentage of people who listen to each type of music:

Country – 19%, Rap – 24%, Pop – 42%, Rock – 15%

Solution

Because the choices are given in %, it is best to display this information on a circle graph. To figure out the angle for each section, multiply the percentage (as a decimal) by 360. Round to nearest degree.

Country – 19% = $0.19 \times 360 = 68.4°$

Rap – 24% = $0.24 \times 360 = 86.4°$

Pop – 42% = $0.42 \times 360 = 151.2°$

Rock – 15% = $0.15 \times 360 = 54°$

Draw the angles in a circle and label each section.

Favourite Music

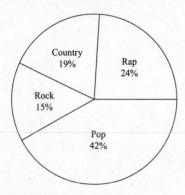

Example 3

Each hour Kyle works he earns $7.50. Show how much he would earn each hour during an 8-hour shift.

Solution

Because this is an amount that Kyle is earning over a continuous time period (his 8-hour shift), this is best displayed on a line graph.
Determine how much Kyle earns each hour by making a table, and then graph the time on the *x*-axis and the dollars earned on the *y*-axis.

Hours Worked	Dollars Earned
1	$7.50
2	$15.00
3	$22.50
4	$30.00
5	$37.50
6	$45.00
7	$52.50
8	$60.00

Plot each point, and then join the points, as shown below.

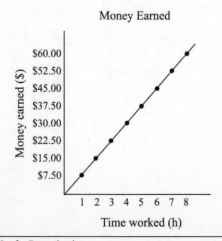

PRACTICE EXERCISE

1. Tell which graph would best represent each situation and why.

   a) Favourite colour of people in Calgary?

   b) Percentage of people who play different types of instruments.

   c) Approximate number of people who read each section of the newspaper.

   d) Amount of annual precipitation in six Canadian cities.

   e) Number of hours of sleep needed over the course of someone's life.

2. Use the following graph to answer the questions below.

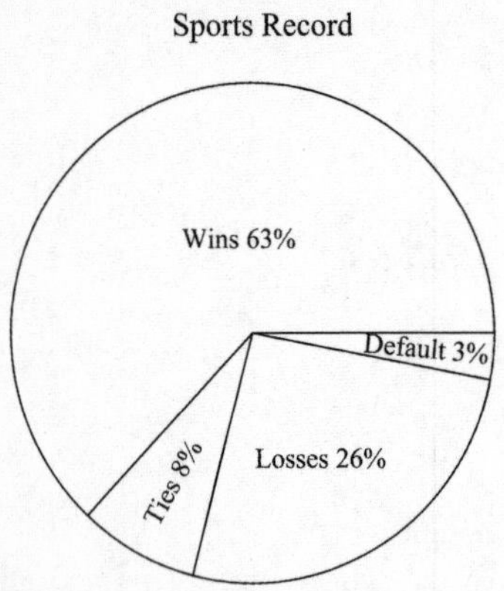

Sports Record

Wins 63%

Default 3%

Losses 26%

Ties 8%

   a) What is being represented by the graph?

   b) What would the angle for number of losses be?

   c) If the team played 25 games, how many did they tie?

3. Use the following graph to answer the questions below.

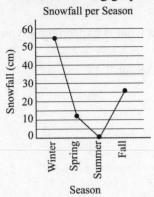

a) Which season has the most snow?

b) Approximately how much more snow falls in fall compared with spring?

c) Approximately how much snow falls in one year?

4. Use the following graph to answer the questions below.

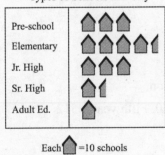

a) How many elementary schools are represented in the pictograph?

b) If there are 32 pre-schools, why are there only 3 pictures drawn?

c) How many schools are there in total in the city?

5. Choose a type of graph to display the following data. Justify your reason for picking that graph, then draw the graph.

a) People's responses to the question: What is the best way of finding out what is happening in your city?

TV News – 51, Newspaper – 28, Magazine – 7, Internet – 46, Word of Mouth – 18

b) People's responses to a survey about car colour.

Silver – 37%, White – 22%, Black – 20%, Blue – 15%, Orange – 6%

c) Number of cows on a dairy farm during the first five years of operation.

First year – 26, Second year – 48, Third year – 103, Fourth year – 240, Fifth year – 512

Lesson 4   DATA SETS

When given a set of data, statistical analysis can be performed to determine information from the data. Central tendency is the tendency of data to merge around certain points near the middle of a set of data. Most random sets of data, when graphed, will result in what is called a bell curve with a few points at either end and the majority of the points in the middle. A typical bell curve looks like this.

NOTES

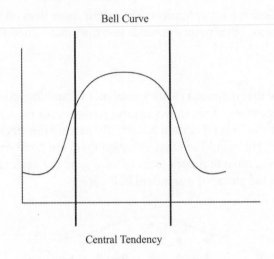

Bell Curve

Central Tendency

The points mean, median, and mode that you learned about in Grade 7 are useful in describing central tendency. Recall the following:

Mean is the average of a set of data. It is calculated by adding all the numbers and dividing the total number of numbers.

Range is not a measure of central tendency, it is the difference between two points in a set of data.

Median is the middle number of a set of data that is in sequential order. If there are two numbers that are in the middle, add them up and divide by two.

Mode is the number or numbers that occur most often. In a set of data there can be no mode, one mode, or many modes.

Example 1

Given the set of data, find the mean, median and the mode.

2, 4, 3, 2, 7, 3, 4, 5, 6, 5, 4

Solution

Always put the data in numerical order first.

2, 2, 3, 3, 4, 4, 4, 5, 5, 6, 7

When calculating the mean, there will usually be many decimal places in the answer. Round to the nearest tenth unless told otherwise.

NOTES

Mean = Average: Add and divide by total number.

$2 + 2 + 3 + 3 + 4 + 4 + 4 + 5 + 5 + 6 + 7 = 45 \div 11 = 4.\overline{09}$

Median = Middle number: Cross out from each side until you get the middle number.

~~2, 2, 3, 3, 4,~~ **4**, ~~4, 5, 5, 6, 7~~

The median is 4.

Mode = Most often

Although there are some numbers that occur more than once, 4 occurs 3 times, whereas, other numbers occur less than that. Therefore 4 is the mode.

You can see that the mean ($4.\overline{09}$), median (4), and the mode (4) are all very close together. This shows central tendency, or the tendency of the data to all occur around certain points. By putting this data on a number line, you would see that although there are numbers at the low and high ends, most numbers seem to be around the peak at the middle, which gives the shape of a standard bell curve.

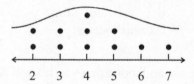

Example 2

Mean, median, and mode can also be used to help analyze real-life situations.

Micah's test scores average out to 63%, and she wants to bring them up to a 65%. Which measure of central tendency is used in this situation.

Solution

Because this is dealing with Micah's average, this is showing mean.

Example 3

Evelyn works in a shoe store. They always seem to be running out of size 7 girls shoes. Which measure of central tendency is described here?

Solution

This situation is describing the mode because size 7 is the most common shoe size.

Example 4

Find the mean, median, and mode of the following set of data.

20, 17, 17, 18, 26, 19, 14, 23, 21, 23

Solution

Rearrange order:

14, 17, 17, 18, 19, 20, 21, 23, 23, 26

Mean: $14 + 17 + 17 + 18 + 19 + 20 + 21 + 23 + 23 + 26 = 198 \div 10$
$= 19.8$

Median: ~~14, 17, 17, 18~~, **19, 20**, ~~21, 23, 23, 26~~ $= 19 + 20 = 39 \div 2 = 19.5$

(Because there are two numbers in the middle, add them up and divide by 2 for the median.)

Mode = 17 and 23 because both those numbers occur most often.

Example 5

Find the mean, median, and mode of the following set of data.

1, 2, 3, 4, 4, 7, 8

Solution

Mean $= 1 + 2 + 3 + 4 + 4 + 7 + 8 = 29 \div 7 = 4.\overline{142857}$

Median $=$ ~~1, 2, 3~~, **4**, ~~4, 7, 8~~ $= 4$

Mode $= 4$

What would happen to the measures of central tendency if all the values in the data set above were increased by 3?

Solution

Write the new data set, then solve for mean, median, and mode.

1, 2, 3, 4, 4, 7, 8 becomes 4, 5, 6, 7, 7, 10, 11

Find mean, median, and mode.

Mean $= 4 + 5 + 6 + 7 + 7 + 10 + 11 = 50 \div 7 = 7.\overline{142\,857}$

Median $=$ ~~4, 5, 6~~, **7** ~~7, 10, 11~~ $= 7$

Mode $= 7$

The new values for mean, median, and mode are each increased by three as well.

What would happen if all the values in the data set were multiplied by 5?

Solution

Write the new data set, then solve for mean, median, and mode.

1, 2, 3, 4, 4, 7, 8 becomes 5, 10, 15, 20, 20, 35, 40

Find mean, median, and mode.

Mean = $5 + 10 + 15 + 20 + 20 + 35 + 40 = 145 \div 7 = 20.\overline{714285}$

Median = $\cancel{5, 10, 15,}$ **20**, $\cancel{20, 35, 40}$ = 20

Mode = 20

The values for mean, median, and mode were all multiplied by 5 as well.

If a constant is added or subtracted to each number in a set of data, the measures of central tendency will be increased or decreased by that amount as well. If they are multiplied or divided by a constant, the values of the mean, median and mode will be increased or decreased by the same factor.

Example 6

Find the mean, median, and mode of the following set of data.

1, 2, 3, 3, 3, 4, 5, 6,

Solution

Mean: 3.4

Median: 3

Mode: 3

Example 7

What measure of central tendency would change the most if three more fives were added to the set of data above?

Solution

Rewrite the data set and recalculate.

1, 2, 3, 3, 3, 4, 5, 5, 5, 5, 6

Mean: 3.8

Median: 4

Mode: 5

The measure of central tendency that changed the most was the mode. It went from 3 to 5.

Example 8

What measure would change the most, if the last number in the data set was changed from 6 to 26?

Solution

1, 2, 3, 3, 3, 4, 5, 26

Mean: 5.9

Median: 3

Mode: 3

The mean would change the most because the sum before being divided by 8 would be much larger: 47 instead of 27.

> An outlier in a set of data is a value that is very different from most others in a set of data.

Example 9

Write a set of data with a median of 4.

Solution

You know that median is the middle number, so as long as 4 is in the middle you can have any amount of numbers on either side. Possible examples include:

a) 1, 2, 4, 6, 8

b) 1, 1, 1, 1, 4, 6, 6, 6, 6

c) 4, 4, 4

> If a significantly different outlier is added to a set of data, the mean is always the most affected because it greatly changes the sum of the numbers but has little, if any, effect on the median or the mode.

> Remember that the numbers should always be listed in order.

Example 10

Write a set of data with a mode of 8.

Solution

Mode is the number that occurs most often, so you need more eights than any other number.

Possible examples include:

a) 4, 5, 8, 8, 9

b) 8, 8, 8, 8, 10, 12, 14, 14, 16

c) 8

Example 11

Write a set of six data points that have a mean of 5.

Solution

You know that the mean is the sum of the points divided by the number. Because there are 6 points, to get a mean of 5, the sum before you divide must be equal to 30 (because $30 \div 6 = 5$). Write any 6 numbers whose sum is 30. Possible examples include:

a) 2, 2, 4, 4, 8, 10

b) 0, 0, 0, 5, 10, 15

c) 3, 4, 5, 5, 6, 7

Example 12

Charles' mean mark on 4 tests is 78%. What mark is needed on his next test to increase his average to 80%?

Solution

You are looking for the average on 5 tests. Multiply 5 times 80 to see what the sum needs to be. $5 \times 80 = 400$.

On 4 tests, the mean was 78 so multiply 4 times 78 to see what the sum was before.

$4 \times 78 = 312$

To go from 312 to 400, Charles will need to get an 88 $(400 - 312)$ on the next test so the marks will average out to 80%.

PRACTICE EXERCISE

1. Calculate the measures of central tendency for the following sets of data.

   a) 3, 6, 2, 3, 7, 4, 3, 5

   b) 12, 18, 23, 27, 12, 21, 18, 24, 17

   c) 35, 50, 56, 73, 30, 44, 62, 51, 32, 47

2. A particular set of data has a mean of 8.2, a median of 6, and a mode of 4.

   a) What will the new mean, median, and mode be if all the numbers in the data set are increased by 6?

   b) What will the new mean, median, and mode be if all the numbers in the data set are divided by 2?

   c) What will the new mean, median, and mode be if all the numbers in the data set are multiplied by 3?

3. List 5 numbers with a mode of 3.

4. List 6 numbers with a mean of 12.

5. List 8 numbers with a median of 35.

6. List 7 numbers with a median of 4, a low value of 1, and a high value of 18.

7. List 5 numbers that have a median of 5, a mode of 3, and a mean of 6.

8. Indicate which measure of central tendency best describes each situation.

a) Shane wants to know his bowling average for the last seven games he has played.

b) Betty needs to know which slurpee flavour runs out most often in her store so she can order extra.

c) Mr. Smith needs to split his class in half by height on picture day.

9. Use the following set of data to answer the questions below.

10, 13, 17, 17, 18, 22, 26.

a) Calculate mean, median, and mode.

b) Which measure would be most affected if 3 more 18s were added? How much does it change?

c) Which measure would be most affected if the number 56 was added to the end? By how much?

Lesson 5 STEM-AND-LEAF PLOTS AND BOX-AND-WHISKER PLOTS

Large sets of data can be displayed in much simpler ways. Two main forms of doing this are with a stem-and-leaf plot and a box-and-whisker plot. A stem-and-leaf plot shows you all the points in a set of data; whereas, a box-and-whisker plot shows five main points and the distribution of the data.

In a stem-and-leaf plot, the numbers are drawn on a T-chart where the left side is the stem and the right side is the leaf. The stem has all the digits of the numbers except for the last, and the leaf side has the last digit of each number. The numbers on the leaf of the chart must be in ascending order.

NOTES

Example 1

This stem-and-leaf plot shows the numbers 44, 44, 46, 49, 54, 57, 67, 68, 70, 72.

Stem	Leaf
4	4, 4, 6, 9
5	4, 7
6	7, 8
7	0, 2

The digits in the tens place are on the left, and the digit in the ones place are on the right.

Consider this set of data.

232, 232, 235, 240, 246, 248, 267, 267, 268, 269

As a stem-and-leaf plot, these data look like this:

Stem	Leaf
23	2, 2, 5
24	0, 6, 8
25	
26	7, 7, 8, 9

Here, the hundreds place and tens place are on the left, because only the last digit may be in the leaf part on the right.

Look at the following stem-and-leaf plot, and tell what numbers are boxed.

Stem	Leaf
8	2, 2, 4, [7]
9	[0], 3, 8
10	1, [4], 9, 9
11	[2], 6, 8

In a box you see a 7, 0, 4, and 2. These are not the complete numbers because you need to see what each last digit corresponds to in the stem.

The 7 is actually from the number 87, the 0 is from the number 90, the 4 is from 104, and the 2 is from 112.

Look at the following stem-and-leaf plot. What are the numbers displayed here?

Stem	Leaf
0	4, 7
1	2, 3, 6
2	7, 7, 9
3	1

If the number in the stem is 0, that means it is just a one-digit number and you do not need to write the 0.

The numbers are 4, 7, 12, 13, 16, 27, 27, 29, 31

When you are given a stem-and-leaf plot, it is possible to calculate the mean, median, and mode.

Consider the first stem-and-leaf plot again.

Stem	Leaf
4	4, 4, 6, 9
5	4, 7
6	7, 8
7	0, 2

Calculate the mean, median, and the mode.

Mean = add all numbers and divide by total numbers

The total of the 10 numbers is 571. $571 \div 10 = 57.1$

Median = middle number

Remove the highest and lowest values alternately until you are left with one number in the middle. If there is an even amount of numbers in a set of data, you will have two numbers that are in the middle. Add up these two numbers and divide by 2 to find the median. Here, when you cross out ones from each side, the middle numbers are 54 and 57. Add them to get 111, divide by 2, $111 \div 2 = 55.5$ for the median.

Mode = most common number

The number that occurs most often is the first number: 44.

Box-and-whisker plots are made using the following five steps:

1. Find the five-number summary. The five number summary is five specific points used for making box-and-whisker plots, they are: lowest number, highest number, the median, the lower quartile, and the upper quartile.

2. Make a number line based on the data set.

3. Plot the points **above** the line.

4. Join the lowest value and the lower quartile to make one whisker, and join the upper quartile and the highest value to make the other whisker.

5. Make a box using the quartiles around the median.

Example 2

Make a box-and-whisker plot using the following set of data representing different shoe sizes.

3, 4, 4, 6, 7, 7, 8, 9, 10, 11, 11, 11, 12

Solution

Step 1

Five main points:

1. Lowest value – 3

2. Highest value – 12

3. Median – 8

4. Lower quartile – remember from Grade 7 that this is the median of the values below the median of the entire set. Use 3, 4, 4, 6, 7, 7 and find the median. The middle numbers work out to be 4 and 6, so add them up and divide by 2. $4 + 6 = 10 \div 2 = 5$.

    The lower quartile is 5

5. Upper quartile – the median of the numbers above the median. Use 9, 10, 11, 11, 11, 12.

    This median, which is the upper quartile, is 11.

Step 2

Draw a number line from at least 3 to 12. It is always a good idea to go a little longer on each side, so you have a little more room to work. Make sure that the numbers on the number line are eventually spaced out.

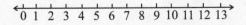

The highest and lowest numbers are also called the upper and lower extremes.

Step 3

The points need to be above the line because the box still needs to be drawn around the median.

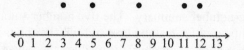

Step 4

Join the whiskers.

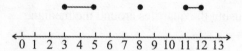

Step 5

Make the box around the median. Do not connect the median with anything, it should be inside the box. Give the plot a title; for example, Shoe Sizes.

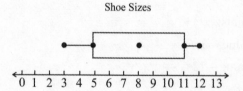

A box and whisker plot is divided into quartiles. This means it is divided into four equal parts. Each whisker contains 25% of the data, and the box represents 50% of the data split by the median in the middle.

Even though each part represents 25% of the data, the lengths of the box and whiskers can vary from one set of data to the other. **Evenly distributed** data has whiskers that are close to the same length and a box that is in the middle of the plot. In an evenly distributed set of data, the length of both whiskers should equal the length of the box. **Unevenly distributed** data usually has one whisker that is longer than the other and a box that is more on the left or the right of the plot. The dot for the median is closer to one edge of the box.

The plot above is one where the data is almost evenly distributed. The next one shows unevenly distributed data.

Example 3

Using the following data, make a box-and-whisker plot.

31, 33, 33, 34, 35, 37, 38, 38, 39, 40, 41, 57

Solution

Step 1

Five main points:

1) Lowest value – 31

2) Highest value – 57. Because this is quite a bit higher than the number before it, the upper whisker of the plot will be much longer than the lower one.

3) Median – (37 + 38) ÷ 2 = 37.5

4) Lower quartile – (33 + 34) ÷ 2 = 33.5

5) Upper quartile – (39 + 40) ÷ 2 = 39.5

Step 2 and 3

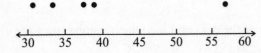

Step 4 and 5

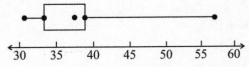

Even though the upper whisker is much longer than the lower one, it still represents 25% of the data.

Looking at the plot, you can answer various questions:

Example 4

Approximately what percentage of the data is below 35?

Solution

You know that a whisker represents 25% and 35 is past the whisker, so it represents more than that. The next 25% of the data is cut off at the median. Because the 35 is about a third of the way between the lower quartile and the median, you can guess that it is about 8% above the lower quartile. The approximate percentage of data below the 35 is the 25% from the whisker and the 8% above the lower quartile, so it is about 33% of the data.

NOTES

Example 5

Approximately what percentage of the data lies between 45 and 55?

Solution

You know an entire whisker represents 25% of the data. The part between 45 and 55 is about half of the whisker so that represents about 12.5% of the data.

Example 6

Consider the following plot.

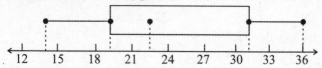

State the five-number summary

Solution

Look at each of the dots and see which number they are closest to.

Lowest value – 14

Highest value – 36

Median – 22.5

Lower quartile – 19.5

Upper quartile – 31

Below what number is approximately 50% of the data situated?

Solution

Look for the median, 50% of the data will be below that. Here, it is 22.5.

What approximate percentage of the data is represented between 21 and 33?

Solution

The number 21 is halfway between the lower quartile and the median, so that part is represented by about 12.5%. Above the median to the 33 is approximately 35% (25% from the second half of the box, and about 10% of the whisker). So, the data represented between 21 and 33 is approximately 47.5%.

PRACTICE EXERCISE

1. Make a stem-and-leaf plot for the following numbers.

    a) 30, 57, 35, 37, 49, 37, 32, 44, 37, 55, 52, 64

    b) 462, 466, 457, 450, 444, 443, 469, 472, 473, 471, 446

2. What are the numbers indicated by the boxes?

Stem	Leaf
79	0, 2, 3
80	1, 6, 6, 7
81	
82	3, 4, 5
83	2, 2, 5, 8, 9

3. Using the stem-and-leaf plot from question 2, write out the data set in ascending order.

4. Make a box-and-whisker plot using the following sets of data.

    a) 10, 10, 14, 16, 16, 18, 18, 19, 20, 20, 22

    b) 16, 23, 18, 31, 31, 26, 19, 20, 26, 4, 25, 26

c)

Stem	Leaf
3	3, 8, 9
4	2, 2, 6, 7
5	3, 5, 8
6	1, 2, 4
7	0, 0, 2

5. Use the following box-and-whisker plot to answer the questions below.

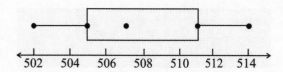

a) What are the highest and lowest numbers?

b) What is the median?

c) What percentage of the numbers are above 505?

d) Approximately what percentage of the numbers are between 504 and 512?

6. Use the following box-and-whisker plot to answer the questions below.

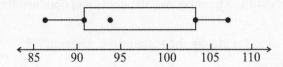

a) What is the approximate difference between the upper quartile and the lower quartile?

b) How would the plot change if the highest value were changed to 125?

c) Explain why the median is not always in the middle of the box.

d) In a box-and-whisker plot of various test scores, the lowest mark is 62 and the range is 24. What is the highest mark?

PRACTICE QUIZ 1

1. Andrea took a survey of people's favourite household chore. She surveyed 50 people and obtained the following results:

   Vacuuming – 9, Laundry—12, Washing dishes – 15, Taking out the garbage – 6, Dusting – 8

   a) Make a complete tally chart for the information above.

   b) Draw a bar graph representing on the results of the survey.

   c) Draw a pictograph representing the results of the survey.

2. Mr. Johnson took a survey to see what colour of towel his students use after they shower. These are his results.

a) Complete the chart.

Colour of Towel Used				
Colour	**Tally**	**Frequency**	**Fraction**	**Percent**
White	卌Ⅰ			
Blue		3		
Green				30%
Pink			$\dfrac{2}{20}$	
Mulicoloured	ⅠⅠⅠⅠ			

b) If only 10 people were surveyed, how many would be expected to use a pink towel?

c) If 70 people were surveyed, how many would be expected to use a green towel?

d) If 350 people were surveyed, how many would be expected to use a blue or white towel?

3. Use the following circle graph to answer the questions below.

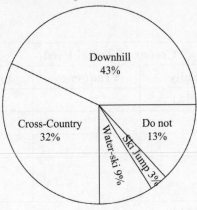

a) Give one example of what the question could be.

b) What is the central angle of the category Water-ski?

c) If 75 people were surveyed, how many people do not ski?

4. Walter wants to take a survey to find out what people's favourite movie is. He goes to a theatre and asks every tenth person as they leave. Is this a fair survey? Justify your answer.

5. Consider the following problem and answer the questions below.

The high school cafeteria wants to update their menu to serve food that is more popular.

a) Who should be surveyed to get unbiased results?

b) How could this survey be conducted?

c) Who would this information be useful to?

d) Once the information is collected, what should the owners do to decide on the new prices?

6. Use the following graph to answer this questions below.

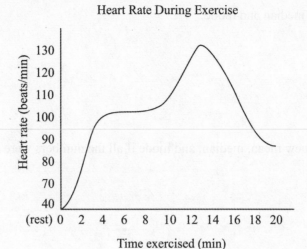

Heart Rate During Exercise

a) Where did the heart rate peak?

b) At how many hearts per minute is happening between 5 min and 8 min?

c) Explain why the heart rate at the beginning of the graph is different from the heart rate at the end of the graph.

d) Why is this information best displayed on a line graph?

7. Calculate the mean, median, and mode of the following set of data.

42, 47, 47, 49, 53, 56, 58, 58, 61, 64, 65

8. Use the following data to answer the questions below.

35, 45, 55, 50, 45, 50, 65, 65, 60, 50, 40

   a) Calculate the mean, median and mode.

   b) What would be the new mean, median, and mode if all the numbers were divided by 5?

9. A set of data has a mean of 54, a median of 56, and a mode of 60.

   a) What would happen if 7 were added to each number in the data set?

   b) What would happen if all the numbers were divided by 4?

10. Create a data set that satisfies the following measures of central tendency.

   a) Five numbers with a mean of 30

   b) Six numbers with a mode of 120

   c) Eight numbers with a median of 20.5

   d) Seven numbers with a median of 12 and a mode of 8

11. Make a stem-and-leaf plot and a box-and-whisker plot from the following set of data.

123, 126, 135, 139, 140, 142, 142, 153, 157

12. From this stem and-leaf plot, make a box-and-whisker plot, and then answer the questions below.

Stem	Leaf
13	2, 2, 3, 5
14	0, 1, 7
15	2, 9
16	1, 8
17	7, 8, 8

a) The lower half of the data is between what two numbers?

b) What is the range between the quartiles?

c) What percentage of the numbers fall between 140 and 160?

13. Use the following diagram to answer the question below.

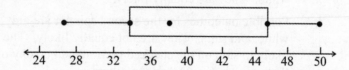

a) What percentage of the data is below 40?

b) What is the value of the upper quartile?

c) What is the range of the data?

Lesson 6 PROBABILITY

Probability is the likelihood that something is going to happen. To calculate probability, you need to know all the possible outcomes of a certain event. The total possible outcomes are all the possible results of that event.

For example: When you flip a coin, the possible outcomes are heads and tails.

When you roll a standard die, the possible outcomes are 1, 2, 3, 4, 5, and 6.

When every outcome has an equal chance of occurring, they are said to be **equally likely**. Tossing a coin and rolling a die are examples where all the outcomes are equally likely.

Example 1

Consider the following spinners.

   a) List the outcomes for each spinner.

   b) Tell if the outcomes are equally likely. If not, tell which is more likely.

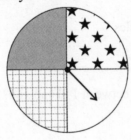 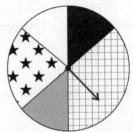

Solution

Possible outcomes for the first spinner are gray, star, checked, and white. They are equally likely.

Possible outcomes for the second spinner are gray, checked, black, white, and stars. They are not equally likely. The spinner is more likely to stop on the checked section than on any other section because that space is bigger than the others.

To calculate the probability of an event happening, you always use the following formula.

$$P(\text{favourable outcome}) = \frac{\text{favourable outcomes}}{\text{total possible outcomes}}$$

When working with probability, you will always get a number that is between 0 and 1. A probability of 1 means that the outcome is guaranteed to occur, and a probability of 0 means that outcome will never occur. Always leave the probability as a fraction in lowest terms unless the question states otherwise.

Example 2

What is the probability of rolling a 3 on a regular, six-sided die?

Solution

When calculating probability, always write capital P and whatever you are looking for in parentheses.

$$P(3) = \frac{\text{favourable outcomes}}{\text{total possible outcomes}}$$

$$= \frac{1 \text{ (because there is one 3)}}{6 \text{ (because there are six possible outcomes)}} = \frac{1}{6}$$

What is the probability of rolling an odd number on a regular, six-sided die?

Solution

$$P(\text{odd}) = \frac{3}{6} \text{ (three odd numbers and six possible outcomes)} = \frac{1}{2}$$

(in lowest terms)

Example 3

In a gumball machine, there are 4 green, 2 blue, 8 red, 6 yellow, 3 purple, and 2 pink gumballs.

Calculate the following probabilities as a fraction and a percentage.

Solution

$$P(\text{green}) = \frac{4}{25} \text{ (4 green gumballs and 25 balls in total)}$$
$$= 4 \div 25$$
$$= 0.16 \times 100$$
$$= 16\%$$

To percentage, convert a fraction to a percentage, divide the numerator by the denominator, and multiply by 100.

$$P(\text{pink and purple}) = \frac{5}{25} \text{ (because you need to add the 2 pink and }$$

$$3 \text{ purple)} = \frac{1}{5} = 20\%$$

$$P(\text{not red}) = \frac{17}{25} = 68\%$$

NOTES

Example 4

Consider a regular deck of cards with no jokers.

Calculate the probability of randomly drawing each of the following cards from a regular deck of cards.

Solution

$$P \text{ (and heart)} = \frac{13}{52} = \frac{1}{4}$$

$$P \text{ (any red card)} = \frac{26}{52} = \frac{1}{2}$$

$$P \text{ (any king)} = \frac{4}{52} = \frac{1}{13}$$

$$P \text{ (any numbered card)} = \frac{36}{52} = \frac{9}{13}$$

In a regular deck of cards, there are 52 cards of which $\frac{1}{2}$ are red and $\frac{1}{2}$ are black; 4 suits (hearts, clubs, diamonds, spades); and 13 cards per suit which are the numbers 2 to 10, and Jack, Queen, King, Ace.

Probability can be used to simulate the results of a real-life event. For example, if you want to figure out the probability of a pregnant couple having a single baby or a set of twins, you can use a coin to determine the likelihood of each. Since there are two outcomes on a coin (heads and tails), you can assign one to represent a single baby and one to represent a set of twins. Flip the coin to determine the probability of the couple having either a single baby or a set of twins.

A simulation to help you choose the answers on a multiple-choice test in which each question has 4 alternatives, could be shown on a spinner like the first spinner below.

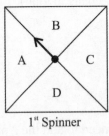

1st Spinner

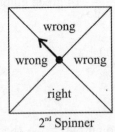

2nd Spinner

The second spinner would show you the probability that any randomly chosen answer is right or wrong.

Different types of simulation work for different real-life situations. Anything with two outcomes is best represented using a coin. Anything with 6 outcomes, is best represented using a die.

PRACTICE EXERCISE

1. For each of the following situation state whether the outcomes are equally likely or not. If not, state which is most likely.

   a) Rolling a 2 on a standard die

   b) Flipping heads on a coin

   c) Randomly drawing a particular coloured marble from a bag of marbles containing 3 blue, 2 yellow, and 1 red marbles.

   d) Spinning one of the colours on the spinner below.

2. What could you use to simulate each of the following events?

   a) Choosing an answer on a true/false question

   b) Likelihood of a candidate with 5 opponents winning an election

3. Find the probability of each of the following events.

   A regular die:

   a) $P(2)$

   b) $P(\text{even number})$

   c) $P(\text{a number less than 5})$

d) $P(8)$

e) P (not a three)

Regular deck of cards:

f) $P(7)$

g) P (face card)

h) P (any numbered card)

i) P (black)

4. Put each letter in of the word MATHEMATICS on a separate piece of paper, place them in a bag, and randomly pick out one.

   a) $P(M)$

   b) P (vowel)

   c) P (consonant)

   d) P (M or T)

5. Draw a spinner that would make all the following probabilities true.

   $P \text{ (black)} = \dfrac{1}{2}, \ P \text{ (grey)} = \dfrac{1}{4}, \ P \text{ (white)} = \dfrac{1}{4}$

6. Consider the following spinner and calculate the following probabilities as a fraction and a percentage.

a) *P* (odd number)

b) *P* (4)

c) *P* (more than 2)

d) *P* (not 3)

7. What is the probability that February 21 will be on a Monday?

8. What does *P* (favourable outcome) = 0 mean?

9. In response to a job advertisement, 5 men and 7 women equally qualified for the job have applied. If no other factors are considered, is a man or a woman more likely to get the job and by what percentage?

Lesson 7 INDEPENDENT EVENTS

The probability of independent events is the probability of two or more events occurring, where the outcome of one event has no effect on the outcome of the other events.

For example, if a person flips a coin and rolls a die the outcome of the coin (H or T) has no effect on the outcome of the die (1, 2, 3, 4, 5, or 6).

To figure out the number of possible outcomes of two independent events, it is easiest to make a tree diagram that shows the outcomes of the second corresponding with the possibilities of the first.

For example, if you flipped a head on the coin you could roll 1, 2, 3, 4, 5 or 6. If you flipped a tail on the coin, you could roll 1, 2, 3, 4, 5, or 6 with the die. As a tree diagram, this would be shown as follows.

Another way to figure out the total number of outcomes is to take the number of outcomes in the first event and multiply that by the total number of outcomes in the second event.

For example, with a coin there are 2 possible outcomes. With a die, there are 6 possible outcomes. $2 \times 6 = 12$ there are 12 possible outcomes when you flip a coin and roll a die. They are:

H1, H2, H3, H4, H5, H6, and T1, T2, T3, T4, T5, T6

Now, consider the example of rolling a die and spinning the spinner shown below. Make a tree diagram, then list all the possible outcomes.

On the die, there are 6 possible outcomes. On the spinner, there are 4 possible outcomes. The total number of outcomes is: $6 \times 4 = 24$.

322

The tree diagram is:

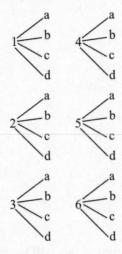

The outcomes are 1a, 1b, 1c, 1d, 2a, 2b, 2c, 2d, 3a, 3b, 3c, 3d, 4a, 4b, 4c, 4d, 5a, 5b, 5c, 5d, 6a, 6b, 6c, and 6d.

How many outcomes would there be if you flipped a coin and then drew a card from a regular deck?

A coin has 2 outcomes, and a deck of cards has 52 outcomes. $2 \times 52 = 104$

The probability of independent events can be calculated in two different ways.

Method 1

Find the total possible outcomes for both events and use the formula:

$$P \text{ (favourable outcome)} = \frac{\text{favourable outcomes}}{\text{total possible outcomes}}$$

Method 2

Find the probability of each single event, and then multiply them together for the total probability of the events together.

Sometimes, you are unable to use method 2 because there are not two separate events, just one result from the two combined events.

Find the probability of the following events.

Example 1

Flip two coins.

Possible outcomes are:

H — H
H — T   H,H
                H,T
T — H   T,H
T — T   T,T

Find P (H, H).

Solution

There are 4 possible outcomes; this will be the denominator.
There is 1 favourable outcome: H, H. Using the formula

$$P\,(\text{H, H}) = \frac{\text{favourable outcomes}}{\text{total possible outcomes}} = \frac{1}{4}$$

$$P\,(\text{first H}) = \frac{1}{2}\,,\ P(\text{second H}) = \frac{1}{2}$$

Multiply the probabilities of each event together.

$$\frac{1}{2} \times \frac{1}{2} = \frac{1}{4}$$

Using either method, $P\,(\text{H,H}) = \frac{1}{4}$

Remember: when you multiply two fractions together, multiply the numerator by numerator and the denominator by denominator.

Leave probabilities as fractions in lowest terms unless told otherwise.

Find P (H, T).

Solution

There are 4 possible outcomes; this will be the denominator. There is 1 favourable outcome: H, T. Using the formula

$$P\,(\text{H, T}) = \frac{\text{favourable outcomes}}{\text{total possible outcomes}} = \frac{1}{4}$$

$$P\,(\text{H}) = \frac{1}{2}\,,\ P\,(\text{T}) = \frac{1}{2}$$ Multiply the probabilities together.

The order that the outcomes are listed in is important. H, T is a different outcome than T, H even though they both involve one head and one tail.

$$\frac{1}{2} \times \frac{1}{2} = \frac{1}{4}$$

Using either method, $P\,(\text{H, T}) = \frac{1}{4}$

Find P (at least one T).

Solution

This probability can only be calculated using the first method because there are not two separate events.

There are 4 total outcomes, 3 with at least one T.

$$P \text{ (at least one T)} = \frac{\text{favourable outcomes}}{\text{total outcomes}} = \frac{3}{4}$$

Example 2

Consider the two spinners below.

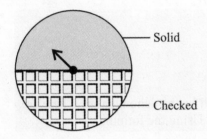 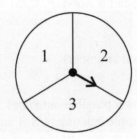

The outcomes for spinning the two spinners are: S1, S2, S3, C1, C2, C3.

Calculate each of the given probabilities as a fraction and as a percentage (round to nearest percentage).

Find P (S, 2).

Solution

There are 6 possible outcomes; this will be the denominator. There is 1 favourable outcome: S, 2. Using the formula

$$P \text{ (S, 2)} = \frac{\text{favourable outcomes}}{\text{total possible outcomes}} = \frac{1}{6}$$

$P \text{ (S)} = \dfrac{1}{2}, P \text{ (2)} = \dfrac{1}{3}$ Multiply the probabilities together.

$$\frac{1}{2} \times \frac{1}{3} = \frac{1}{6}$$

Using either method, $P \text{ (S, 2)} = \dfrac{1}{6} = 17\%$

NOTES

Find P (C, 3).

Solution

There are 6 possible outcomes; this will be the denominator. There is 1 favourable outcome: C, 3. Using the formula

$$P\text{ (C, 3)} = \frac{\text{favourable outcomes}}{\text{total possible outcomes}} = \frac{1}{6}$$

$P\text{ (C)} = \dfrac{1}{2}$, $P(3) = \dfrac{1}{3}$ Multiply the probabilities together.

$$\frac{1}{2} \times \frac{1}{3} = \frac{1}{6}$$

Using either method, P (C, 3) $= \dfrac{1}{6} = 17\%$

Find P (S, odd number).

Solution

There are 6 possible outcomes; this will be the denominator. There are 2 favourable outcomes: S, 1 and S, 3. Using the formula

$$P\text{ (S, odd number)} = \frac{\text{favourable outcomes}}{\text{total possible outcomes}} = \frac{2}{6} = \frac{1}{3}\text{ in lowest terms}$$

$P\text{ (S)} = \dfrac{1}{2}$, $P(\text{odd}) = \dfrac{2}{3}$ Multiply the probabilities together.

$$\frac{1}{2} \times \frac{2}{3} = \frac{2}{6} = \frac{1}{3}$$

Using either method, P (S, odd number) $= \dfrac{1}{3} = 33\%$

Find P (S or C, 4).

Solution

There are 6 possible outcomes; this will be the denominator. There are no favourable outcomes for S, 4 or C, 4 because there is no 4 on the spinner. Using the formula

$$P\text{ (S or C, 4)} = \frac{\text{favourable outcomes}}{\text{total possible outcomes}} = \frac{0}{6} = 0$$

$P \text{ (S or C)} = \dfrac{2}{2}, P(4) = \dfrac{0}{3}$ 　　　　Multiply the probabilities together.

$\dfrac{2}{2} \times \dfrac{0}{3} = \dfrac{0}{6} = 0$

Using either method, $P \text{ (S or C, 4)} = 0 = 0\%$

Example 3

Consider rolling a die, then drawing a card. You know there are 312 possible outcomes because for a die there are 6 and for drawing a card there are 52. $6 \times 52 = 312$; when calculating probabilities with numbers this high, use method 2 because it would take too long to make a tree diagram for these events listing all the possible outcomes.

Find $P \text{ (2, red)}$.

Solution

$P(2) = \dfrac{1}{6}, P \text{ (red)} = \dfrac{26}{52}$ 　　　　Multiply the probabilities together.

$\dfrac{1}{6} \times \dfrac{26}{52} = \dfrac{26}{312} = \dfrac{1}{12}$

If you put the fractions into lowest terms first and then multiply, it is much easier to calculate the probabilities and you still get the same answer.

$P(2) = \dfrac{1}{6}, P \text{ (red)} = \dfrac{1}{2}$ 　　　　Multiply the probabilities together.

$\dfrac{1}{6} \times \dfrac{1}{2} = \dfrac{1}{12}$

Either way, $P \text{ (2, red)} = \dfrac{1}{12}$

Find $P \text{ (odd, 7)}$

Solution

$P \text{ (odd)} = \dfrac{1}{2}, P(7) = \dfrac{1}{13}$

$\dfrac{1}{2} \times \dfrac{1}{13} = \dfrac{1}{26}$

Find P (less than 5, face card)

Solution

P (less than 5) $= \dfrac{2}{3}$, P (face card) $= \dfrac{3}{13}$

$\dfrac{2}{3} \times \dfrac{3}{13} = \dfrac{6}{39} = \dfrac{2}{13}$

Find P (a number, a card)

Solution

P (a number) $= \dfrac{1}{1}$, P (a card) $= \dfrac{1}{1}$

$\dfrac{1}{1} \times \dfrac{1}{1} = \dfrac{1}{1} = 1$

This means that no matter what you roll and what card you pick, you will always get a number and a card.

What is the probability of rolling two dice and getting at least one 2?

You cannot solve this by multiplying probabilities because there are not two specific outcomes; there is one possibility that involves both events. Use method 1.

For two dice, there are 36 possible outcomes ($6 \times 6 = 36$).

The outcomes that have a 2 are:
1,2 2,1 2,2 2,3 2,4 2,5 2,6 3,2 4,2 5,2 6,2.

P (at least one 2) $= \dfrac{11}{36}$

PRACTICE EXERCISE

1. Draw a tree diagram for the following events and then list all the possible outcomes.

a) Flip a coin, roll a die

b) Roll a die, spin the spinner shown below

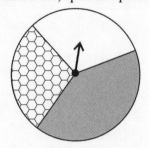

c) Spin the two spinners shown below

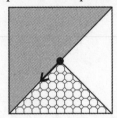 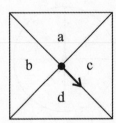

2. Calculate the following probabilities.

Spin the spinner shown below, roll a die

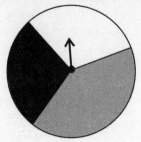

a) P (white, 1)

b) P (black, even number)

c) P (gray, a number)

d) P (white or Gray, 2 or 6)

e) P (a colour, a number less than 3)

3. Spin the two spinners shown below

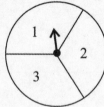 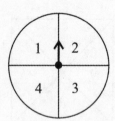

a) P (1, 1)

b) P (1, 4)

c) P (3, odd)

d) P (sum of 6)

e) P (sum of 4)

4. A couple is having twins. Find the following probabilities for first-born, second-born children as a fraction and a percentage.

a) P (B, B)

b) P (G, B)

c) P (at least 1 girl)

d) P (no boys)

5. Ian has the following coins in his pocket: 11 quarters, 6 loonies, 3 toonies. He randomly picks out a coin, replaces it, then randomly picks out another coin. Calculate the following probabilities for the coins Ian picks.

a) P (quarter, loonie)

b) P (loonie, toonie)

c) P (toonie, quarter)

d) P (quarter, quarter)

e) P (loonie or toonie, quarter)

6. A coin is flipped, and a card is drawn. Find the following probabilities for these results.

 a) P (H, red)

 b) P (T, face card)

 c) P (T, ace)

 d) P (H, a number)

 e) P (T, 6)

 f) P (H or T, 7)

7. Meredith and Cathy are playing a game in which they roll two dice and find the sum. If the sum is 11, Meredith wins. If it is 6, Cathy wins. Who is more likely to win? By what percentage?

PRACTICE QUIZ 2

1. State whether each of the following outcomes are equally likely or not for each event. If not, tell which is the most   likely outcome.

   a) Flipping heads or tails on a coin

   b) Rolling a die with sides 1, 1, 2, 2, 3, 4 and getting a number

   c) Spinning the spinner to get a colour

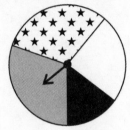

   d) Drawing a random card out of a standard deck of cards

   e) Picking a random coin out of a pocket containing 8 dimes, 6 quarter, and 4 pennies

2. Given each of the following situations, what could be used to simulate the probability?

   a) The probability of 1 of 6 finalists winning the title of Miss Canada

   b) The probability of 1 of 8 companies being the first to discover a cure for the common cold

   c) The probability that someone who has narrowed his or her vacation possibilities to 2 places will go to 1 of them.

3. Given each situation related to the spinner shown below, find the probability.

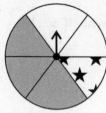

   a) P (white)

   b) P (grey)

   c) P (stars)

   d) P (not stars)

   e) P (stars or grey)

4. For a regular deck of cards, find each of the following probabilities.
   a) P (3)

   b) P (face card)

   c) P (a number)

   d) P (a black 4)

5. A jar contains 800 jelly beans. If you randomly pull out 10 and get 7 red and 3 white, how many white jelly beans would you predict are in the jar?

6. In the last hour, a company has sold 22 large pizzas, 17 medium pizzas, and 8 small pizzas. What is the likelihood, to the nearest whole percentage, that the next pizza sold will be a medium one?

7. Draw a tree diagram to represent each set of events below, and then list the outcomes.

  a) A coin is flipped, and the spinner shown below is spun.

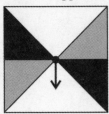

  b) A die is rolled, and one coin is picked from a pocket containing a penny, nickel, and dime.

8. State the total number of possible outcomes for each set of events below.

  a) A card is drawn and a die is rolled

  b) A letter from the alphabet is selected and a card is drawn from a deck

9. Calculate the probability of each event below.

One marble of the marbles represented below is randomly chosen and regular die is rolled.

  a) P (gray, 6)

  b) P (brick, even)

  c) P (swirl, not a 4)

  d) P (marble, odd)

e) P (gray or brick, 3)

f) P (swirl, a number)

10. A coin is flipped, and 1 coin is drawn from a pocket containing 2 pennies, 1 nickel, and 7 quarters. Calculate the probability of each event below.

a) P (H, penny)

b) P (H, nickel)

c) P (T, not a quarter)

d) P (T, not a nickel)

e) P (H or T, quarter)

f) P (T, loonie)

11. Murray wants to win a particular lottery in which a person needs three out of three numbers to win. To do this, he needs to pick three out of the following numbers: 1, 2, 3, 4, 5, 6, 7, 8, 9, 10. If he is allowed to pick the same number more than once, what are his chances of having all three of his numbers match up with the winning numbers?

Review Summary

- A survey is a way of collecting information. In a random survey, each answer has an equal chance of being chosen and the results are fair. In a biased survey, not every answer has an equal chance of being chosen. The results are not fair.

- A tally sheet is a way of representing the data collected from a survey. It contains all the choices, the tally, and the frequency of the choices.

- The fractions and percentage of each choice in a survey can be used to make predictions for an entire population. To do this, either set up a proportion and cross-multiply, or calculate the percentage of the population by converting the percentage to a decimal and multiplying by the population.

- Graphs are used to represent different types of information. Bar graphs are used for data with   distinct categories, line graphs are used to graph changes over time, pictographs use pictures to compare two or more things, and circle graphs use percentages to show how much out of a whole circle is represented by each category.

- Central tendency is the tendency of data to converge around specific points in the middle of a set of data. The points are the *mean*, which is the average of the data, the *median*, which is the middle point, and the *mode*, which is the point or points that occur most often.

- If a set if data is changed by a certain amount, the mean, median, and mode also change by that amount. If an outlier that is very different than the rest of the data is added, the mean is the measure most affected.

- Stem-and-leaf plots are a way of representing a long set of data. The leaf contains the last digit in each number, and the stem contains all the other digits.

- A box-and-whisker plot is made using the low and high values, the lower and upper quartile, and the median. Each section of the box-and-whisker plot represents 25% of the data.

- Probability is the chance that an event will occur. If all the events have the same chance of occurring, each outcome is said to be equally likely. Probability is always calculated using the formula:

$$P \text{ (favourable outcome)} = \frac{\text{favourable outcomes}}{\text{total possible outcomes}}$$

- Probability is always a number between 0 and 1. If something has a probability of 0, it means that outcome will never occur. If probability is 1, it means that outcome is guaranteed to always happen. Probability should be written as a fraction unless stated otherwise.

- Independent events are two or more events where the outcome of one has no effect on the other. The outcomes are best displayed in a tree diagram. The probably of independent events can be calculated in two ways using the probability formula, or by calculating the probability of each specific event and multiplying them together.

PRACTICE TEST

1. In a survey, 40 people were asked what type of TV show they watch most. The results are given in the following incomplete chart.

   a) Complete the chart.

Favourite Types of Shows on TV				
Type	Tally	Frequency	Fraction	Percentage
News		9		
Soap Operas				15%
Sitcoms			$\frac{10}{40}$	
Educational Programs	I I			
Sports				32.5%

   b) How many more people liked soap operas than educational programs?

   c) What percentage liked sports over news?

   d) If 500 people were surveyed, how many would you expect to enjoy sitcoms?

2. The Kim family calculated their monthly expenses and converted the amounts to percentages, as follow: Mortgage – 36%, Bills – 20%, Food – 12%, Car – 16%, Entertainment – 10%, Other – 6%

   a) Make a bar graph based on the percentages of the Kim family's expenses.

b) If this information were graphed on a circle graph, how many degrees would the angle for "Bills" be?

c) If each 10% was represented by a dollar bill on a pictograph, how many bills would be used for the "Car" section?

3. Explain if each of the following surveys is biased or not.

   a) Every fifth person entering West Edmonton Mall is asked what their favourite shopping mall is.

   b) At a large school, 10% of the students are surveyed about their opinion on the school dress code.

   c) Two hundred lawyers were asked if they thought that lawyer fees were reasonable.

4. Use the graph below to answer the following questions.

Each 🍦 =10 people

   a) What is the most popular type of ice cream?

   b) How many more people like vanilla than those who like strawberry?

5. Use the graph below to answer the following questions.

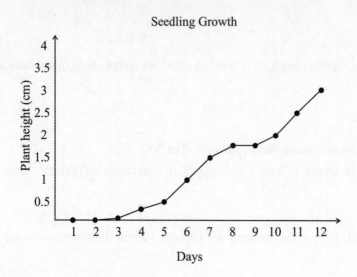

Seedling Growth

a) What is happening in the first two days?

b) How much did the plant grow between day 5 and day 10?

6. In her last eight games of golf, Emily had the following scores: 63, 62, 59, 65, 71, 62, 58, 67.

a) Calculate her average score.

b) Calculate median and the mode of her scores.

7. Given the set of data 2, 2, 4, 6, 6, 6, 7, 8,

   a) find the measures of central tendency

   b) write the new set of data that will result and find the measures of central tendency if all the values are decreased by 3

8. Write a set of five numbers where the highest value is 80, the range is 60, and the median is 55.

9. Consider the following numbers: 55, 50, 50, 47, 49, 73, 71, 76, 45

   a) Make a stem-and-leaf plot of the data

   b) Make a box-and-whisker plot of the data

   c) Approximately what percentage of the data lies between 55 and 70?

   d) How would the appearance of the box-and-whisker plot change if 14 were added to the set of data?

10. State whether the following outcomes for each event are equally likely. If not, tell which is most likely to occur.

   a) Randomly picking a letter of the word MISSISSIPPI out of a hat.

   b) Spinning the spinner to get a colour

   c) Rolling a ten-sided die with all the digits from 0 to 9 on it to randomly get any number.

11. The letters of the word BANANA are put into a hat and then 1 letter is randomly drawn out. Calculate the following probabilities as both a fraction and as a percentage.

a) P (B)

b) P (N)

c) P (not an A)

d) P (consonant)

e) P (S)

12. In Ben's office, $\dfrac{35}{150}$ people are allergic to cats. What is the probability that the next person to work in this office will not be allergic to cats?

13. For each of the following situations, make a tree diagram, list the outcomes, and then calculate the probability.

A coin is tossed, and a die is rolled

a) P (H, 3)

b) P (T, not 1)

c) P (T, 9)

d) P (H, composite number)

14. The two spinners shown below are spun.

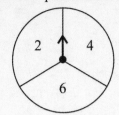

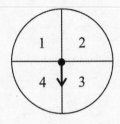

Calculate the following probabilities.

   a) $P(2, 3)$

   b) $P(1, 3)$

   c) $P(2 \text{ or } 4, 1 \text{ or } 3)$

   d) $P(\text{two even numbers})$

   e) $P(\text{two of the same numbers})$

   f) $P(\text{two different numbers}$

NOTES

NOTES

NOTES

Student Notes and Problems

Answers
and
Solutions

Research Corp

NOTES

NUMBER CONCEPTS

Lesson 1—Negative Exponents

PRACTICE EXERCISE
Answers and Solutions

1.

	Standard Form			Exponential Form
	Fraction	Decimal	Positive Exponent	Negative Exponent
a)	$\dfrac{1}{10}$	0.1	$\dfrac{1}{10^1}$	10^{-1}
b)	$\dfrac{1}{1\,000}$	0.001	$\dfrac{1}{10^3}$	10^{-3}
c)	$\dfrac{1}{100}$	0.01	$\dfrac{1}{10^2}$	10^{-2}
d)	$\dfrac{1}{100\,000}$	0.000 01	$\dfrac{1}{10^5}$	10^{-5}

2. **a)** $10^{-2}, \dfrac{10^{-2}}{1}$

$$\frac{1}{100} = \frac{1}{10 \times 10} = \frac{1}{10^2}$$

$$\frac{1}{10^2} = \frac{10^{-2}}{1} = 10^{-2}$$

b) $10^{-4}, \dfrac{1}{10^4}$

$$\frac{1}{10\,000} = \frac{1}{10 \times 10 \times 10 \times 10} = \frac{1}{10^4}$$

$$\frac{1}{10^4} = \frac{10^{-4}}{1} = 10^{-4}$$

c) $10^{-3}, \dfrac{1}{10^3}$

$$\frac{1}{1\,000} = \frac{1}{10 \times 10 \times 10} = \frac{1}{10^3}$$

$$\frac{1}{10^3} = \frac{10^{-3}}{1} = 10^{-3}$$

d) $\dfrac{1}{10^1}, 10^{-1}$

$$\frac{1}{10} = \frac{1}{10^1}$$

$$\frac{1}{10^1} = \frac{10^{-1}}{1} = 10^{-1}$$

3. **a)** $10^{-2}, \dfrac{1}{100}$

$$\frac{1}{100} = \frac{1}{10 \times 10} = \frac{1}{10^2} = \frac{10^{-2}}{1} = 10^{-2}$$

b) $10^{-5}, \dfrac{1}{100\,000}$

$$\frac{1}{100\,000} = \frac{1}{10 \times 10 \times 10 \times 10 \times 10} = \frac{1}{10^5}$$
$$= \frac{10^{-5}}{1} = 10^{-5}$$

c) $10^{-1}, \dfrac{1}{10}$

$$\frac{1}{10} = \frac{1}{10^1} = \frac{10^{-1}}{1} = 10^{-1}$$

d) $\dfrac{1}{100\,000\,000} = 10^{-8}$

$$\frac{1}{100\,000\,000} = \frac{1}{10 \times 10 \times 10 \times 10 \times 10 \times 10 \times 10 \times 10}$$
$$= \frac{1}{10^8} = \frac{10^{-8}}{1} = 10^{-8}$$

4. **a)** $\dfrac{1}{100\,000}$

$$10^{-5} = \frac{1}{10^5} = \frac{1}{100\,000}$$

b) $\dfrac{1}{100}$

$$10^{-2} = \dfrac{1}{10^2} = \dfrac{1}{100}$$

c) $\dfrac{1}{10\ 000}$

$$10^{-4} = \dfrac{10^{-4}}{1} = \dfrac{1}{10^4} = \dfrac{1}{10\ 000}$$

d) $\dfrac{1}{10\ 000\ 000}$

$$10^{-7} = \dfrac{10^{-7}}{1} = \dfrac{1}{10^7} = \dfrac{1}{10\ 000\ 000}$$

5. **a)** $0.000\ 001,\ \dfrac{1}{1\ 000\ 000}$

$$10^{-6} = \dfrac{1}{10^6} = \dfrac{1}{1\ 000\ 000} = 0.000\ 001$$

b) $0.001,\ \dfrac{1}{1\ 000}$

$$10^{-3} = \dfrac{1}{10^3} = \dfrac{1}{1\ 000} = 0.001$$

c) $0.1,\ \dfrac{1}{10}$

$$10^{-1} = \dfrac{1}{10^1} = \dfrac{1}{10} = 0.1$$

d) $0.000\ 000\ 01,\ \dfrac{1}{100\ 000\ 000}$

$$10^{-8} = \dfrac{1}{10^8} = \dfrac{1}{100\ 000\ 000} = 0.000\ 000\ 01$$

6. **a)** $10^{-5} < 0.001$

$\quad 0.00\ 001 < 0.001$

b) $10^{-7} < \dfrac{1}{100\ 000}$

$\quad 0.000\ 000\ 1 < 0.000\ 001$

c) $10^{-2} = 0.01$

$\quad 0.01 = 0.01$

d) $10^{-2} > \dfrac{1}{1\ 000}$

$\quad 0.01 > 0.001$

Lesson 2—Scientific Notation

PRACTICE EXERCISE
Answers and Solutions

1. **a)** $80 = 8 \times 10^1$

Count the number of spaces that you move the decimal from the end of the number so it is immediately to the right of the first digit in the number. This is the power of 10.

80.
   1

b) $200 = 2 \times 10^2$

c) $93\ 000 = 9.3 \times 10^4$

d) $45\ 600 = 4.56 \times 10^4$

e) $6\ 770 = 6.77 \times 10^3$

f) $1\ 908\ 000 = 1.908 \times 10^6$

For b) to f) count the number of spaces you move the decimal from the end of the number so it is immediately to the right of the first digit in the number. This is the power of 10.

2. **a)** $4\ 600 = 4.6 \times 10^3$

b) $590 = 5.9 \times 10^2$

c) $70\ 000 = 7 \times 10^4$

d) $34\ 000 = 3.4 \times 10^4$

e) $2\ 430\ 000 = 2.43 \times 10^6$

f) $750\ 000 = 7.5 \times 10^5$

g) $21\ 300\ 020 = 2.130\ 002 \times 10^7$

h) $901\ 000\ 000 = 9.01 \times 10^8$

For b) to h) use the same procedures as in question part a

3. a) $3.6 \times 10^2 = 360$

Move the decimal to the right the same number of spaces indicated by the exponent on the 10. Fill in any extra spaces with zeros

3.6×10^2

$3.6 \rightarrow 360$

b) $10.5 \times 10^4 = 105\,000$

c) $5.9 \times 10^3 = 5\,900$

d) $8.8 \times 10^5 = 880\,000$

e) $6.02 \times 10^6 = 6\,020\,000$

f) $7.893 \times 10^4 = 78\,930$

For b) to f) move the decimal to the right the same number of spaces indicated by the exponent on the 10. Fill in any extra spaces with zeros.

4. a) $0.005 = 5 \times 10^{-3}$

The decimal is currently behind the first 0. It needs to be moved to the right until it is to the right of the first number, which is 5. The number of places it moves becomes the power on the 10. It has moved 3 places to the right so the power is 10^{-3}

0.005

b) $0.8 = 8 \times 10^{-1}$

c) $0.06 = 6 \times 10^{-2}$

d) $0.43 = 4.3 \times 10^{-1}$

e) $0.009\,8 = 9.8 \times 10^{-3}$

f) $0.000\,005 = 5 \times 10^{-6}$

For b) to f) use the same procedure as a).

5. a) $0.000\,4 = 4 \times 10^{-4}$

b) $0.09 = 9 \times 10^{-2}$

c) $0.005\,4 = 5.4 \times 10^{-3}$

d) $0.000\,001 = 1 \times 10^{-6}$

e) $0.000\,007\,3 = 7.3 \times 10^{-6}$

f) $0.004\,05 = 4.05 \times 10^{-3}$

g) $0.305\,06 = 3.050\,6 \times 10^{-1}$

For a) to g) use the same prodecure as question 4.

6. a) $5 \times 10^{-3} = 0.005$

Move the decimal from where it is to the left because the exponent is negative. The decimal moves 3 places. Fill in the extras places with zeros.

0.005

b) $3.4 \times 10^{-4} = 0.000\,34$

c) $7.07 \times 10^{-7} = 0.000\,000\,707$

d) $5.28 \times 10^{-5} = 0.000\,052\,8$

e) $8.01 \times 10^{-2} = 0.080\,1$

f) $5.6 \times 10^{-3} = 0.005\,6$

g) $4.01 \times 10^{-8} = 0.000\,000\,040\,1$

For b) to g) use the same procedure as in a).

Lesson 3—Rational Numbers

PRACTICE EXERCISE
Answers and Solutions

1. a) rational

776.0 is rational because the decimal number terminates.

b) rational

$\sqrt{121}$ is rational because it is a perfect square.

c) rational

$\dfrac{0}{8}$ is rational because it is a fraction with a denominator other than 0.

d) rational

$4.\overline{76}$ is rational because the decimal number repeats.

e) not rational

$\dfrac{7}{0}$ is not rational because the fraction has zero as a denominator.

f) rational

$-\dfrac{3}{4}$ is rational because the fraction has a denominator other than 0.

g) rational

$\dfrac{66}{99}$ is rational because the fraction has a denominator other than 0.

h) not rational

$\sqrt{23}$ is not rational because the decimal number does not terminate or repeat.

i) rational

−2.48 is rational because the decimal number terminates.

j) not rational

π is not rational because the decimal number (3.14159…) does not terminate or repeat.

2. For a) to j) answers may vary. Any fraction where the numerator and denominator have been multiplied or divided by the same number produces an equivalent fraction.

a) $\dfrac{10}{16}$ and $\dfrac{15}{24}$

$\dfrac{5}{8} = \dfrac{5(\times 2)}{8(\times 2)} = \dfrac{10}{16}$ and $\dfrac{5}{8} = \dfrac{5(\times 3)}{8(\times 3)} = \dfrac{15}{24}$

b) $\dfrac{18}{30}$ and $\dfrac{3}{5}$

$\dfrac{9}{15} = \dfrac{9(\times 2)}{15(\times 2)} = \dfrac{18}{30}$ and $\dfrac{9}{15} = \dfrac{9(\div 3)}{15(\div 3)} = \dfrac{3}{5}$

c) $\dfrac{-6}{20}$ and $\dfrac{-30}{100}$

$\dfrac{-3}{10} = \dfrac{-3(\times 2)}{10(\times 2)} = \dfrac{-6}{20}$ and

$\dfrac{-3}{10} = \dfrac{-3(\times 10)}{10(\times 10)} = \dfrac{-30}{100}$

d) $\dfrac{8}{3}$ and $\dfrac{16}{6}$

$2\dfrac{2}{3} = \dfrac{2\times 3 + 2}{3} = \dfrac{8}{3}$ and $\dfrac{8}{3} = \dfrac{8(\times 2)}{3(\times 2)} = \dfrac{16}{6}$

e) $1\dfrac{2}{5}$ and $1\dfrac{4}{10}$

$\dfrac{7}{5} = 1\dfrac{2}{5} = 1\dfrac{2(\times 2)}{5(\times 2)} = 1\dfrac{4}{10}$

f) $\dfrac{8}{2}$ and $\dfrac{16}{4}$

$4 = \dfrac{4}{1} = \dfrac{4(\times 2)}{1(\times 2)} = \dfrac{8}{2}$ and $\dfrac{4}{1} = \dfrac{4(\times 4)}{1(\times 4)} = \dfrac{16}{4}$

g) $\dfrac{5}{10}$ or $\dfrac{1}{2}$ and $\dfrac{2}{4}$

$0.5 = \dfrac{1}{2} = \dfrac{1(\times 2)}{2(\times 2)} = \dfrac{1}{4}$

h) $1\dfrac{1}{4}$ and $1\dfrac{25}{100}$

$1.25 = 1\dfrac{25}{100}$ or $1\dfrac{1}{4}$ and $1\dfrac{25(\div 25)}{100(\div 25)} = 1\dfrac{1}{4}$

i) $\dfrac{-2}{10}$ and $\dfrac{-1}{5}$

$-0.2 = \dfrac{-2}{10}$ and $\dfrac{-2(\times 2)}{10(\times 2)} = \dfrac{-4}{20}$

j) $\dfrac{-66}{100}$ and $\dfrac{-33}{50}$

$-0.66 = \dfrac{-66}{100}$ and $\dfrac{-66(\div 2)}{100(\div 2)} = \dfrac{-33}{50}$

3. a) $\dfrac{6}{8} > \dfrac{2}{8}$

> because 6 is greater than 2

b) $\dfrac{0}{4} = 0$

= because both have a value of 0

c) $\dfrac{-7}{2} < \dfrac{-3}{2}$

< because −7 is less than −3

d) −2.46 > −6.42

> because −2.46 is greater than −6.42

e) 12.457 8 > 12.454 8

> because 12.457 8 is greater than 12.454 8

f) $3\dfrac{1}{4} < 3.75$

< because 3.25 is less than 3.75

g) $0.63 < \dfrac{2}{3}$

$<$ because 0.63 is lessthan 0.6 repeating

h) $0.29 < 2\dfrac{9}{10}$

$<$ because 0.29 is less than 2.9

i) $-6\dfrac{2}{10} = \dfrac{-31}{5}$

$=$ because the numbers are the same in lowest terms

4. **a)** $-3\dfrac{1}{2}$ $4\dfrac{3}{9}$ $\sqrt{49}$ 12.5

b) $-1\dfrac{4}{100}$ $-\sqrt{1}$ $\dfrac{3}{12}$ 2.08

Lesson 4—Ratio

PRACTICE EXERCISE
Answers and Solutions

1. **a)** 4 red, 3 yellow = 4:3 and 4 to 3

b) 7 green, 4 red = 7:4 and 7 to 4

c) 3 yellow, 7 green, 14 total (4 + 3 + 7)
= 3:7:14 and 3 to 7 to 14

2. Answers may vary.

a) 8 × 2 to 9 × 2 = 16 to 18, 8 × 3 to 9 × 3 = 24 to 27

b) 2 × 2:11 × 2 = 4:22, 2 × 4:11 × 4 = 8:44

c) 2 × 2:8 × 2: 16 × 2 = 4:16:32, 2 ÷ 2: 8 ÷ 2 : 16 ÷ 2 = 1:4:8

3. **a)** 36 ÷ 12:12 ÷ 12 = 3:1

b) 28 ÷ 7:77 ÷ 7 = 4:11

c) 13 ÷ 13 to 26 ÷ 13 to 52 ÷ 13 = 1 to 2 to 4

4. **a)** 10 blue, 4 brown = 10:4 =
10 ÷ 2 : 4 ÷ 2 = 5:2

b) 8 green, 1 hazel, 23 total = 8 to 1 to 23 This ratio is already in lowest terms because the only factor that divides into 8, 1, and 23 is 1.

c) 4 brown, 10 blue, 22 not hazel = 4:10:22 =
4 ÷ 2:10 ÷ 2: 22 ÷ 2 = 2:5:11

d) 4 brown = double means multiply by 2 so
4 × 2 = 8

Lesson 5—Percentage

PRACTICE EXERCISE
Answers and Solutions

1. **a)** Half the diagram is shaded, which is 50%.

b) $\dfrac{5}{8}$ of the diagram is shaded, which is approximately 60%.

c) $\dfrac{1}{10}$ is shaded, which is 10%.

2. **a)** $\dfrac{32}{100} = 32\%$

b) $\dfrac{76}{100} = 76\%$

c) $\dfrac{16}{20} = \dfrac{16(\times 5)}{20(\times 5)} = \dfrac{80}{100} = 80\%$

d) $\dfrac{4}{10} = \dfrac{4(\times 10)}{10(\times 10)} = \dfrac{40}{100} = 40\%$

e) $\dfrac{23}{25} = \dfrac{23(\times 4)}{25(\times 4)} = \dfrac{92}{100} = 92\%$

f) $\dfrac{52}{50} = \dfrac{52(\times 2)}{50(\times 2)} = \dfrac{104}{100} = 104\%$

g) $\dfrac{4}{5} = \dfrac{4(\times 20)}{5(\times 20)} = \dfrac{80}{100} = 80\%$

h) $\dfrac{3}{2} = \dfrac{3(\times 50)}{2(\times 50)} = \dfrac{150}{100} = 150\%$

i) $0.59 \times 100 = 59\%$

Multiply the decimal number by 100 to find the percent.

j) $0.125 \times 100 = 12.5\%$

Multiply the decimal number by 100 to find the percent.

k) $1.13 \times 100 = 113\%$

Multiply the decimal number by 100 to find the percent.

l) $0.07 \times 100 = 7\%$

Multiply the decimal number by 100 to find the percent.

3.

Fraction	Ratio	Decimal	Percent
$\dfrac{1}{4}$	1:4	0.25	25%
$\dfrac{1}{1}$	1:1	1.00	100%
$1\dfrac{2}{10}$	6:5	1.20	120%
$\dfrac{9}{20}$	9:20	0.45	45%
$\dfrac{5}{8}$	5:8	0.625	62.5%

Fraction to ratio: make an improper fraction if possible and rewrite with a colon or the word *to*

Fraction to decimal: numerator divided by denominator

Fraction to percent: numerator divided by denominator times 100

Ratio to anything: convert the ratio to a fraction and use the above rules

Decimal to percent: multiply 100

Decimal to fraction: make a percent, and put the percent over 100. Reduce to lowest terms

Decimal to ratio: find the fraction and rewrite

Percent to decimal: divide by 100

Percent to a fraction: put percent over 100 and reduce

Percent to a ratio: find the fraction and write in the different form

4. a) Order is 39%, 0.425, $\dfrac{7}{10}$, 39:50

$0.425 \times 100 = 42.5\%$,

$\dfrac{7}{10} = 7 \div 10 \times 100 = 70\%$

$39\%, 39{:}50 = 39 \div 50 \times 100 = 78\%$

b) Order is 0.5%, 2:25, 0.125, $\dfrac{1}{5}$

$0.125 \times 100 = 12.5\%$, $\dfrac{1}{5} = 1 \div 5 \times 100 = 20\%$

$0.5\%, 2{:}25 = 2 \div 25 \times 100 = 8\%$

5. a) 30%

3 nickels, 2 quarters, and 5 pennies = $3 + 2 + 5 = 10$ coins in total

Nickels ÷ total $\times 100 = 3 \div 10 \times 100 = 30\%$

b) 80%

Not quarters ÷ total $\times 100 =$ $8 \div 10 \times 100 = 80\%$

c) 70%

Percent of a dollar is the total value of coins (in cents) out of $1 (100 cents).

3 nickels = 15
2 quarters = 50
5 pennies = 5

Value = $15 + 50 + 5 = 70$
Percent = $70 \div 100 \times 100 = 70\%$

6. a) 40%

Vowels ÷ total letters $\times 100 = 4 \div 10 \times 100 = 40\%$

b) 30%

Es ÷ total letters $\times 100 = 3 \div 10 \times 100 = 30\%$

Lesson 6—Square Root

PRACTICE EXERCISE
Answers and Solutions

1. a) $\sqrt{49} = 7$

$7 \times 7 = 49$

b) $\sqrt{0.16} = 0.4$

$0.4 \times 0.4 = 0.16$

c) $\sqrt{1} = 1$

$1 \times 1 = 1$

d) $\sqrt{196} = 14$

$14 \times 14 = 196$

2. a) $\sqrt{20}$, $16 = 4 \times 4$, $25 = 5 \times 5$. 20 is about halfway between so it will be about 4.5

b) $\sqrt{104}$, $100 = 10 \times 10$, $121 = 11 \times 11$. 104 is much closer to 100 than 121 so it will be about 10.2

c) $\sqrt{66}$, $64 = 8 \times 8$, $81 = 9 \times 9$. 66 is much closer to 64 than 81 so it will be about 8.1

d) $\sqrt{171}$, $169 = 13 \times 13$, $196 = 14 \times 14$. 171 is much closer to 169 than 196 so it will be about 13.1

For a) to d), find the two perfect squares close to each number and determine which value the number under the square root sign is closest to. Estimate the decimal part of the number based on which perfect square the number is closest to.

3. a) $\sqrt{11} = 3.32$

b) $\sqrt{119} = 10.91$

c) $\sqrt{54} = 7.35$

d) $\sqrt{213} = 14.59$

For a) to d), use the $\sqrt{}$ button on your calculator to get the answers, then round to the nearest hundredth.

4. 8 m

Because you know mat is square, you know each side must be the same length. Sometimes it is easiest to draw a diagram to help you see this.

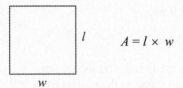

You need to determine what number multiplied by itself gives you 64. In other words, you need to take the square root of 64.

$\sqrt{64} = 8$ so you know that each side is 8 m.

5. a) 16 km^2

There are 9 sections so divide $144 \div 9 = 16$ km^2 for each section.

b) 4 km by 4 km

Take the square root of 16 to find the length of each side.

$\sqrt{16} = 4$, so each small field is 4 km by 4 km

Practice Quiz 1

Answers and Solutions

1. a) 81

3^4 means 3 multiplied by itself 4 times
$3 \times 3 \times 3 \times 3 = 81$

b) 1

$8^0 = 1$ (anything to the exponent 0 is equal to 1)

c) 0.001

$$10^{-3} = \frac{10^{-3}}{1} = \frac{1}{10^3} = \frac{1}{1\,000} = 0.001$$

d) $10^{-5} = \dfrac{10^{-5}}{1} = \dfrac{1}{10^5} = \dfrac{1}{100\,000} = 0.000\,01$

e) $2.79 \times 10^6 = 2\,790\,000$

Move the decimal from the number 6 places right (because the exponent is positive) because the exponent on the power of 10 is a 6. Delete the power of 10 and fill in any extra places with zeros.

f) $5.8 \times 10^{-2} = 0.058$

Move the decimal from the number 2 places left (because the exponent is negative) because the exponent on the power of 10 is 2. Delete the power of 10 and fill in any extra places with zeros.

2. a) $4\,420 = 4.42 \times 10^3$

b) $0.000\,000\,723 = 7.23 \times 10^{-7}$

3. Answers may vary.

a) $\dfrac{5}{12} = \dfrac{10}{24}$

$\dfrac{5(\times 2)}{12(\times 2)} = \dfrac{10}{24}$

b) $2\dfrac{2}{3} = 2\dfrac{2(\times 2)}{3(\times 2)} = 2\dfrac{4}{6}$

c) $0.49 = \dfrac{49}{100}$

d) $8 = \dfrac{8}{1}$

4. a) $1\dfrac{7}{8} > 1\dfrac{5}{6}$ because

$1\dfrac{7}{8} = \dfrac{15}{8} = 15 \div 8 = 1.875$

$1\dfrac{5}{6} = \dfrac{11}{6} = 11 \div 6 = 1.83$

and $1.875 > 1.83$

b) $-0.547 > -0.574$ is closer to 0 on the number line

5. a) ☆ to ♡

2 stars to 5 hearts

2 to 5 or 2:5 or $\dfrac{2}{5}$

b) 😊 to all pictures

3 faces to $(5 + 3 + 2) = 10$ total pictures

3 to $(5 + 3 + 2) = 3$ to 10, 3:10, $\dfrac{3}{10}$

c) 😊 and ♡ to ☆

3 faces, 5 hearts, 2 stars

$8:2 \rightarrow 4:1$ or 4 to 1 or $\dfrac{4}{1}$

d) ⚡ to 😊

no lightening bolts, 3 faces

0 (no lightening bolts) : 3

0:3 or 0 to 3

6. a) 2 setters, 12 others $= 2:12 = 2 \div 2 :$
$12 \div 2 = 1:6$

b) 2 setters, 10 other players $= 2:10 = 2 \div 2 :$
$10 \div 2 = 1:5$

c) $2 \times 2 = 4$ setters

7.

Fraction	Ratio	Decimal	Percent
$\dfrac{4}{5}$	4:5	0.8	80%
$\dfrac{3}{2}$	3:2	1.5	150%
$\dfrac{3}{8}$	3:8	0.375	37.5%
$\dfrac{11}{25}$	11:25	0.44	44%

8. 18%, 0.42, $\dfrac{2}{3}$, 9:10

0.66, 0.42, 0.18, 0.9

9. a) $\sqrt{81} = 9$ (perfect square)

b) $\sqrt{1.44} = 1.2$ (not a whole number)

c) $\sqrt{76}$, $64 = 8 \times 8$, $81 = 9 \times 9$. 76 is much closer to 81 than 64, so it will be about 8.7

d) $\sqrt{129}$, $121 = 11 \times 11$, $144 = 12 \times 12$. 129 is much closer to 121 than 144 so it will be about 11.3

10. a) $\sqrt{225} = 15.0$

b) $\sqrt{45} = 6.7$

c) $\sqrt{98} = 9.9$

d) $\sqrt{3} = 1.7$

For a) to d), use the $\sqrt{}$ button on your calculator and round to the nearest tenth.

11. a) 36 cows, 12 pigs = 36:12 = 36 ÷ 12: 12 ÷ 12
= 3:1

b) chickens and cows = 28 + 36 = 64, horses
and pigs = 24 + 12 = 36

64:36 = 64 ÷ 4 : 36 ÷ 4 = 16:9

c) 24 horses, 100 total = $\dfrac{24}{100}$ = 24%

d) Not chickens = 36 + 24 + 12 = 72

72 not chickens, 100 total = $\dfrac{72}{100}$ = 72%

Lesson 7—Operations with Fractions

PRACTICE EXERCISE
Answers and Solutions

1. a) $\dfrac{2}{6}+\dfrac{3}{6}=\dfrac{5}{6}$

b) $\dfrac{7}{9}-\dfrac{2}{9}=\dfrac{5}{9}$

2. $\dfrac{1}{3}+\dfrac{1}{2}=\dfrac{5}{6}$

3. a) $\dfrac{1}{2}+\dfrac{2}{2}=\dfrac{3}{2}=1\dfrac{1}{2}$

b) $\dfrac{9}{10}+\dfrac{3}{4}=\dfrac{18}{20}+\dfrac{15}{20}=\dfrac{33}{20}=1\dfrac{13}{20}$

c) $6\dfrac{4}{5}+2\dfrac{4}{3}=\dfrac{34}{5}+\dfrac{10}{3}$

$=\dfrac{102}{15}+\dfrac{50}{15}=\dfrac{152}{15}=10\dfrac{2}{15}$

d) $3+4\dfrac{1}{2}=\dfrac{3}{1}+\dfrac{9}{2}=\dfrac{6}{2}+\dfrac{9}{2}=\dfrac{15}{2}=7\dfrac{1}{2}$

To add the fractions, in a) to d), convert any mixed numbers to improper fractions first. Check to see if you have a common denominator. If not, write equivalent fractions with a common denominator. Add the numerators, keep the denominators the same, and reduce at the end, making a mixed number if necessary.

4. a) $\dfrac{6}{7}-\dfrac{2}{7}=\dfrac{4}{7}$

b) $\dfrac{3}{5}-\dfrac{4}{10}=\dfrac{6}{10}-\dfrac{4}{10}=\dfrac{2}{10}=\dfrac{1}{5}$

c) $7\dfrac{1}{6}-\dfrac{3}{8}=\dfrac{43}{6}-\dfrac{3}{8}=\dfrac{172}{24}-\dfrac{9}{24}=\dfrac{163}{24}=6\dfrac{19}{24}$

d) $3\dfrac{1}{3}-2\dfrac{1}{8}=\dfrac{10}{3}-\dfrac{17}{8}=\dfrac{80}{24}-\dfrac{51}{24}=\dfrac{29}{24}=1\dfrac{5}{24}$

To subtract the fractions in a) to d), convert any mixed numbers to improper fractions first. Check to see if you have a common denominator. If not, write equivalent fractions with a common denominator. Subtract the numerators, keep the denominators the same, and reduce at the end, making a mixed number if necessary.

5. a) $\dfrac{2}{3}\times\dfrac{1}{5}=\dfrac{2}{15}$

b) $3\dfrac{1}{8}\times\dfrac{4}{6}=\dfrac{25}{8}\times\dfrac{4}{6}=\dfrac{100}{48}=2\dfrac{4}{48}=2\dfrac{1}{12}$

c) $\dfrac{1}{3}$ of $\dfrac{12}{15}=\dfrac{1}{3}\times\dfrac{12}{15}=\dfrac{12}{15}=\dfrac{4}{15}$

d) $\dfrac{11}{20}$ of $4=\dfrac{11}{20}\times\dfrac{4}{1}=\dfrac{44}{20}=2\dfrac{4}{20}=2\dfrac{1}{5}$

To multiply the fractions in a) to d), convert any mixed numbers to improper fractions first. Multiply numerator by numerator and denominator by denominator and reduce at the end. Make a mixed number if necessary.

6. a) $\dfrac{2}{5}\rightarrow\dfrac{5}{2}$

b) $\dfrac{13}{25}\rightarrow\dfrac{25}{13}$

c) $\dfrac{1}{6}\rightarrow\dfrac{6}{1}=6$

d) $2\dfrac{7}{8} = \dfrac{23}{8} \rightarrow \dfrac{8}{23}$

e) $5 = \dfrac{5}{1} \rightarrow \dfrac{1}{5}$

7. **a)** $\dfrac{2}{7} \div \dfrac{5}{6} = \dfrac{2}{7} \times \dfrac{6}{5} = \dfrac{12}{35}$

b) $\dfrac{7}{10} \div 3 = \dfrac{7}{10} \div \dfrac{3}{1} = \dfrac{7}{10} \times \dfrac{1}{3} = \dfrac{7}{30}$

c) $4 \div \dfrac{5}{8} = \dfrac{4}{1} \div \dfrac{5}{8} = \dfrac{4}{1} \times \dfrac{8}{5} = \dfrac{32}{5} = 6\dfrac{2}{5}$

d) $8\dfrac{2}{3} \div 5\dfrac{1}{4} = \dfrac{26}{3} \div \dfrac{21}{4} = \dfrac{26}{3} \times \dfrac{4}{21} = \dfrac{104}{63} = 1\dfrac{41}{63}$

To divide the fractions in a) to d), convert any mixed numbers to improper fractions first. Take the reciprocal of the second fraction and change the $\div$ to a $\times$. Multiply the fractions and reduce. Make a mixed number if necessary.

8. **a)** $2\dfrac{3}{4} \times 3 = \dfrac{11}{4} \times \dfrac{3}{1} = \dfrac{33}{4} = 8\dfrac{1}{4}$ cups

b) $\dfrac{1}{16} \times 7 = \dfrac{1}{16} \times \dfrac{7}{1} = \dfrac{7}{16}$ of a tank.

$\dfrac{7}{16}$ of 40 L =

$\dfrac{7}{16} \times 40 = \dfrac{7}{16} \times \dfrac{40}{1} = \dfrac{280}{16} = 17\dfrac{8}{16}$

$= 17\dfrac{1}{2}$ litres were used.

c) $7\dfrac{5}{8} \div 5 = \dfrac{61}{8} \div \dfrac{5}{1} = \dfrac{61}{8} \times \dfrac{1}{5} = \dfrac{61}{40} = 1\dfrac{21}{40}$ m^2

d) $\dfrac{2}{3} + \dfrac{1}{6} = \dfrac{4}{6} + \dfrac{1}{6} = \dfrac{5}{6}$ is done.

For the amount left, subtract from the whole yard (= 1)

$1 - \dfrac{5}{6} = \dfrac{1}{1} - \dfrac{5}{6} = \dfrac{6}{6} - \dfrac{5}{6} = \dfrac{1}{6}$ left to rake.

Lesson 8—Operations with Rational Numbers

PRACTICE EXERCISE
Answers and Solutions

1. **a)** $4.68 + (-1.2) = 5 + (-1) = 4$

b) $-81.8 + (-33.47) = -82 + (-33) = -115$

c) $2.19 - 5.92 = 2 - 6 = -4$

d) $-0.74 - (-1.3) = -1 - (-1) = -1 + (+1) = 0$

e) $3.27 \times (-22.4) = 3 \times (-22) = -66$

f) $-10.6 \times (-7.99) = -11 \times (-8) = 88$

g) $-24.5 \div 6.2 = -24 \div 6 = -4$

h) $-9.57 \div (-5.1) = -10 \div (-5) = 2$

2. **a)** $3.13 + (-19.16) = -16.03$

b) $-4.13 + (-1.56) = -5.69$

c) $-1.2 + 3.16 = 1.96$

d) $1.8 + (-4.3) = -2.5$

3. **a)** $-6.17 - (-21.4) = 15.23$

b) $5.21 - 3.28 = 1.93$

c) $32.11 - (-4.2) = 36.31$

d) $1.719 - 3.287 = -1.568$

4. **a)** $1.19 \times (-2.4) = -2.856$

b) $-71.7 \times (-1.1) = 78.87$

c) $-25.16 \times (-6.3) = 158.508$

d) $3.1 \times (-1.5) = -4.65$

5. **a)** $-33.58 \div (-4.6) = 7.3$

b) $-19.32 \div 6 = -3.22$

c) $5.992 \div (-0.7) = -8.56$

d) $-18.5 \div (-0.5) = 37$

6. a) -15.2

$-4.5 \div 0.5 + (-6.2) =$

$-9 + (-6.2) = (-15.2)$

b) -10.31

$7.33 + 2.1 \times (-8.4) =$

$7.33 + (-17.64) = -10.31$

c) -2.46

$(1.2) + (-3.9) =$

$1.44 + (-3.9) = -2.46$

d) 30.34

$(2.5 + (-9.1)) \times 4.4 - (-1.3) =$

$29.04 - (-1.3) = 30.34$

7. a) $1.6 \times 15 = 24$ cm

b) $33.5 + 2.8 - 14.6 = 21.7$ m

Lesson 9—Ratio, Rate, Proportion, and Percentage

PRACTICE EXERCISE
Answers and Solutions

1. a) $25:20 = 25 \div 5:20 \div 5 = 5:4$

b) $\dfrac{26}{104} = \dfrac{26(\div 26)}{104(\div 26)} = \dfrac{1}{4}$

c) 8 to $48 = 8 \div 8$ to $48 \div 8 = 1$ to 6

2. a) $\dfrac{175}{x} = \dfrac{5}{3} = 175 \times 3 \div 5 = 105$

b) $\dfrac{6}{7} = \dfrac{a}{91} = 91 \times 6 \div 7 = 78$

c) $24:96 = r:24 = \dfrac{24}{96} = \dfrac{r}{24}$

$24 \times 24 \div 96 = 6$

3. a) $\dfrac{48}{j} = \dfrac{4}{1} = \dfrac{g}{7}$ is the same as $\dfrac{48}{j} = \dfrac{4}{1}$ and

$\dfrac{4}{1} = \dfrac{g}{7}$

Cross-multiply to solve for the missing part:

$\dfrac{48}{j} = \dfrac{4}{1} = 48 \times 1 \div 4 = 12$

$\dfrac{4}{1} = \dfrac{g}{7} = 7 \times 4 \div 1 = 28$

b) $5:9 = y:6$

Set up an equivalent proportion and cross-multiply:

$\dfrac{5}{y} = \dfrac{9}{36} = 5 \times 36 \div 9 = 20$

4. a) 15 girls, 33 total $= 15:33 = 5:11$

b) $\dfrac{\$14.25}{5h} = \dfrac{\$x}{3h} = 14.25 \times 3 \div 5 = \$8.55$

c) $\dfrac{6}{\$9} = \dfrac{x}{\$12} = 12 \times 6 \div 9 = 8$

d) 4 green, if three times as many, $14 \times 3 = 42$

e) VHS to total $= 1:4$

$\dfrac{1}{4} = \dfrac{x}{440}$ $1 \times 440 \div 4 = 110$ VHS tapes

f) Change $6\dfrac{1}{2}$ to 6.5.

$\dfrac{95\,\text{km}}{1\text{h}} = \dfrac{x}{6.5\text{h}} = 95 \times 6.5 \div 1 = 617.5$ km

g) 88% is the same as 88 out of 100.

$\dfrac{88}{100} = \dfrac{154}{x} = 100 \times 154 \div 88 = 175$

h) Perimeter would be $3 + 3 + 5 + 5 = 16$

$\dfrac{3}{16} = \dfrac{12}{x} = 12 \times 16 \div 3 = 64$ cm

i) $\dfrac{75}{100} = \dfrac{45}{x} = 100 \times 45 \div 75 = 60$ kg

Lesson 10—Calculating Percentage

PRACTICE EXERCISE
Answers and Solutions

1. **a)** 30% of 45 = $0.30 \times 45 = 14$

    b) 110% of 600 = $1.10 \times 600 = 660$

    c) 83% of 22 = $0.83 \times 22 = 18$

    d) 7.5% of 20 = $0.075 \times 20 = 2$

    e) $9\frac{1}{2}$% of 38 = 9.5% of 38 = $0.095 \times 38 = 4$

    f) 140% of 77 = $1.40 \times 77 = 108$

For a) to f), convert the percent to a decimal by dividing by 100, multiply by the given amount, and then round to the nearest whole number.

2. **a)** 12% of 504 > 48% of 93

      $0.12 \times 504 = 60.48 > 0.48 \times 93 = 44.64$

    b) 30% of 130 > 60% of 60

      $0.30 \times 130 = 39 > 0.6 \times 60 = 36$

3. $0.15 \times 24.32 = \$3.65$

4. $0.12 \times 17.95 = \$2.15$

    $0.15 \times 17.95 = \$2.69$

    Tip = $2.15 + 2.96 = \$4.84$

5. $2\,200 \div 2\,499 = 0.88 \times 100 = 88\%$. That means the TV sold for 88% of its original price. The discount is $100\% - 88\% = 12\%$

6. $0.3 \times 28.49 = \$8.55$ off

    $28.49 - 8.55 = \$19.94$

7. $0.07 \times \$150 = \$10.50$

8. $0.07 \times 4.50 = 0.32$

    $0.06 \times 4.50 = 0.27$

    Total = $4.50 + 0.32 + 0.27 = \$5.09$

9. $0.065 \times 3\,400 = \$221$

10. $4\,875 \div 195\,000 = 0.025 \times 100 = 2.5\%$

11. **a)** $0.15 \times 3\,175 = \$476.25$

      $\$3\,175 - \$476.25 = \$2\,698.75$

    b) $0.07 \times \$2\,698.75 = \$188.91$

      $0.08 \times \$2\,698.75 = \$161.93$

      Total = $\$2\,698.75 + 188.91 + 161.93 = \$3\,103.56$

    c) $0.03 \times 2\,698.75 = \$80.96$

Lesson 11—Ratios and Rates

PRACTICE EXERCISE
Answers and Solutions

1. **a)** $\dfrac{15}{18} = \dfrac{15(\div 3)}{18(\div 3)} = \dfrac{5}{6}$

    b) $\dfrac{13}{52} = \dfrac{13(\div 13)}{52(\div 13)} = \dfrac{1}{4}$

    c) $\dfrac{66}{154} = \dfrac{66(\div 22)}{154(\div 22)} = \dfrac{3}{7}$

2. **a)** $\dfrac{3}{8} = \dfrac{f}{24} = 24 \times 3 \div 8 = 9$

    b) $\dfrac{39}{k} = \dfrac{156}{144} = 39 \times 144 \div 156 = 36$

3. **a)** Doug ran 18 laps in 15 minutes, not in 1 minute = rate

    b) Kate drove 105 km/h, 1 hour = unit rate

    c) There are 24 students in each Grade 8 class, each class = unit rate

    d) Ricky scored 150 points in 7 games, not in 1 game = rate

4. **a)** Phillip can type 102 words in 3 min. Divide each term by 3 = 34 words per minute or 34 words/min.

    b) A 10 kg bag of flour costs $4.95. Divide each term by 10 = $0.495 per kg or $0.495/kg = $0.50/kg to the nearest cent.

c) Grace read 18 pages in 30 min. Divide each term by 30 = 0.6 pages per minute or 0.6 pages/min.

5. a) $\dfrac{400}{30} = \dfrac{x}{1} = 400 \times 1 \div 30 = 13.3$ km/L

$\dfrac{400}{30} = \dfrac{x}{50} = 400 \times 50 \div 30 = 666.6$ km with 50 L

b) $\dfrac{15}{2} = \dfrac{x}{1} = 15 \times 1 \div 2 = \$7.50/\text{h}$

$\dfrac{15}{2} = \dfrac{x}{25} = 15 \times 25 \div 2 =$ $187.50 for 25 hours

6. a) $90 \div 8 = \$11.25$

$75 \div 6 = \$12.50$
$\$12.50 - \$11.25 = \$1.25$
8 tickets for $90 is better by $1.25 per ticket.

b) $\$4.99 \div 5 = \$0.998$
$\$2.59 \div 3 = \$0.68$
$\$0.998 - \$0.863 = \$0.135$ or $0.14
3 pounds is the better by $0.14 per pound.

Practice Quiz 2

Answers and Solutions

1. a) $\dfrac{3}{5} + \dfrac{1}{4} = \dfrac{12}{20} + \dfrac{5}{20} = \dfrac{17}{20}$

b) $2\dfrac{5}{6} - 1\dfrac{1}{3} = \dfrac{17}{6} - \dfrac{8}{6} = \dfrac{9}{6} = 1\dfrac{3}{6} = 1\dfrac{1}{2}$

c) $\dfrac{1}{3} \times 2\dfrac{1}{7} = \dfrac{1}{3} \times \dfrac{15}{7} = \dfrac{15}{21} = \dfrac{5}{7}$

d) $1\dfrac{1}{5}$ of $12 = \dfrac{6}{5} \times \dfrac{12}{1} = \dfrac{72}{5} = 14\dfrac{2}{5}$

e) $9\dfrac{2}{4} \div \dfrac{5}{7} = \dfrac{38}{4} \div \dfrac{5}{7} = \dfrac{38}{4} \times \dfrac{7}{5} = \dfrac{266}{20}$

$= 13\dfrac{6}{20} = 13\dfrac{3}{10}$

f) $5\dfrac{3}{7} \div 6 = \dfrac{38}{7} \div \dfrac{6}{1} = \dfrac{38}{7} \times \dfrac{1}{6} = \dfrac{38}{42} = \dfrac{19}{21}$

g) $1.07 + (-12.9) = -11.83$

h) $-4.83 - (-5.96) = 1.13$

i) $3.4x - 2.6 = -8.84$

j) $-6.5 \div (-1.3) = 5$

2. a) $\dfrac{3}{4} = \dfrac{t}{72} = 72 \times 3 \div 4 = 54$

b) $\dfrac{h}{25} = \dfrac{40}{200} = 25 \times 40 \div 200 = 5$

c) $\dfrac{2}{3} = \dfrac{60}{c} = 60 \times 3 \div 2 = 90$

d) $\dfrac{86}{w} = \dfrac{15}{30} = 86 \times 30 \div 15 = 172$

3. a) $\dfrac{7}{20} = 7 \div 20 \times 100 = 35\%$

b) $\dfrac{10}{16} = 10 \div 16 \times 100 = 62.5\%$

c) $\dfrac{66}{50} = 66 \div 50 \times 100 = 132\%$

d) $2\dfrac{7}{25} = \dfrac{57}{25} = 57 \div 25 \times 100 = 228\%$

4. a) 20% of $60 = 0.2 \times 60 = 12$

b) 6.5% of $182 = 0.065 \times 182 = 11.83$

c) 144% of $13 = 1.44 \times 13 = 18.72$

5. a) A heart beats 292 times in 4 minutes.

Divide each term by 4 = 73 beats/min.

b) Carl sells 6 vacuums in 2.5 hours.

Divide each term by 2.5 = 2.4 vacuums per hour

c) $2.98 \div 3 = 0.99$

$6.55 \div 7 = 0.94$

$0.99 - 0.94 = 0.05$

The better buy is 7 kg of by $0.05 per kg or $0.05/kg

d) $\dfrac{12\,\text{km}}{30\,\text{min}} = \dfrac{150\,\text{km}}{x} = 30 \times 150 \div 12 =$

375 min $\div$ 60 min/h = 6.25 h or 6 hours,

15 minutes

e) 3 wins, 9 games

3:9 (divide each term by 3) = 1:3

f) $6\dfrac{3}{8} + 2\dfrac{3}{4} = \dfrac{51}{8} + \dfrac{11}{4} = \dfrac{51}{8} + \dfrac{22}{4} = \dfrac{73}{8} =$

$9\dfrac{1}{8}$ hours

g) $159 \div 199 = 0.8 \times 100 = 80\%$ is paid of original price.

$100 - 80 = 20\%$ is the discount

h) Marie works in a clothing store where she earns $3\dfrac{1}{2}\%$ commission on her sales. What does she earn in a week if she sells \$800 worth of clothes?

3.5% of 800 = $0.035 \times 800 = \$28$

Practice Test

Answers and Solutions

1. a) $4^2 = 4 \times 4 = 16$

b) $7^0 = 1$

c) $10^3 = 10 \times 10 \times 10 = 1\ 000$

d) $10^{-4} = 0.000\ 1$

e) $10^{-1} = 0.1$

f) $\dfrac{1}{10^5} = \dfrac{1}{100\ 000} = 0.000\ 01$

g) $3.45 \times 10^1 = 34.5$

h) $5.55 \times 10^{-5} = 0.000\ 055\ 5$

2. a) $9\ 260\ 000 = 9.26 \times 10^6$

b) $0.000\ 000\ 24 = 2.4 \times 10^{-7}$

3. $\dfrac{1}{5}, \cancel{\sqrt{26}}, -2.2, -\dfrac{1}{3}, \cancel{\pi}, 0, 4.751,$

$\dfrac{4}{0}$ (undefined), $1\dfrac{2}{8}$

Rewrite remaining ones as decimals, then order.

$0.2, -2.2, -0.3, 0, 4.751, 1.25$

$4.751, 1\dfrac{2}{8}, \dfrac{1}{5}, 0, -\dfrac{1}{3}, -2.2,$

4. a) $-4 \div 1 = -4$

$-1 \div 4 = -0.25$

$-4 < -0.25$ so the sign is <

b) $2\dfrac{5}{6} = \dfrac{17}{6} = 17 \div 6 = 2.83$

$2.83 > 2.56$ so the sign is >

c) $-1.7 > -1.782$ so the sign is >

d) $4 \div 6 = 0.67$

$6 \div 4 = 1.5$

$0.67 < 1.5$ so the sign is <

e) $\dfrac{2}{3} = 2 \div 3 = 0.6\overline{6}$

$0.66 < 0.\overline{6}$ so the sign is <

f) $\sqrt{144} = 12$ because $12 \times 12 = 144$

$12 = 12$ so the sign is =

5. a) White diamonds to gray diamonds

5:4

b) Gray diamonds to striped diamonds

$4:4 = (4 \div 4):(4 \div 4) = 1:1$

c) 5:13

d) Striped diamonds to spotted diamonds

4:0, because there are no spotted diamonds

6. a) $\dfrac{73}{100} = 73 \div 100 \times 100 = 73\%$

b) $0.475 = 0.475 \times 100 = 47.5\%$

c) $12:10 = 12 \div 10 \times 100 = 120\%$

d) $\dfrac{20}{32} = 20 \div 32 \times 100 = 62.5\%$

7. a) $\dfrac{2}{8} = 2 \div 8 = 0.25$

b) $18:12 = 18 \div 12 = 1.5$

c) $163\% = 163 \div 100 = 1.63$

d) $0.7\% = 0.7 \div 100 = 0.007$

8. a) $\sqrt{36} = 6$ (a perfect square)

b) $\sqrt{1.96} = 1.4$

c) $\sqrt{97}$ = between 81 and 100 about 9.8, actual value 9.85

d) $\sqrt{128}$ = between 121 and 144 about 11.2, actual value 11.31

9. a) $\dfrac{j}{42} = \dfrac{5}{7}$ $5 \times 42 \div 7 = 30$

b) $\dfrac{4}{8} = \dfrac{x}{6}$ $4 \times 6 \div 8 = 3$

10. a) 84 beats in a minute

If there are 7 beats in 5 seconds, you need to know how many beats in 1 min, which is 60 s. Set up proportions and cross multiply.

$\dfrac{7 \text{ beats}}{5 \text{ sec}} = \dfrac{x}{60 \text{ sec}}$

$= 7 \times 60 \div 5 = 84$ beats in a minute

b) 12 misses in 48 attempts

Since she made 3 baskets for 4 attempts, this means there is also 1 miss in 4 attempts. Set up with a proportion for misses with 48 attempts and cross-multiply.

$\dfrac{1 \text{ miss}}{4 \text{ attempts}} = \dfrac{x}{48 \text{ attempts}}$

$= 48 \times 1 \div 4 = 12$ misses in 48 attempts

c) The bridge is 42.5 m wide.

The bridge is 11 times as long as it is wide, so the ratio of length to width is 11:1. Since you know it is 467.5 m long, set up a proportion and solve.

$\dfrac{11 \text{ length}}{1 \text{ width}} = \dfrac{467.5 \text{ long}}{x}$

$= 467.5 \times 1 \div 11 = 42.5$ wide

d) 156 gumballs are not blue.

The ratio of red to green to blue is 5:8:3. To find how many are not blue, you need to add red and green $5 + 8 = 13$ and put it over the total $5 + 8 + 3 = 16$. Set up a proportion of not blue to total with 192 gumballs.

$\dfrac{13 \text{ not blue}}{16 \text{ total}} = \dfrac{x}{192 \text{ total}} = 192 \times 13 \div 16$

$= 156$ gumballs are not blue.

11. a) 60 markers in 4 packs

(Divide each by 4) = 15 markers per pack

b) $84 earned in 8 hours

(Divide each by 8) = $10.50 per hour

c) $5.25 \div 12 = 0.44$
$7.50 \div 20 = 0.38$
$0.44 - 0.38 = 0.06$
The better buy is the box of 20 by $0.06 per bar.

12. a) $\dfrac{1}{2} + \dfrac{7}{11} = \dfrac{11}{22} + \dfrac{14}{22} = \dfrac{25}{22} = 1\dfrac{3}{22}$

b) $5\dfrac{2}{3} - \dfrac{4}{9} = \dfrac{17}{3} - \dfrac{4}{9} = \dfrac{51}{9} - \dfrac{4}{9} = \dfrac{47}{9} = 5\dfrac{2}{9}$

c) $\dfrac{3}{5} \times 3\dfrac{3}{4} = \dfrac{3}{5} \times \dfrac{15}{4} = \dfrac{45}{20} = 2\dfrac{5}{20} = 2\dfrac{1}{4}$

d) $\dfrac{1}{2} \div 4 = \dfrac{1}{2} \div \dfrac{4}{1} = \dfrac{1}{2} \times \dfrac{1}{4} = \dfrac{1}{8}$

e) $-1.55 + 2.3 = 0.75$

f) $-6.5 + (-13.4) = -19.9$

g) $25.7 - (-15.9) = 41.6$

h) $-30.08 \div 9.4 = -3.2$

i) $-63.64 \div 7.4 \times 1.285 = -11.051$

j) $-1.4 \times (-18.5 - (-27.93)) = -13.202$

13. Leslie $= 24 \div 30 = 0.8$ laps per min or 0.8 laps/min

Dave $= 10 \div 10 = 1$ lap per min or 1 lap/min
$1 - 0.8 = 0.2$
Dave is a faster swimmer by 0.2 laps per min or 0.2 laps/min

14. Together they change 10 diapers a day.
$10 \times 7 = 70$ diapers per week or 70 diapers/week

15. $1\ 895 - (-225) = 2\ 150$. Jane is winning by 2 150 points.

16. Make the percent a fraction with a denominator of 100.

$$\frac{85}{100} = \frac{x}{420} = 85 \times 420 \div 100 = 357$$

357 people voted for Denise.

$420 - 375 = 63$ voted for the opponent.

17. $0.12 \times 249.99 = \$30$

$249.99 - 30 = \$219.99 = $ discounted price
GST $= 0.07 \times 219.99 = 15.40$
PST $= 0.06 \times 219.99 = 13.20$
Final price $= 219.99 + 15.40 + 13.20 = \$248.59$

18. $\frac{75}{15} = \frac{n}{20} = 75 \times 20 \div 15 = 100$ people in total

$100 - 75 = 25$ more people needed

19. Take the square root to find the length of each side of a stamp.

$$\sqrt{225} = 15 \text{ mm long}$$

5 stamps $= 15 \times 5 = 75$ mm long

PATTERNS AND RELATIONS

Lesson 1—Expressions and Equations

PRACTICE EXERCISE
Answers and Solutions

1. a) expression

Two more than a number, not equal to anything: expression

b) equation

The difference between six and a number is twelve, is equal to something: equation

c) equation

Fourteen is the product of seven and a number, is equal to something: equation

d) expression

Eight more than the quotient of three and a number, not equal to anything: expression

e) equation

A number increased by seven and then multiplied by four is twenty-four, is equal to something: equation

2. i) b

ii) c

iii) f

iv) d

v) j

3. Answers may vary.

a) The product of four and a number increased by six is negative eighteen.

b) A number divided by two decreased by three is eight.

c) The sum of nine and a number is ten.

d) The product of three and a number taken away from five is seven.

e) The sum of two and six all multiplied by a number gives sixty-four.

4. a) $8b + 4 = 2$

b) $\dfrac{e}{3} = 33$ kg

c) $a - 3 = 12$

d) $3x = 27$

e) $5x = 95$

f) $4x = 160$

The two things are Matt and his brother
You know the least about the brother $= x$
Matt three times as tall as the brother $= 3x$
Matt + Brother $= 160$
$x + 3x = 160$
$4x = 160$

g) The two things are Jenn and Chad.

You know the least about Chad $= x$
Jenn has 15 more dollars than Chad $= x + 15$
Jenn + Chad $= \$55$
$x + x + 15 = 55$
$2x + 15 = 55$

Lesson 2—Substituting Variables

PRACTICE EXERCISE
Answers and Solutions

1. a) 10

$x + 7 = (3) + 7 = 10$

b) 5

$5x - 10 = 5(x) - 10 = 15 - 10 = 5$

c) 21

$3(x + 4) = 3((3) + 4) = 3(7) = 21$

d) -11

$-x - 8 = (-3) - 8 = -11$

2. a) -7

$4a + b = 4(-2) + (1) = -8 + 1 = -7$

b) -1

$(a + b) = (-2) + (1) = -1$

c) 17

$-9a - b = -9(-2) - (1) = 18 - 1 = 17$

d) 0

$\dfrac{a}{2} + b = \dfrac{(-2)}{2} + (1) = -1 + 1 = 0$

3. a) $2x + 3 = 2(5) + 3 = 10 + 3 = 13$

"more" shows adding, "twice" shows multiply by 2

b) $100 - 7x = 100 - 7(5) = 100 - 35 = 65$

"product" shows multiplication, "subtract from" shows taking away from something that is given

c) $\dfrac{x + x}{2} = \dfrac{5 + 5}{2} = \dfrac{10}{2} = 5$

"increased" shows adding, "all divided" shows that you add first, then divide.

d) $\dfrac{6x}{3} = \dfrac{6(5)}{3} = \dfrac{30}{3} = 10$

"one-third" shows the division "times" shows multiplication

Lesson 3—Relations

PRACTICE EXERCISE
Answers and Solutions

1. a) $2x = y$

Both numbers are increasing: x by 1, y by 2. This shows that it is a type 2 equation, where x is multiplied by something to equal y. Guess and check to see if anything needs to be added to the $2x$ to equal y.

b) $x + y = 3$

Here, x goes up by 1 and y goes down by 1. This shows that it is a type 3 equation, where one variable is increasing and the other is decreasing. This means that the x and y are added or subtracted to equal something.
Guess and check by adding and subtracting x and y.

c) $x + 2 = y$

Both x and y are increasing by 3.
This shows that it is a type 1 equation, where x plus or minus something equals y. Guess and check to see what is to be added or subtracted.

2. a) Answers may vary based on numbers chosen.

x	y
1	5
2	9
3	13
4	17
5	21

b)

x	y
1	6
2	7
3	8
4	9
5	10

c)

x	y
−2	3
−1	2
0	1
1	0
2	−1

3. a) $x + y = 7$

x goes up, y goes down
Type 3
$x + y = 7$

x	y
1	6
2	5
3	4
4	3
5	2

b) $3x - 2 = y$

y increases by 2 every $1x$
Type 2
$3x - 2 = y$

x	y
2	4
4	10
6	16
8	22
10	28

4. $2n + (-1) = d$

Diagram number (n)	Number of circles (s)
1	1
2	3
3	5
4	7
5	9

Both numbers are increasing: n by 1, s by 2. This shows that it is a type 2 equation, where n is multiplied by something to equal s.
Guess and check to see if anything needs to be added to the $2n$ to equal s and you will figure out that -1 must be added (or 1 subtracted).

5. $30l + 10 = C$

Length of Call (l)	Cost (C)
1	40
2	70
3	100
4	130
5	160

Both numbers are increasing: l by 1, C by 30. This shows that it is a type 2 equation, where l is multiplied by something to equal C.
Guess and check to see if anything needs to be added to the $30l$ to equal C and you figure out that 10 must be added.

6. $5w + 1 = c$

Week (w)	Cars sold (c)
2	11
4	21
6	31
8	41
10	51

Both numbers are increasing: w by 2, c by 10. This shows that it is a type 2 equation, where w is multiplied by something to equal c.

Guess and check to see if anything needs to be added to the $5w$ to equal c and you will figure out that 1 must be added.

7. $5w + 1 = C$
$5(15) + 1 = C$
$75 + 1 = 76$ cars sold

$5w + 1 = C$
$5(20) + 1 = C$
$100 + 1 = 101$ cars sold

Lesson 4—Graphing Relations

PRACTICE EXERCISE
Answers and Solutions

1. **a)** $(2, 8)$

$2 + 6 = y$
$2 + 6 = 8$
$y = 8$

b) $(-6, 0)$

$x + 6 = 0$
-6

c) $(10, 16)$

$10 + 6 = y$
$10 + 6 = 16$
$y = 16$

d) $(-3, 3)$

$x + 6 = 3$
$-3 + 6 = 3$
$x = -3$

2. **a)** $x - 1 = y$

$(0, -1)$
$(1, 0)$
$(2, 1)$

x	y
0	-1
1	0
2	1
3	2
4	3

Both x and y are changing by 1. This shows that it is a type 1 equation, where x plus or minus something equals y. Guess and check to see what needs to be added or subtracted.

b) $x + y = 1$

$(1, 0)$
$(2, -1)$
$(3, -2)$

x	y
1	0
2	-1
3	-2
4	-3
5	-4

Here, x goes up by 1 and y goes down by 1. This shows that it is a type 3 equation, where one variable is increasing and the other is decreasing. This means that the x and y are added or subtracted to equal something. Guess and check by adding and subtracting x and y.

c) $3x - 2 = y$

$(0, -2)$
$(1, 1)$
$(2, 4)$

x	y
0	−2
1	1
2	4
3	7
4	10

Both numbers are increasing: x by 1 and y by 3. This shows that it is a type 2 equation, where x is multiplied by something to equal y. Guess and check to see if anything needs to be added to the $3x$ to equal y. Here, you see that you need to add $a - 2$ (or subtract 2) to get the value of y.

3. a)

x	y
1	2
2	4
3	6
4	8
5	10

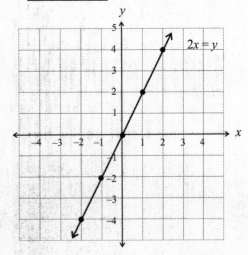

b)

x	y
1	3
2	2
3	1
4	0
5	−1

c)

x	y
1	−2
2	−1
3	0
4	1
5	2

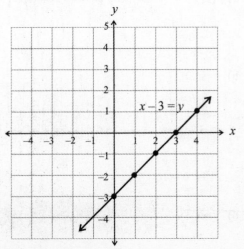

4. **a)** The distance travelled in a certain amount of time

b) Each hour the person travels 110 km, so the rate is 110 km per hour

c) The equation is $d = 110t$, where d = distance (km) and t = time (h)

d) Use the equation $d = 110t$ and substitute for 7 hours

$d = 110t$
$d = 110\,(7)$
$d = 770$ km

5. **a)** 60¢

Look at the y value on the graph when x is 2. The cost is 60¢.

b) $1.20

Look at the graph and determine what the value at $x = 8$ would be. The cost is $1.20.

c) 40¢

The y-axis starts at 40 so that is the base amount no matter if you talk for 1 min or 10 min.

d) $10t + 40 = c$

Goes up by 10 each time with a base rate of 40. Equation is $10t + 40 = c$.

6.

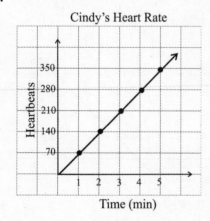

Cindy's Heart Rate

7.

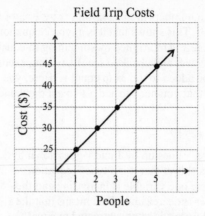

Field Trip Costs

Extending the line from the graph, you could find that the cost would be $70

$5x + 20 = y$ $\qquad\qquad$ x = student

Practice Quiz 1

Answers and Solutions

1. Answers may vary.

a) The sum of a number and five gives a result of negative eight.

b) A number divided by three, decreased by two is twelve.

c) The product of six and a number all increased by four totals negative fourteen.

2. **a)** $3x + 6 = 69$

"More than" shows addition, and "times" shows multiplication.

b) $\dfrac{n}{2} - 3 = 22$

"Less than" is subtraction, and "half" is division.

c) $-7a = 49$

"Product" is multiplication.

3. **a)** $(5) - 8 = -3$

b) $2\,(-7) + 14 = -14 + 14 = 0$

c) $\dfrac{(56)}{7} - 9 = 8 - 9 = -1$

4. a) $3x + 1 = y$

Both numbers are increasing: x by 1 and y by 3. This shows that it is a type 2 equation, where x is multiplied by something to equal y. Guess and check to see if anything needs to be added to the $3x$ to equal y. Here, you see that you need to add a 1 to get the value of y.

b) $x + y = 10$

Here, x goes up by 1 and y goes down by 1. This shows that it is a type 3 equation, where one variable is increasing and the other is decreasing. This means that the x and y are added or subtracted to equal something. Guess and check by adding and subtracting x and y

c) $x - 6 = y$

Both x and y are changing by 1.

This shows that it is a type 1 equation, where x plus or minus something equals y. Guess and check to see what needs to be added or subtracted.

5. Answers will vary based on numbers chosen

a)

x	y
1	5
2	6
3	7
4	8
5	9

$(1, 5)$
$(2, 6)$

b)

x	y
1	6
2	5
3	4
4	3
5	2

$(1, 6)$
$(2, 5)$

c)

x	y
1	–1
2	1
3	3
4	5
5	7

$(1, -1)$

$(2, 1)$

6. a) $(2, 4) = 2 + 2 = 4$

b) $(6, 8) = 6 + 2 = 8$

c) $(0, 2) = 0 + 2 = 2$

7. a) $2n = d$

The diagram number to the total number of squares:

In each diagram, there are twice as many squares as the diagram number.

b) $n - 1 = d$

diagram number to number of shaded squares:

In each diagram, there is one less shaded on than the diagram number.

$n - 1 = d$

8. a) $x + 1 = y$

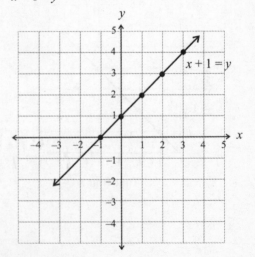

b) $3x = y$

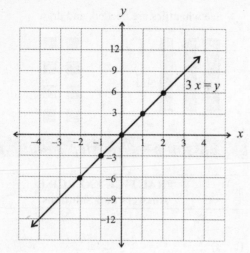

c) $x + y = 5$

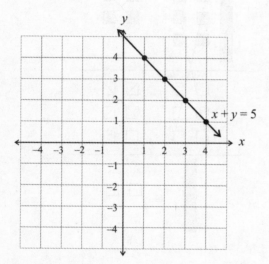

9. a) $0.05t = d$

Dave moves half a km every 10 minutes.

b) $0.05t = d$
$0.05 (90) = d$
$4.5 \text{ km} = d$

$0.05 (90 \text{ min}) = 4.5 \text{ km}$

An hour and a half is 90 minutes. Substitute that value in for time and solve.

Lesson 5—Algebra Tiles

PRACTICE EXERCISE
Answers and Solutions

1. a) $x - 3 = -2$

There is 1 x tile. There are 3, –1 tiles.
Equation is equal to –2

b) $2x - 5 = 4$

There are 2 x tiles. There are 5, –1 tiles.
Equation is equal to 4.

c) $-2x + 2 = -4$

There are 2, –x tiles. There are 2, 1 tiles.
Equation is equal to –4.

2. a)

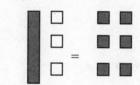

b)

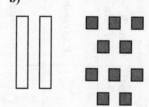

c)

3. a)

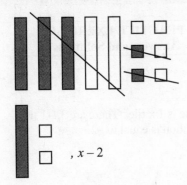

, $x - 2$

b)

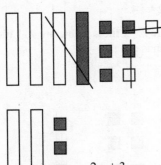

, $-2x + 3$

4.

	Tiles	Simplified Form	Expression	Substitute with $x = 2$
a)			x	$x = (2) = 2$
b)			$-x - 2$	$-x - 2$ $-(2) - 2 =$ -4
c)			$2x - 2$	$2x - 2$ $2(2) - 2 = 2$

5. Equation is $3x - 1 = 8$

See what tiles are needed, and draw.

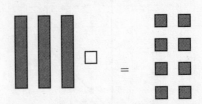

Lesson 6—One-step equations

PRACTICE EXERCISE
Answers and Solutions

1. a)

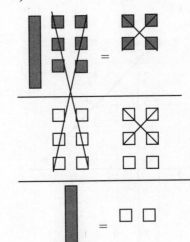

b)

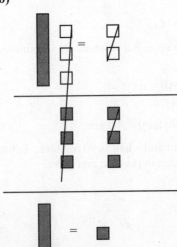

2. a) $t = 6$

$t = 18$
$t \div 3 = 18 \div 3$
$t = 6$

b) $m = 50$

$\dfrac{m}{5} \times 5 = 10 \times 5$
$m = 50$

c) $c = -11$

$c \div 2 = -22 \div 2$
$c = -11$

d) $j = 34$

$j - 13 = 21$
$j - 13 + 13 = 21 + 13$
$j = 34$

e) $h = 30$

$\dfrac{h}{-5} = -6$

$\dfrac{h}{-5} \times -5 = -6 \times -5$
$h = 30$

f) $n = +4$

$-7n = -28$
$-7n \div (-7) = -28 \div (-7)$
$n = +4$

g) $v = -44$

$v + 14 = -30$
$v + 14 - 14 = -30 - 14$
$v = -44$

h) $g = 4$

$g - 12 = -8$
$g - 12 + 12 = -8 + 12$
$g = 4$

3. a) $s = 7$ Check

$s + 4 = 11$ $s + 4 = 11$
$s + 4 - 4 = 11 - 4$ $(7) + 4 = 11$
$s = 7$ $11 = 11$

b) $e = -4$ Check

$e - 6 = -10$ $e - 6 = -10$
$e - 6 + 6 = -10 + 6$ $(-4) - 6 = -10$
$e = -4$ $-10 = -10$

c) $t = -3$ Check

$9t = -27$ $9t = -27$

$\dfrac{9t}{9} = \dfrac{-27}{9}$ $9(-3) = -27$

$t = -3$ $-27 = -27$

d) $w = -16$ Check

$\dfrac{w}{-2} = 8$ $\dfrac{w}{-2} = 8$

$\dfrac{w}{-2} \times -2 = 8 \times -2$ $\dfrac{(-16)}{-2} = 8$

$w = -16$ $8 = 8$

e) $p = 7$ Check

$-8p = -56$ $-8p = -56$

$\dfrac{-8p}{-8} = \dfrac{-56}{-8}$ $-8(7) = -56$

$p = 7$ $-56 = -56$

4. a) $-7 = w$

$10 - w = 17$
$10 - w + w = 17 + w$
$10 = 17 + w$
$10 - 17 = 17 - 17 + w$
$-7 = w$

b) $6 = y$

$5 - y = -1$
$5 - y + y = -1 + y$
$5 = -1 + y$
$5 + 1 = -1 + 1 + y$
$6 = y$

c) $3 = p$

$\dfrac{18}{p} \times p = 6 \times p$

$18 = 6p$

$\dfrac{18}{6} = \dfrac{6p}{6}$

$3 = p$

d) $-2 = t$

$\dfrac{10}{t} \times t = -5 \times t$

$10 = -5t$

$\dfrac{10}{-5} = \dfrac{-5t}{-5}$

$-2 = t$

5. **a)** $n = 4$

$n - 9 = -5$
$n - 9 + 9 = -5 + 9$
$n = 4$

b) $x = 22$

$\dfrac{x}{2} = 11$

$\dfrac{x}{2} \times 2 = 11 \times 2$

$x = 22$

c) $d = 25$

$20 + d = 45$
$20 - 20 + d = 45 - 20$
$d = 25$

d) $f = 12$

$-6f = -72$
$-6f \div (-6) = -72 \div (-6)$
$f = 12$

e) $t = 63$

$\dfrac{t}{-9} = 7$

$\dfrac{t}{-9} \times -9 = 7 \times -9$

$t = 63$

f) $s = 12$ years old

$s + 5 = 17$
$s + 5 - 5 = 17 - 5$

$s = 12$ years old

g) $m = 9$ cm

$4m = 36$
$4m \div 4 = 36 \div 4$
$m = 9$ cm

Lesson 7—Two-step equations

PRACTICE EXERCISE
Answers and Solutions

1. **a)** $f = 2$

$3f + 4 = 10$
$3f + 4 - 4 = 10 - 4$
$\dfrac{3f}{3} = \dfrac{6}{3}$
$3f = 6$
$f = 2$

b) $a = 4$

$4a - 16 = 0$
$4a - 16 + 16 = 0 + 16$
$4a = 16$
$\dfrac{4a}{4} = \dfrac{16}{4}$
$a = 4$

c) $q = -7$

$-4q - 8 = 20$

$-4q - 8 + 8 = 20 + 8$
$-4q = 28$
$\dfrac{-4q}{-4} = \dfrac{28}{-4}$
$q = -7$

d) $z = 0$

$3z - 3 = -3$
$3z - 3 + 3 = -3 + 3$
$3z = 0$
$\dfrac{3z}{3} = \dfrac{0}{3}$
$z = 0$

e) $r = 21$

$\dfrac{r}{3} + 6 - 6 = 13 - 6$

$\dfrac{r}{3} = 7$

$\dfrac{h}{3} \times 3 = 7 \times 3$

$r = 21$

f) $d = -48$

$\dfrac{d}{-4} - 7 = 5$

$\dfrac{d}{-4} - 7 + 7 = 5 + 7$

$\dfrac{d}{-4} = 12$

$\dfrac{d}{-4} \times -4 = 12 \times -4$

$d = -48$

g) $w = 10$

$$\frac{w}{2} + 11 = 16$$

$$\frac{w}{2} + 11 - 11 = 16 - 11$$

$$\frac{w}{2} = 5$$

$$\frac{w}{2} \times 2 = 5 \times 2$$

$$w = 10$$

h) $k = -50$

$$\frac{k}{10} + 1 = -4$$

$$\frac{k}{10} + 1 - 1 = -4 - 1$$

$$\frac{k}{10} = -5$$

$$\frac{k}{10} \times 10 = -5 \times 10$$

$$k = -50$$

2. a) $x = 5$

$$3x - 6 = 9$$ Check

$$3x - 6 + 6 = 9 + 6$$ $3x - 6 = 9$

$$3x = 15$$ $3(5) - 6 = 9$

$$\frac{3x}{3} = \frac{15}{3}$$ $15 - 6 = 9$

             $9 = 9$

$$x = 5$$ $Ls = Rs$

b) $t = -0.5$

$$4t - 8 = -10$$ Check

$$4t - 8 + 8 = -10 + 8$$ $4t - 8 = -10$

$$4t = -2$$ $4(0.5) - 8 = -10$

$$\frac{4t}{4} = \frac{-2}{4}$$ $-2 - 8 = -10$

             $-10 = -10$

$$t = -0.5$$ $Ls = Rs$

c) $b = -7$

$$7 - 2b = 21$$ Check

$$7 - 7 - 2b = 21 - 7$$ $7 - 2b = 21$

$$-2b = 14$$ $7 - 2(-7) = 21$

$$\frac{-2b}{-2} = \frac{14}{-2}$$ $7 - (-14) = 21$

             $21 = 21$

$$b = -7$$ $Ls = Rs$

d) $r = -3$

$$-3r - 4 = 5$$ Check

$$-3r - 4 + 4 = 5 + 4$$ $-3r - 4 = 5$

$$-3r = 9$$ $-3(-3) - 4 = 5$

$$\frac{-3r}{-3} = \frac{9}{-3}$$ $9 - 4 = 5$

             $5 = 5$

$$r = -3$$ $Ls = Rs$

e) $1 = y$

$$5 = 4y + 1$$ Check

$$5 - 1 = 4y + 1 - 1$$ $5 = 4y + 1$

$$4 = 4y$$ $5 = 4(1) + 1$

$$\frac{4}{4} = \frac{4y}{4}$$ $5 = 4 + 1$

             $5 = 5$

$$1 = y$$ $Ls = Rs$

f) $l = 9$

$$\frac{l}{3} - 1 = 2$$ Check

$$\frac{l}{3} - 1 + 1 = 2 + 1$$

$$\frac{l}{3} = 3$$ $\frac{l}{3} - 1 = 2$

$$\frac{l}{3} \times 3 = 3 \times 3$$ $\frac{(9)}{3} - 1 = 2$

$$l = 9$$ $3 - 1 = 2$

             $2 = 2$

             $Ls = Rs$

g) $g = 40$

$$\frac{g}{5} + 4 = 12$$ Check

$$\frac{g}{5} + 4 - 4 = 12 - 4$$

$$\frac{g}{5} = 8$$ $\frac{g}{5} + 4 = 12$

$$\frac{g}{5} \times 5 = 8 \times 5$$ $\frac{(40)}{5} + 4 = 12$

$$g = 40$$ $8 + 4 = 12$

             $12 = 12$

             $Ls = Rs$

h) $r = -18$

$$\frac{e}{9} - 2 = -4 \qquad \text{Check}$$

$$\frac{e}{9} - 2 + 2 = -4 + 2 \qquad \frac{e}{9} - 2 = -4$$

$$\frac{e}{9} = -2 \qquad \frac{(-18)}{9} - 2 = -4$$

$$\frac{r}{9} \times 9 = -2 \times 9 \qquad -2 - 2 = -4$$

$$r = -18 \qquad -4 = -4$$

$$Ls = Rs$$

3. a) $-3 = w$

$$7 + \frac{15}{w} = 2$$

$$7 - 7 + \frac{15}{w} = 2 - 7$$

$$\frac{15}{w} = -5$$

$$\frac{15}{w} \times w = -5 \times w$$

$$15 = -5w$$

$$\frac{15}{-5} = \frac{-5w}{-5}$$

$$-3 = w$$

b) $-4 = x$

$$4 - \frac{24}{x} = -2$$

$$4 - 4 - \frac{24}{x} = -2 - 4$$

$$-\frac{24}{x} = -6$$

$$-\frac{24}{x} \times x = -6 \times x$$

$$-24 = -6$$

$$\frac{-24}{-6} = \frac{-6x}{-6}$$

$$-4 = x$$

c) $k = -1$

$$1 - 4k = 5$$
$$1 - 1 - 4k = 5 - 1$$
$$-4k = 4$$
$$k = -1$$

d) $q = -18$

$$-11 - 3q = 43$$
$$-11 + 11 - 3q = 43 + 11$$
$$-3q = 54$$
$$q = -18$$

4. a) $x = 4.5$

$$4x + 3 = 21$$
$$4x + 3 - 3 = 21 - 3$$
$$4x = 18$$
$$\frac{4x}{4} = \frac{18}{4}$$
$$x = 4.5$$

b) $x = 6$

$$2x - 4 = 8$$
$$2x - 4 + 4 = 8 + 4$$
$$2x = 12$$
$$\frac{2x}{2} = \frac{12}{2}$$
$$x = 6$$

c) $x = -18$

$$\frac{x}{3} - 4 = -10$$

$$\frac{x}{3} - 4 + 4 = -10 + 4$$

$$\frac{x}{3} = -6$$

$$\frac{x}{3} \times 3 = -6 \times 3$$

$$x = -18$$

d) $x = -4$

$$\frac{x}{-4} + 1 = 2$$

$$\frac{x}{-4} + 1 - 1 = 2 - 1$$

$$\frac{x}{-4} = 1$$

$$\frac{x}{-4} \times -4 = 1 \times -4$$

$$x = -4$$

5. Corey = 16, Darren = 31

Corey = x
Darren = $x + 16$
Together they are 46.

$x + x + 16 = 46$
$2x + 16 = 46$
$2x + 16 - 16 = 46 - 16$
$2x = 30$
$2x \div 2 = 30 \div 2$
$2 = 15$

If $x = 15$, this means Corey is 16.
$(15) + 16 = 31$, this means Darren is 31.

6. Numbers = 37 and 47

First number = x
Second number = $x + 10$
Sum of 84

$x + x + 10 = 84$
$2x + 10 = 84$
$2x + 10 - 10 = 84 - 10$
$2x = 74$
$x = 37$
$x + 10 = 47$

The numbers are 37 and 47.

Practice Quiz 2

Answers and Solutions

1. **a)** $2x - 5 = 2$

    b) $-2x - 2 = 3$

2.

	Tiles	Simplified Form	Expression	Substitute with $x = -2$
a)			$4x$	$4x = 4(-2) = -8$
b)			$-5x$	$-5x = -5(-2) - 2 = 10$

3. **a)**

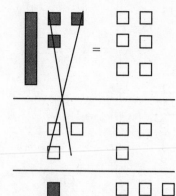

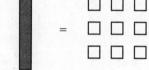

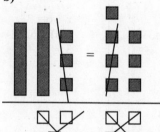

b)

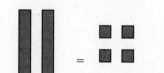

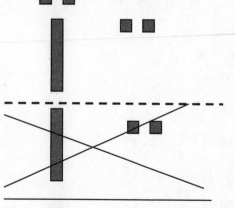

4. a) $x = 22$

$x - 7 = 15$
$x - 7 + 7 = 15 + 7$
$x = 22$

b) $c = 9$

$-3c = -27$
$\dfrac{-3c}{-3} = \dfrac{-27}{-3}$
$c = 9$

5. a) $j = -40$

$\dfrac{j}{5} = -8$

$\dfrac{j}{5} \times 5 = -8 \times 5$

$j = -40$

Check

$\dfrac{j}{5} = -8$

$\dfrac{(-40)}{5} = -8$

$-8 = -8$

b) $x = -3$

$x + 6 = 3$
$x + 6 - 6 = 3 - 6$
$x = -3$

Check

$x + 6 = 3$
$(-3) + 6 = 3$
$3 = 3$

6. a) $g = 14$

$3g - 9 = 33$
$3g - 9 + 9 = 33 + 9$
$\dfrac{3g}{3} = \dfrac{42}{3}$
$g = 14$

b) $u = -10$

$-5u + 45 = 95$
$-5u + 45 - 45 = 95 - 45$
$-\dfrac{5u}{5} = \dfrac{50}{-5}$
$u = -10$

c) $60 = n$

$18 = \dfrac{n}{4} + 3$

$18 - 3 = \dfrac{n}{4} + 3 = -3$

$4 \times 15 = \dfrac{n}{4} \times 4$

$60 = n$

d) $b = 0$

$\dfrac{b}{-10} - 1 = -1$

$\dfrac{b}{-10} - 1 + 1 = -1 + 1$

$-10 \times \dfrac{b}{-10} = 0 \times (-10)$

$b = 0$

7. a) $q = 9$

$2q - 2 = 16$

$2q - 2 + 2 = 16 + 2$

$\dfrac{2q}{2} = \dfrac{18}{2}$

$q = 9$

Check

$2q - 2 = 16$
$2(9) - 2 = 16$
$19 - 2 - 6$
$16 - 16$
$Ls = Rs$

b) $d = -2$

$-7d + 8 = 22$
$-7d + 8 - 8 = 22 - 8$
$-\dfrac{7d}{7} = \dfrac{14}{-7}$
$d = -2$

Check

$-7d + 8 = 22$
$-7(-2) + 8 = 22$
$14 + 8 = 22$
$22 = 22$
$Ls = Rs$

c) $y = 75$

$\dfrac{y}{3} - 10 = 15$

$\dfrac{y}{3} - 10 + 10 = 15 + 10$

$3 \times \dfrac{y}{3} = 25 \times 3$

$y = 75$

Check

$\dfrac{y}{3} - 10 = 15$

$\dfrac{75}{3} - 10 = 15$

$25 - 10 = 15$

$15 = 15$

$Ls = Rs$

d) $l = -5$

$\dfrac{l}{-1} + 4 = 9$

$\dfrac{l}{-1} + 4 - 4 = 9 - 4$

$-\times\dfrac{l}{-1} = 5 \times -1$

$l = -5$

Check

$\dfrac{l}{-1} + 4 = 9$

$\dfrac{(-5)}{-1} + 4 = 75$

$5 + 4 = 9$

$9 = 9$

$Ls = Rs$

8 a) $17 - 5y = -13$

$\quad\quad \underline{-17 \quad\quad -17}$

$\quad\quad \dfrac{-5y}{-5} = \dfrac{-30}{-5}$

$\quad\quad y = +6$

b) $\dfrac{36}{z} + 4 = 10$

$\quad\quad \underline{\quad -4 \;\; -4}$

$\quad\quad \dfrac{36^{\times z}}{2} = 6^{\times z}$

$\quad\quad \dfrac{36}{6} = \dfrac{6z}{6}$

$\quad\quad 6 = z$

9. a) $n = 5$

$\quad\quad 10n - 7 = 43$

$\quad\quad 10n - 7 + 7 = 43 = 7$

$\quad\quad \dfrac{10n}{10} = \dfrac{50}{10}$

$\quad\quad n = 5$

b) $n = 52$

$\quad\quad \dfrac{n}{4} + 8 = 21$

$\quad\quad \dfrac{n}{4} + 8 - 8 = 21 - 8$

$\quad\quad 4 \times \dfrac{n}{4} = 13 \times 4$

$\quad\quad n = 52$

c) $m = 42$

$\quad\quad \dfrac{m}{7} = 6$

$\quad\quad 7 \times \dfrac{m}{7} = 6 \times 7$

$\quad\quad m = 42$

d) Shawn $= x$

Cheri $= x + 7$

Together they have 41

$x + x + 7 = 41$

$2x + 7 = 41$

$2x + 7 - 7 = 47 - 7$

$\dfrac{2x}{2} = \dfrac{40}{2}$

$x = 20$

Shawn has 20 dollars, and Cheri has 27 dollars.

Practice Test

Answers and Solutions

1. a) equation

"is" represents equals. This is an equation.

b) expression

There is nothing to represent "equals" so this is an expression.

c) equation

"totals" represents equals. This is an equation.

2. a) The sum of a number and two all multiplied by three gives a result of six.

b) Negative four increased by a number is twenty-nine.

3. a) $x^2 + 4 = 20$

b) $14 = 3(n - 7)$

4. a) $= 2$

$2a + b$

$2(-1) + (4) = 2 + 4 = 2$

b) $= 11$

$-3a + 2b$

$-3(-1) + 2(4) = 3 + 8 = 11$

5. **a)** $(0, 2)$

$3(0) + 2 = 2$

b) $(2, 8)$

$3(2) + 2 = 8$

c) $(-3, -7)$

$3(-3) + 2 = -7$

b)

x	y
–2	0
–1	–1
0	–2
1	–3
2	–4

6. **a)**

x	y
5	1
4	0
3	–1
2	–2
1	–3

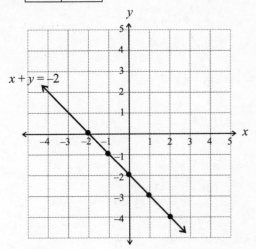

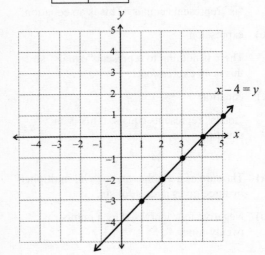

7. $x - 1 = y$

Guess and check to find out how x and y are related. You see that y is always one less than x so: $x - 1 = y$

8. **a)** $y = 6$

$17 - 5y = -13$
$17 - 17 - 5y = -13 - 17$
$-5y = -30$
$y = 6$

b) $18 = z$

$\dfrac{36}{z} + 8 - 8 = 10 - 8$

$\dfrac{36}{z} = 2$

$\dfrac{36}{z} \times z = 2 \times z$

$36 = 2z$

$18 = z$

9. a) The relationship between the amount of gas used each hour that someone is driving

b) $0.25\,t = g$

A quarter of a tank is being used each hour, so the equation is $0.25\,t = g$

c) = 2 tanks

$0.25t = g$
$0.25(8) - g$
$2 = g$

d) The person driving uses 1 tank in 2 hours or $\dfrac{1}{2}$ tank in an hour.

10. a)

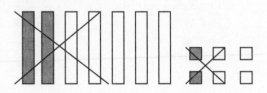

$-2x + 3$

Simplify to get $-2\,x + 3$

b) Simplify to get $2x + 2 = -2$

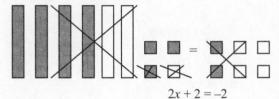

$2x + 2 = -2$

11. Simplify to get $-3x + 2$

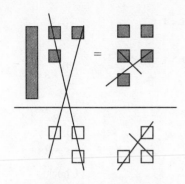

$-3x + 2$
$-3(5) + 2 =$
$-15 + 2 = -13$

12. a)

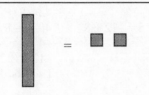

b)

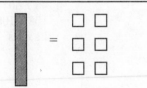

13. a) $m = -14$ Check

$m + 5 = -9$ $m + 5 = -9$
$m + 5 - 5 = -9 - 5$ $(-14) + 5 = -9$
$m = -14$ $-9 = -9$
     Ls = Rs

b) $s = 5$ Check

$3s - 4 = 11$ $3s - 4 = 11$
$3s - 4 + 4 = 11 + 4$ $3(5) - 4 = 11$
$3s = 15$ $15 - 4 = 11$
$s = 5$ $11 = 11$
     Ls = Rs

c) $x = 20$ Check

$$\frac{x}{5} - 8 = -4$$ $$\frac{x}{5} - 8 = -4$$

$$\frac{x}{5} - 8 + 8 = -4 + 8$$ $$\frac{20}{5} - 8 = -4$$

$$\frac{x}{5} = 4$$

               $$4 - 8 = -4$$
$$x = 20$$ $$-4 = -4$$
               Ls = Rs

d) $a = -1$ Check

$4a - 8 = -12$ $4a - 8 = -12$
$4a - 8 + 8 = -12 + 8$ $4(-1) - 8 = -12$
$4a = -4$ $-4 - 8 = -12$
$a = -1$ $-12 = -12$
               Ls = Rs

e) $e = 6$ Check

$$\frac{e}{-3} - 11 = -13$$ $$\frac{e}{-3} - 11 = -13$$

$$\frac{e}{-3} - 11 + 11 =$$ $$\frac{6}{-3} - 11 = -13$$

$$-13 + 11$$ $$-2 - 11 = -13$$

$$\frac{e}{-3} = -2$$ $$-13 = -13$$

$$e = 6$$ Ls = Rs

f) $t = 16$ Check

$3t + 60 = 108$ $3t + 60 = 108$
$3t + 60 - 60 = 108 - 60$ $3(16) + 60 = 108$
$3t = 48$ $48 + 60 = 108$
$t = 16$ $108 = 108$
               Ls = Rs

14. a) $w = -7$

$$\frac{4w}{4} = \frac{-28}{4}$$

$$w = -7$$

b) $m = 20$

$m - 3 + 3 = 17 + 3$

$m = 20$

c) $x = 52$

$$\frac{x}{4} \times 4 = 13 \times 4$$

$$x = 52$$

d) $2 = y$

$6 - y = 4$
$6 - y + y = 4 + y$
$6 = 4 + y$
$6 - 4 = 4 - 4 + y$
$2 = y$

e) $-5 = b$

$$\frac{-50}{b} = 10$$

$$\frac{-50}{b} \times b = 10 \times b$$

$$-50 = 10b$$

$$\frac{-50}{10} = \frac{10b}{10}$$

$$-5 = b$$

f) $d = 56$

$$\frac{d}{8} + 19 = 26$$

$$\frac{d}{8} + 19 - 19 = 26 - 19$$

$$\frac{d}{8} = 7$$

$$\frac{d}{8} \times 8 = 7 \times 8$$

$$d = 56$$

g) $4 = x$

$13 - 4x = -3$
$13 - 4x + 4x = -3 + 4x$
$13 = -3 + 4x$
$13 + 3 = -3 + 3 + 4x$
$16 = 4x$

$$\frac{16}{4} = \frac{4x}{4}$$

$$4 = x$$

h) $8 = h$

$$\frac{96}{h} + 18 = 30$$

$$\frac{96}{h} + 18 - 18 = 30 - 18$$

$$\frac{96}{h} = 12$$

$$\frac{96}{h} \times h = 12 \times h$$

$$96 = 12h$$

$$\frac{96}{12} = \frac{12h}{12}$$

$$8 = h$$

15. a) $x = -12$

$-6x = 72$

$x = -12$

b) $x = 11$

$5x + 4 = 59$

$5x + 4 - 4 = 59 - 4$

$5x = 55$

$x = 11$

c) Book 1 = 353, Book 2 = 201

Book 1 = $x + 152$

Book 2 = x

$x + x + 152 = 554$

$2x + 152 = 554$

$2x + 152 - 152 = 554 - 152$

$2x = 402$

$x = 201$

$x + 152 = 201 + 152 = 353$

Book 1 has 353 pages and book 2 has 201 pages.

d) Ostrich egg = 302 g, Chicken egg = 40 g

Ostrich = $8x$

Chicken = x

$8x - x = 280$

$7x = 280$

$x = 40$

$8x = 8(40) = 320$

The ostrich egg is 320 g, and the chicken egg is 40 g.

SHAPE AND SPACE

Lesson 1—Pythagorean Theorem

PRACTICE EXERCISE
Answers and Solutions

Look at triangles and see which sides make up the right angle. Those are sides a and b. Side c is the hypotenuse. It is the longest side, and it is always directly across from the right angle.

1. a)

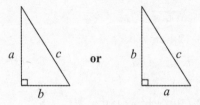

b)

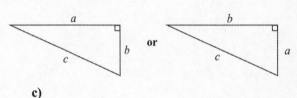

c)

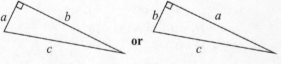

2. a) $c = 10$ m

$a^2 + b^2 = c^2$

$(6)^2 + (8)^2 = c^2$

$36 + 64 = c^2$

$100 = c^2$

$\sqrt{100} = \sqrt{c^2}$

10 m $= c$

b) $c = 17.0$ m

$a^2 + b^2 = c^2$

$(11)^2 + (13)^2 = c^2$

$121 + 169 = c^2$

$290 = c^2$

$\sqrt{290} = \sqrt{c^2}$

17.0 m $= c$

c) $c = 12.1$ cm

$a^2 + b^2 = c^2$

$(7.5)^2 + (9.5)^2 = c^2$

$56.25 + 90.25 = c^2$

$146.5 = c^2$

$\sqrt{146.5} = \sqrt{c^2}$

12.1 cm $= c$

d) $b = 13.4$ cm

$a^2 + b^2 = c^2$

$(30)^2 + b^2 = (45)^2$

$900 + b^2 = 2025$

$900 - 900 + b^2 = 2025 - 900$

$b^2 = 1\,125$

$\sqrt{b^2} = \sqrt{1\,125}$

$b = 33.5$ cm

e) $b = 13.4$ m

$a^2 + b^2 = c^2$

$(4)^2 + b^2 = (14)^2$

$16 + b^2 = 196$

$16 - 16 + b^2 = 196 - 16$

$b^2 = 180$

$\sqrt{b^2} = \sqrt{180}$

$b = 13.4$ m

f) $b = 8.2$ mm

$a^2 + b^2 = c^2$

$(16)^2 + b^2 = (18)^2$

$256 + b^2 = 324$

$256 - 256 + b^2 = 324 - 256$

$b^2 = 68$

$\sqrt{b^2} = \sqrt{68}$

$b = 8.2$ mm

3. $c = 3.6$ m

$a^2 + b^2 = c^2$

$(2)^2 + (3)^2 = c^2$

$4 + 9 = c^2$

$13 = c^2$

$\sqrt{13} = \sqrt{c^2}$

3.6 m $= c$

4. $b = 7.8$ m

$a^2 + b^2 = c^2$

$(4.5)^2 + b^2 = (9)^2$

$20.25 + b^2 = 81$

$20.25 - 20.25 + b^2 = 81 - 20.25$

$b^2 = 60.75$

$\sqrt{b^2} = \sqrt{60.75}$

$b = 7.8$ m

5. $c = 42.4$ m

$a^2 + b^2 = c^2$

$(30)^2 + (30)^2 = c^2$

$900 + 900 = c^2$

$1\,800 = c^2$

$\sqrt{1\,800} = \sqrt{c^2}$

42.4 m $= c$

6. 20.9 km shorter

$a^2 + b^2 = c^2$

$(75)^2 + (25)^2 = c^2$

$5625 + 625 = c^2$

$6250 = c^2$

$\sqrt{6250} = \sqrt{c^2}$

79.1 km $= c$

Total travelled $= 75$ km $+ 25$ km $= 100$ km

100 km $- 79.1$ km $= 20.9$ km shorter

7. $c = 19.8$ m

$a^2 + b^2 = c^2$

$(14)^2 + (14)^2 = c^2$

$196 + 196 = c^2$

$392 = c^2$

$\sqrt{392} = \sqrt{c^2}$

19.8 m $= c$

Lesson 2—Perimeter

PRACTICE EXERCISE
Answers and Solutions

1. **a)** $P = 17$ m

   $P = 6 + 5 + 4 + 2 = 17$ m

   b) $P = 62$ mm

   $P = 7 + 5 + 7 + 7 + 7 + 5 + 7 + 17 = 62$ mm

   c) $C = 50.24$ cm

   $C = \pi d$
   $C = (3.14)(16)$
   $C = 50.24$ cm

   d) $P = 80$ mm

   $P = 10 \times 8 = 80$ mm

   e) $P = 48$ cm

   $P = 12 \times 4 = 48$ cm

   f) $P = 22$ cm

   $P = 7 + 7 + 4 + 4 = 22$ cm

   g) $C = \pi d = 3.4, d = 3.4 \times 2 = 6.8$
   $C = (3.14)(6.8)$
   $C = 21.35$ m

2. **a)** $S = 23$ cm

   $S = 142 - 33 - 12 - 20 - 18 - 22 - 14 =$ 23 cm

   b) $S = 22$ m

   $S = 132 \div 6 = 22$ m

   c) $S = 109$ mm

   $S = 545 \div 5 = 109$ mm

   d) $S = 23$ m

   $S = 69 \div 3 = 23$ m

3. $C = 7.5$ cm

   $C = 47.1$ Divide by 3.14 to find d
   $47.1 \div 3.14 = 15$
   Diameter divided by 2 = radius
   $15 \div 2 = 7.5$ cm

4. $w = 9$ m

   $46 - 14 - 14 = 18$
   Divide by 2 (two sides are widths)
   $18 \div 2 = 9$ m

5. $P = 78$ mm

   If width is 13, then 13×2 = length = 26
   $P = 13 + 13 + 26 + 26 = 78$ mm

6. $P = 15$ m longer

   Old perimeter = $12 + 14 + 16 = 42$ m
   New perimeter = $17 + 19 + 21 = 57$ m
   It is 15 m larger.
   Or
   3 sides + 5m/side
   $3 \times 5 = 15$ cm

Lesson 3—Area

PRACTICE EXERCISE
Answers and Solutions

1. **a)** $A = 96$ m^2

   $A = l \times w$
   $A = 8 \times 12$
   $A = 96$ m^2

   b) $A = 34$ cm^2

   $A = \dfrac{b \times h}{2}$

   $A = \dfrac{17 \times 4}{2}$

   $A = \dfrac{68}{2}$

   $A = 34$ cm^2
   Or
   $A = \dfrac{170 \times 40}{2}$

   $A = \dfrac{6800}{2}$

   $A = 3400$ mm^2

c) $A = 112 \text{ mm}^2$

$A = b \times h$
$A = (14) \times (8)$
$A = 112 \text{ mm}^2$

d) $A = 562.5 \text{ m}^2$

$A = \dfrac{h(a+b)}{2}$

$A = \dfrac{25(32+13)}{2}$

$A = \dfrac{25(45)}{2}$

$A = \dfrac{1125}{2}$

$A = 562.5 \text{ m}^2$

e) $A = 226.865 \text{ mm}^2$

$A = \pi\, r^2$
$A = (3.14)\,(8.5)^2$
$A = (3.14)\,(72.25)$
$A = 226.865 \text{ mm}^2 \text{ or } 226.87 \text{ mm}^2$

2. $A = 2.52 \text{ m}^2$

$A = l \times w$
$A = (1.8) \times (1.4)$
$A = 2.52 \text{ m}^2$
2.52 m^2 carpet is needed to cover the floor

3. 10 cm^2

$A = l \times w$
$A = (8) \times (10)$
$A = 80 \text{ cm}^2$

$A = \dfrac{h(a+b)}{2}$

$A = \dfrac{5(16+20)}{2}$

$A = \dfrac{5(36)}{2}$

$A = \dfrac{180}{2}$

$A = 90 \text{ cm}^2$
90 cm^2 − 80 cm^2 = 10 cm^2
The trapezoid is bigger by 10 cm^2.

4. $A = 200.96 \text{ mm}^2$

Divide circumference by 3.14 to find diameter. Divide diameter by 2 to get radius. Solve for area with the radius.

$50.24 \div 3.14 = 16$
$16 \div 2 = 8$
$A = \pi r^2$
$A = (3.14)\,(8)^2$
$A = (3.14)\,(64)$
$A = 200.96 \text{ mm}^2$

5. $A = 121.5 \text{ cm}^2$

Base = 27
Height = $27 \div 3 = 9$

$A = \dfrac{b \times h}{2}$

$A = \dfrac{(27) \times (9)}{2}$

$= \dfrac{243}{2}$

$A = 121.5 \text{ cm}^2$

6. $A = 84 \text{ m}^2$

Old $A = l \times w$
$A = (3) \times (7)$
$A = 21 \text{ m}^2$
New $A = l \times w$
$A = (6) \times (14)$
$A = 84 \text{ m}^2$
The new area is 4 times bigger; or, the new area is 63 m^2 more than the old area.

7. a) $h = 5.5 \text{ m}$

$A = b \times h$
$95.15 = 17.3 \times h$

$\dfrac{95.15}{17.3} = \dfrac{17.3 \times h}{17.3}$

$5.5 \text{ m} = h$

b) $r = 4.7$ m

$A = \pi r^2$

$69.08 = (3.14) r^2$

$\dfrac{69.08}{3.14} = \dfrac{3.14 r^2}{3.14}$

$22 = r^2$

$\sqrt{22} = \sqrt{r^2}$

4.7 m $= r$ or 4.69 m

c) $S = 12$ cm

$A = 144$

Since this is a square, you know that length and width are the same size. Take the square root to find the missing sides.

$\sqrt{144} = 12$ cm

8. $l = 10$ m

$A = l \times w$

$\dfrac{400}{40} = \dfrac{l \times 40}{40}$

$10 = l$

$l = 10$ m

Or

$A = l \times w$

$A \div l = w$

$400 \div 40 = 10$ m

9. $A = 400$ m^2

$P = 4l$

$P \div 4 = l$

$80 \div 4 = 20$

$l = 20$ m

$A = l \times w$

$A = (20) \times (20)$

$A = 400$ m^2

10. 6 cm and 12 cm

List all the factors of 72 and find two, one of which is twice the other, that multiply to 72.

1, 2, 3, 4, 6, 12, 18, 24, 36, 72

The factors are 6 cm and 12 cm

11. If you use a radius of 1, you get $A = 3.14$.

If you use a radius of 2, you get $A = 12.56$.

$12.56 \div 3.14 = 4$

Each time the radius is doubles, the area gets 4 times lager.

Lesson 4—2-D Composite Figures

PRACTICE EXERCISE
Answers and Solutions

1. a) $A = 35.375$ mm^2

Area of rectangle – Area of circle

Rectangle

$A = l \times w$

$A = (11) \times (5)$

$A = 55$ mm^2

Circle

$A = \pi r^2$

$A = (3.14)(2.5)^2$

$A = (3.14)(6.25)$

$A = 19.625$ mm^3

Shaded area $= 55 - 19.625 = 35.375$ mm^2

b) $A = 16$ cm^2

Area of triangle – Area of rectangle

Triangle

$A = \dfrac{b \times h}{2}$

$A = \dfrac{(10) \times (8)}{2}$

$= \dfrac{80}{2}$

Remember to convert to one unit.

$A = 40$ cm^2

Rectangle

$A = l \times w$

$A = (4) \times (6)$

$A = 24$ cm^2

Shaded area $= 40 - 24 = 16$ cm^2

c) $A = 116 \text{ mm}^2$

Area of top rectangle + Area of bottom rectangle

Top rectangle
$A = l \times w$
$A = (8) \times (7)$
$A = 56 \text{ mm}^2$

Bottom rectangle
$A = l \times w -$ (the length of this rectangle if found by subtracting $14 - 8 = 6$)
$A = (6) \times (10)$
$A = 60 \text{ mm}^2$
Shaded area $= 56 + 60 = 116 \text{ mm}^2$

d) $A = 203 \text{ cm}^2$

Area triangle + Area of rectangle
Triangle
$A = \dfrac{b \times h}{2}$

$A = \dfrac{(14) \times (15)}{2}$

$= \dfrac{210}{2}$

$A = 105 \text{ cm}^2$

Rectangle
$A = l \times w$
$A = (7) \times (14)$
$A = 98 \text{ cm}^2$
Shaded Area $= 105 + 98 = 203 \text{ cm}^2$

e) $A = 27.31 \text{ m}^2$

Area of triangle + Area of rectangle – Area of half circle

Triangle
$A = \dfrac{b \times h}{2}$

$A = \dfrac{(4.2 \times (3.3)}{2}$

$= \dfrac{13.86}{2}$

$A = 6.93 \text{ m}^2$

Rectangle
$A = l \times w$
$A = (6.5) \times (4.2)$
$A = 27.3 \text{ m}^2$

Circle
$A = \pi r^2$
$A = (3.14) \, (2.1)^2$
$A = (3.14) \, (4.41)$
$A = 13.847 \div 2$ Half a circle must be removed.
$A = 6.923 \, 7 \text{ m}^2$
Shaded area $= 6.93 + 27.3 - 6.92 =$ 27.306 3 m^2

f) $A = 360 \text{ cm}^2$

Area of parallelogram – Area of rectangle

Parallelogram
$A = b \times h$
$A = (24) \times (18)$
$A = 432 \text{ cm}^2$

Rectangle
$A = l \times w$
$A = (18) \times (4)$
$A = 72 \text{ cm}^2$
Shaded area $= 432 - 72 = 360 \text{ cm}^2$

2. $A = 211.74 \text{ m}^2$

Area of rectangle – Area of circle
Rectangle
$A = l \times w$
$A = (20) \times (12)$
$A = 240 \text{ m}^2$

Circle
$A = \pi r^2$
$A = (3.14) \, (3)^2$
$A = (3.14) \, (9)$
$A = 28.26 \text{ m}^2$
Area of grass $= 240 - 28.26 = 211.74 \text{ m}^2$

Practice Quiz 1

Answers and Solutions

1. a) $7.8 \text{ m} = c$

$a^2 + b^2 = c^2$
$(6)^2 + (5)^2 = c^2$
$36 + 25 = c^2$
$61 = c^2$
$\sqrt{61} = \sqrt{c^2}$
$7.8 \text{ m} = c$

b) $b = 8.3$ mm

$a^2 + b^2 = c^2$

$(10)^2 + b^2 = (13)^2$

$100 + b^2 = 169$

$100 - 100 + b^2 = 169 - 100$

$b^2 = 69$

$\sqrt{b^2} = \sqrt{69}$

$b = 8.3$ mm

c) $b = 15.5$ m

$a^2 + b^2 = c^2$

$(9.2)^2 + b^2 = (18)^2$

$84.64 + b^2 = 324$

$84.64 - 84.64 + b^2 = 324 - 84.64$

$b^2 = 239.36$

$\sqrt{b^2} = \sqrt{239.36}$

$b = 15.5$ m

2. $c = 36.1$ cm

$a^2 + b^2 = c^2$

$(30)^2 + (20)^2 = c^2$

$900 + 400 = c^2$

$1300 = c^2$

$\sqrt{1300} = \sqrt{c^2}$

36.1 cm $= c$

3. $b = 7.2$ m

$a^2 + b^2 = c^2$

$(4)^2 + b^2 = (8.2)^2$

$16 + b^2 = 67.24$

$16 - 16 + b^2 = 67.24 - 16$

$b^2 = 51.24$

$\sqrt{b^2} = \sqrt{51.24}$

$b = 7.2$ m

4. $P = 55$ mm

$P = 8 + 10 + 4 + 6 + 10 + 17 = 55$ mm

5. $C = 50.24$ m

$C = \pi d$

$C = (3.14)\,(16)$

$C = 50.24$ m

6. $S = 4$ cm

$S = 129 - 22 - 25 - 33 - 10 - 20 - 15 = 4$ cm

7. $S = 14$ cm

$S = 84 \div 6 = 14$ cm

8. **a)** $A = 40$ m^2

$A = l \times w$

$A = (8) \times (5)$

$A = 40$ m^2

b) $A = 126$ mm^2

$A = \dfrac{h(a+b)}{2}$

$A = \dfrac{9(11+17)}{2}$

$A = \dfrac{9(28)}{2}$

$A = \dfrac{252}{2}$

$A = 126$ mm^2

c) $A = 17.01$ m^2

$A = \dfrac{b \times h}{2}$

$A = \dfrac{(6.3) \times (5.4)}{2}$

$= \dfrac{34.02}{2}$

$A = 17.0$ m^2

d) $A = 46.53$ mm^3

$A = \pi r^2$

$A = (3.14)\,(3.85)^2$

$A = (3.14)\,(14.82)$

$A \div 46.53$ mm^2

9. $A = 32$ cm^2

$A = b \times h$

$A = (4) \times (8)$

$A = 32$ cm^2

10. a) $h = 15$ cm

$A = b \times h$

$300 = 20 \times h$

$\dfrac{300}{20} = \dfrac{300 \times h}{20}$

$15 \, \text{cm} = h$

b) $b = 7$ m

$A = \dfrac{b \times h}{2}$

$14 = \dfrac{b \times 4}{2}$

$14 \times 2 = b \times 4$

$28 = b \times 4$

$\dfrac{28}{4} = \dfrac{b \times 4}{4}$

$7 \, \text{m} = b$

11. a) Shaded area = 368 m^2

Area = Area of rectangle + Area of triangle

$A = l \times w$

$A = (16) \times (18)$

$A = 288$ m^2

$A = \dfrac{b \times h}{2}$

$A = \dfrac{(16) \times (10)}{2}$

$= \dfrac{160}{2}$

$A = 80$ m^2

Shaded area = $288 + 80 = 368$ m^2

b) $A = 390.8$ cm^2

Area = Area of half circle + Area of rectangle + Area of trapezoid

$A = \pi r^2$

$A = (3.14)(7.5)^2$

$A = (3.14)(56.25)$

$A = 176.625 \div 2$ because half circle

$A = 88.312\,5$ cm^2

$A = l \times w$

$A = (15) \times (12)$

$A = 180$ cm^2

$A = \dfrac{h(a + b)}{2}$

$A = \dfrac{7(15 + 20)}{2}$

$A = \dfrac{7(35)}{2}$

$A = \dfrac{245}{2}$

$A = 122.5$ cm^2

Area = 88.31 cm^2 + 180 cm^2 + 122.5 cm^2

$A = 390.81$ cm^2

c) $A = 722$ mm^2

Area = Area of triangle – Area of half-circle

$A = \dfrac{b \times h}{2}$

$A = \dfrac{(45) \times (60)}{2}$

$= \dfrac{2700}{2}$

$A = 1\,350$ mm^2

$A = \pi r^2$

$A = (3.14)(20)^2$

$A = (3.14)(400)$

$A = 1\,256 \div 2$ (half-circle)

$A = 628$ mm^2

$A = 1\,350$ mm^2 – 628 mm^2 = 722 mm^2

d) $A = 438$ m^2

Area of rectangle – Area of parallelogram

$A = l \times w$

$A = (30) \times (25)$

$A = 750$ m^2

$A = b \times h$

$A = (39) \times (8)$

$A = 312$ m^2

$A = 750 - 312$ m^2

$A = 438$ m^2

13. $P = 43$ m $\quad A = 82$ m^2

Area of parallelogram + Area of side rectangle + Area of left rectangle

$A = b \times h$

$A = (5) \times (4)$

$A = 20$ m^2

$A = l \times w$

$A = (5) \times (4)$

$A = 20$ m^2

$A = l \times w$

$A = (7) \times (6)$

$A = 42$ m^2

$A = 20 + 20 + 42 = 82$ m^2

$P = 5 + 5 + 5 + 4 + 5 + 4 + 2 + 6 + 7 = 43$ m

14. $A = 169$ cm^2

$P = 52$ cm

$S = 52 \div 4 = 13$ cm

$A = l \times w$

$A = (13) \times (13)$

$A = 169$ cm^2

15. $A = 12$ m^2

$b = 6$ m

$h = 6 - 2 = 4$ m

$A = \dfrac{b \times h}{2}$

$A = \dfrac{(6) \times (4)}{2}$

$= \dfrac{24}{2}$

$A = 12$ m^2

16. $A = 50.24$ mm^2

$C = \pi d$

$25.12 = (3.14)\, d$

Divide each side by 3.14

$d = 8$ m

$8 \div 2 = 4 = $ radius

$A = \pi r^2$

$A = (3.14)(4)^2$

$A = (3.14)(16)$

$A = 50.24$ mm^2

Lesson 5—3-D Objects

PRACTICE EXERCISE
Answers and Solutions

1. **a)** 1 pentagon, 5 triangles

   b) 2 octagons, 8 rectangles

   c) 2 circles, 1 rectangle

2. cylinder, cone, sphere

3. cylinder, cone, sphere

4. Any prism, cylinder, square, or rectangular pyramid

5. cylinder, cone, sphere

6. pentagonal pyramid or triangular prism

7.

a) Rectangular prism

   i)

   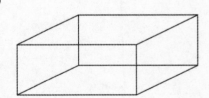

   ii)

   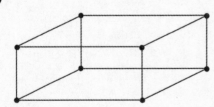

   iii)

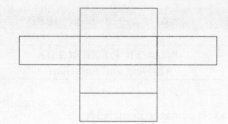

iv) 12

v) 8

b) Square pyramid

i)

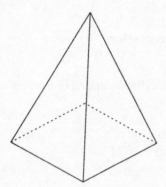

ii)

iii)

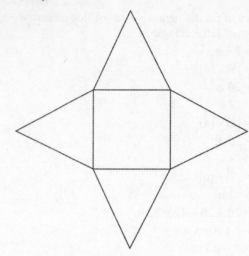

iv) 8

v) 5

c) Cube

i)

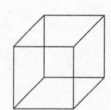

ii)

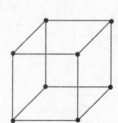

iii)

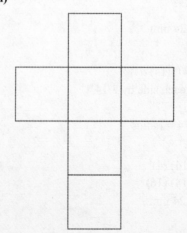

iv) 12

v) 8

d) Triangular pyramid

i)

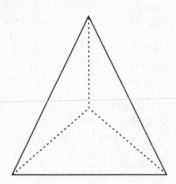

ii)

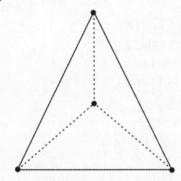

iii)

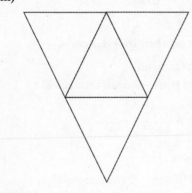

iv) 6

v) 4

PRACTICE EXERCISE
Answers and Solutions

1. **a)** $SA = 382 \text{ m}^2$

Front and Back – 2 equal rectangles
$A = l \times w$
$A = 5 \times 13$
$A = 65 \times 2$
$A = 130 \text{ m}^2$

Top and Bottom – 2 equal rectangles
$A = l \times w$
$A = 13 \times 7$
$A = 91 \times 2$
$A = 182 \text{ m}^2$

Sides – 2 equal rectangles
$A = l \times w$
$A = 5 \times 7$
$A = 35 \times 2$
$A = 70 \text{ m}^2$
Surface Area $= 130 \text{ m}^2 + 182 \text{ m}^2 + 70 \text{ m}^2$
$= 382 \text{ m}^2$

b) $SA = 727 \text{ cm}^2$

Triangular Prism
Left and right side – two equal rectangles
$A = l \times w$
$A = 22 \times 11$
$A = 242 \times 2$
$A = 484 \text{ cm}^2$

Bottom
$A = l \times w$
$A = 9 \times 22$
$A = 198 \text{ cm}^2$
Ends – two equal triangles

$A = \dfrac{b \times h}{2}$

$A = \dfrac{(9) \times (5)}{2}$

$= \dfrac{45}{2}$

$A = 22.5 \times 2 \text{ because two triangles}$
$A = 45 \text{ cm}^2$
$SA \text{ (surface area)} = 198 + 484 + 45$
$= 727 \text{ cm}^2$

c) $SA = 168.5$ mm^2

$A = l \times w$

$A = 5.3 \times 5.3$

$A = 28.06 \times 6$ because there are 6 equal squares

$A = 168.5$ mm^2

$SA = 168.5$ mm^2

d) $SA = 36$ m^2

Bottom rectangle

$A = l \times w$

$A = 2 \times 3$

$A = 6$ m^2

Left Rectangle

$A = l \times w$

$A = 4 \times 2$

$A = 8$ m^2

Diagonal Rectangle

$A = l \times w$

$A = 5 \times 2$

$A = 10$ m^2

Sides – two equal triangles

$A = \dfrac{b \times h}{2}$

$A = \dfrac{(3) \times (4)}{2}$

$\quad = \dfrac{12}{2}$

$A = 6 \times 2$

$A = 12$ m^2

$SA = 6 + 8 + 10 + 12 = 36$ m^2

e) $SA = 244.9$ cm^2

Bottom – square

$A = l \times w$

$A = 8.3 \times 8.3$

$A = 68.7$ cm^2

Sides – 4 equal triangles

$A = \dfrac{b \times h}{2}$

$A = \dfrac{(8.3) \times (10.6)}{2}$

$\quad = \dfrac{87.98}{2}$

$A = 43.99 \times 4$ (4 equal triangles)

$A = 175.96$ cm^2

$SA = 68.69 + 175.96 = 244.9$ cm^2

f) $SA = 100.5$ m^2

Circles – two equal

$A = \pi r^2$

$A = (3.14)(2)^2$

$A = (3.14)(4)$

$A = 12.56 \times 2$

$A = 25.12$ m^2

Rectangle

$A = h \times \pi d$

$A = 6 \times (3.14)(4)$

$A = 75.36$ m^2

$SA = 25.12 + 75.36 = 100.5$ m^2

g) $SA = 57.5$ mm^2

Circles – two equal

$A = \pi r^2$

$A = (3.14)(1.5)^2$

$A = (3.14)(2.25)$

$A = 7.065 \times 2$

$A = 14.1$ mm^2

Rectangle

$A = h \times \pi d$

$A = 4.6 \times (3.14)(3)$

$A = 43.33$ m^2

$SA = 14.13 + 43.33 = 57.46$ mm^2

$\quad\quad = 57.5$ mm^2

2. Cylinder is bigger by 941.8 cm^2

Rectangular prism

Front and Back – 2 equal rectangles

$A = l \times w$

$A = 10 \times 8$

$A = 80 \times 2$

$A = 160$ cm^2

Top and Bottom – 2 equal rectangles

$A = l \times w$

$A = 8 \times 25$

$A = 200 \times 2$

$A = 400$ cm^2

Sides – 2 equal rectangles

$A = l \times w$

$A = 25 \times 10$

$A = 250 \times 2$

$A = 500$ cm^2

Surface Area $= 160 + 400 + 500 = 1\ 060$ cm^2

Cylinder
Circles – two equal
$A = \pi r^2$
$A = (3.14)(7.5)^2$
$A = (3.14)(56.25)$
$A = 176.625 \times 2$
$A = 353.25 \text{ cm}^2$

Rectangle
$A = h \times \pi d$
$A = 35 \times (3.14)(15)$
$A = 1648.5 \text{ cm}^2$
$SA = 353.25 + 1648.5 = 2\,001.75 \text{ cm}^2$
Cylinder is bigger by $2\,001.75 - 1\,060 =$
941.8 cm^2

3. $A = 241.78 \text{ cm}^2$

The label that goes around is only the rectangle part of the cylinder.
Rectangle
$A = h \times \pi d$
$A = 11 \times (3.14)(7)$
$A = 241.78 \text{ cm}^2$

4. $SA = 6450 \text{ mm}^2$

Front, back, bottom – three equal rectangles
$A = l \times w$
$A = 25 \times 80$
$A = 2\,000 \times 3$
$A = 6\,000 \text{ mm}^2$

Sides – two equal triangles
$A = \dfrac{b \times h}{2}$

$A = \dfrac{(25) \times (18)}{2}$

$= \dfrac{450}{2}$

$A = 225 \times 2$
$A = 450 \text{ mm}^2$
$SA = 6\,000 + 450 = 6\,450 \text{ mm}^2$

Lesson 7—Volume

PRACTICE EXERCISE
Answers and Solutions

1. **a)** $V = 75\,000 \text{ cm}^3$

$V =$ area of the base $\times$ height of object
$V = (l \times w) \times \text{height}$
$V = (40 \times 25) \times 75$
$V = 75\,000 \text{ cm}^3$

b) $V = 5.8 \text{ m}^3$

$V =$ area of the base $\times$ height of object
$V = (l \times w) \times \text{height}$
$V = (1.8 \times 1.8) \times 1.8$
$V = 5.8 \text{ m}^3$

c) $V = 210 \text{ m}^3$

$V =$ area of the base $\times$ height of object
$V = \dfrac{b \times h}{2} \times \text{height}$

$V = \dfrac{5 \times 12}{2} \times 7$

$V = \dfrac{60}{2} \times 7$

$V = 30 \times 7$
$V = 210 \text{ m}^3$

d) $V = 115.2 \text{ m}^3$

$V =$ area of the base $\times$ height of object
$V = \dfrac{b \times h}{2} \times \text{height}$

$V = \dfrac{4.5 \times 3.2}{2} \times 16$

$V = \dfrac{14.4}{2} \times 16$

$V = 7.2 \times 16$
$V = 115.2 \text{ m}^3$

e) $V = 7\,474.8 \text{ cm}^3$

$V =$ area of the base $\times$ height of object
$V = \pi r^2 \times \text{height}$
$V = (3.14)(11.5)^2 \times 18$
$V = (3.14)(132.25) \times 18$
$V = 7\,474.8 \text{ cm}^3$

f) $V = 5\ 444.8\ \text{m}^3$

V = area of the base × height of object

$V = \pi r^2 \times$ height

$V = (3.14)\,(8.5)^2 \times 24$

$V = (3.14)\,(72.25) \times 24$

$V = 5\ 444.8\ \text{m}^3$

2. $V = 405\ 000\ \text{cm}^3$

V = area of the base × height of object

$V = (l \times w) \times$ height

$V = (90 \times 75) \times 60$

$V = 405\ 000\ \text{cm}^3$

3. $V = 121\ 500\ \text{cm}^3$

V = area of the base × height of object

$V = (l \times w) \times$ height

$V = (54 \times 30) \times 24$

$V = 405\ 000 \times 3$ because there are 3 planters

Total $V = 121\ 500\ \text{cm}^3$

4. $A = 7\ \text{cm}^2$

Volume equals the area of the base times height of the object.

If you are given the volume and know the height, divide to find the area of the base.

$35 \div 5 = 7\ \text{cm}^2$

The area of the base of the cheese wedge is $7\ \text{cm}^2$.

5. $V = 166\ 375\ \text{cm}^3$

Because it's a cube, all the sides are the same.

V = area of the base × height of object

$V = (l \times w) \times$ height

$V = (55 \times 55) \times 55$

$V = 166\ 375\ \text{cm}^3$

Mark needs $166\ 375\ \text{cm}^3$ of peanuts to fill the box.

Lesson 8—3-D Composite Figures

PRACTICE EXERCISE
Answers and Solutions

1. **a)** $SA = 724\ \text{m}^2$, $V = 1\ 320\ \text{m}^3$

Rectangular prism: there is no top to this because the triangular prism is sitting on top of the prism.

Front and Back – 2 equal rectangles

$A = l \times w$

$A = 12 \times 9$

$A = 108 \times 2$

$A = 216\ \text{m}^2$

Bottom: no top

$A = l \times w$

$A = 12 \times 10$

$A = 120$

$A = 120\ \text{m}^2$

Sides – 2 equal rectangles

$A = l \times w$

$A = 10 \times 9$

$A = 90 \times 2$

$A = 180\ \text{m}^2$

Surface Area of rectangular prism =
$216\ \text{m}^2 + 120\ \text{m}^2 + 180\ \text{m}^2 = 516\ \text{m}^2$

Triangular prism: There is no bottom to this figure.

Sides: 2 equal rectangles

$A = l \times w$

$A = 8 \times 10$

$A = 80 \times 2$

$A = 160\ \text{m}^2$

Sides – two equal triangles

$A = \dfrac{b \times h}{2}$

$A = \dfrac{(12) \times (4)}{2}$

$\quad = \dfrac{48}{2}$

$A = 24 \times 2$ because there are 2 triangles that are equal

$A = 48\ \text{m}^2$

Surface area of triangular prism =
$160\ \text{m}^2 + 48\ \text{m}^2 = 208\ \text{m}^2$

Surface area of composite figure =
Rectangular prism + triangular prism
= 516 m^2 + 208 m^2 = 724 m^2

V = Volume of rectangular prism +
Volume of triangular prism
Rectangular prism
V = area of the base × height of object
$V = (l \times w) \times$ height
$V = (12 \times 10) \times 9$
$V = 120 \times 9$
$V = 1080$ m^3

Volume of triangular prism (remember
think of this shape as sitting on the triangle
as the base)

V = area of the base × height of object
$V = \dfrac{b \times h}{2} \times$ height
$V = \dfrac{12 \times 4}{2} \times 10$
$V = \dfrac{48}{2} \times 10$
$V = 24 \times 10$
$V = 240$ m^3
V = Volume of rectangular prism +
Volume of triangular prism
$V = 1808$ m^3 + 240 m^3 = 1320 m^3

b) $SA = 296.73$ cm^2, $V = 197.82$ cm^3

Large Cylinder
Circles – two equal
$A = \pi r^2$
$A = (3.14)(2.5)^2$
$A = (3.14)(6.25)$
$A = 19.625 \times 2$
$A = 39.25$ cm^2

Rectangle
$A = h \times \pi d$
$A = 12 \times (3.14)(5)$
188.4 cm^2
SA of large cylinder =
39.25 cm^2 + 188.4 cm^2 = 227.65 cm^2

Small cylinder
Circles – end pieces that will be subtracted
$A = \pi r^2$
$A = (3.14)(1)2$
$A = (3.14)(1)$
$A = 3.14 \times 2$
$A = 6.28$ cm^2

Rectangle – middle that will be added
$A = h \times \pi d$
$A = 12 \times (3.14)(2)$
75.36 cm^2
Total surface area large cylinder – end
pieces of small + middle of small
$SA = 227.65$ cm^2 – 6.28 cm^2 + 75.36 cm^2 =
296.73 cm^2

V = Volume of large cylinder – volume of
small cylinder

Large Cylinder
V = area of the base × height of object
$V = \pi r^2 \times$ height
$V = (3.14)(2.5)^2 \times 12$
$V = (3.14)(6.25) \times 12$
$V = 19.625 \times 12$
$V = 235.5$ cm^3

Small Cylinder
V = area of the base × height of object
$V = \pi r^2 \times$ height
$V = (3.14)(1)^2 \times 12$
$V = (3.14)(1) \times 12$
$V = 3.14 \times 12$
$V = 37.68$ cm^3
V = Volume of large cylinder – Volume of
small cylinder
$V = 235.5$ cm^3 – 37.68 cm^3
$V = 197.82$ cm^3

c) $SA = 600$ cm^2, $V = 672$ cm^3

Top Rectangular Prism:
For this prism, there is a front and back
pieces, a top, and left and right pieces.
There is no bottom piece.
Front and Back – 2 equal rectangles
$A = l \times w$
$A = 8 \times 3$
$A = 24 \times 2$
$A = 48$ cm^2

Top
$A = l \times w$
$A = 8 \times 4$
$A = 32$
$A = 32$ cm^2

Left and right sides

$A = l \times w$

$A = 4 \times 3$

$A = 12 \times 2$

$A = 24 \text{ cm}^2$

Surface area of top rectangular prism
$= 48 \text{ cm}^2 + 32 \text{ cm}^2 + 24 \text{ cm}^2 = 104 \text{ cm}^2$

Bottom Rectangular Prism:

For this prism, there are front and back pieces, a bottom piece, two top pieces, and left and right pieces.

Front and Back – 2 equal rectangles

$A = l \times w$

$A = 24 \times 6$

$A = 144 \times 2$

$A = 288 \text{ cm}^2$

Bottom

$A = l \times w$

$A = 24 \times 4$

$A = 96$

$A = 96 \text{ cm}^2$

Top pieces – 2 equal

$A = l \times w$

$A = 8 \times 4$

$A = 32 \times 2$

$A = 64 \text{ cm}^2$

Left/Right sides

$A = l \times w$

$A = 4 \times 6$

$A = 24 \times 2$

$A = 48 \text{ cm}^2$

Surface area of bottom rectangular prism =
$288 \text{ cm}^2 + 96 \text{ cm}^2 + 64 \text{ cm}^2 + 48 \text{ cm}^2 = 496 \text{ cm}^2$

Surface area of composite figure =
top prism + bottom prism
$= 104 \text{ cm}^2 + 496 \text{ cm}^2 = 600 \text{ cm}^2$

V = Volume of top rectangular prism + Volume of bottom rectangular prism

Top prism

V = area of the base $\times$ height of object

$V = (l \times w) \times$ height

$V = (8 \times 4) \times 3$

$V = 32 \times 3$

$V = 96 \text{ cm}^3$

Bottom prism

V = area of the base $\times$ height of object

$V = (l \times w) \times$ height

$V = (24 \times 4) \times 6$

$V = 96 \times 6$

$V = 576 \text{ cm}^3$

V = Volume of top rectangular prism + Volume of bottom rectangular prism

$V = 96 \text{ cm}^3 + 576 \text{ cm}^3 = 672 \text{ cm}^3$

d) $SA = 67.625 \text{ m}^2$, $V = 28.125 \text{ m}^3$

Large Prism

Front and Back – 2 equal rectangles

$A = l \times w$

$A = 3 \times 5$

$A = 15 \times 2$

$A = 30 \text{ m}^2$

Top and Bottom – 2 equal rectangles

$A = l \times w$

$A = 3 \times 2$

$A = 6 \times 2$

$A = 12 \text{ m}^2$

Sides – 2 equal rectangles

$A = l \times w$

$A = 2 \times 5$

$A = 10 \times 2$

$A = 20 \text{ m}^2$

Surface area of large prism = $30 \text{ m}^2 + 12 \text{ m}^2 + 20 \text{ m}^2 = 62 \text{ m}^2$

Smaller Prism

Triangles – end pieces to be subtracted

$$A = \frac{b \times h}{2}$$

$$= \frac{1 \times 0.75}{2}$$

$$= \frac{0.75}{2}$$

$= 0.375 \text{ m}^2$

Rectangular Sides – middle to be added

$A = l \times w$

$A = 1 \times 2$

$A = 2 \times 3$ (3 rectangles)

$A = 6 \text{ m}^2$

Total surface area = large prism – end pieces of small + middle of small

$SA = 62 \text{ m}^2 - 0.375 \text{ m}^2 + 6 \text{ m}^2 = 67.625 \text{ m}^2$

V = Volume of Rectangular Prism – Volume of Triangular Prism

Rectangular prism

V = area of the base $\times$ height of object

$V = (l \times w) \times$ height

$V = (3 \times 2) \times 5$

$V = 6 \times 5$

$V = 30 \text{ m}^3$

Volume of triangular prism (remember to think of this shape as sitting on the triangle as the base

V = area of the base $\times$ height of object

$V = \dfrac{b \times h}{2} \times$ height

$V = \dfrac{1 \times 0.75}{2} \times 5$

$V = \dfrac{0.75}{2} \times 5$

$V = 0.375 \times 5$

$V = 1.875 \text{ m}^3$

V = Volume of rectangular prism $\times$ Volume of triangular prism

$V = 30 \text{ m}^3 - 1.875 \text{ m}^3 = 28.125 \text{ m}^3$

e) $A = 3221.5 \text{ mm}^2$, $V = 10\ 785 \text{ mm}^3$

Prism

Front and Back – 2 equal rectangles

$A = l \times w$

$A = 40 \times 10$

$A = 400 \times 2$

$A = 800 \text{ mm}^2$

Sides – 2 equal rectangles

$A = l \times w$

$A = 25 \times 10$

$A = 250 \times 2$

$A = 500 \text{ mm}^2$

Bottom

$A = l \times w$

$A = 40 \times 25$

$A = 1000 \text{ mm}^2$

Top = 1000 mm^2 (same as bottom) – area of the base of the cylinder which is a circle

Base of cylinder

$A = \pi r^2$

$A = (3.14)(5)^2$

$A = (3.14)(25)$

$A = 78.5 \text{ mm}^2$

Top = $1000 - 78.5 = 921.5 \text{ mm}^2$

Surface area of prism = 800 mm^2 + 500 mm^2 + 1000 mm^2 + 921.5 mm^2

= 3 221.5mm^2

Cylinder – not including the bottom

Circles (only 1)

$A = \pi r^2$

$A = (3.14)(5)^2$

$A = (3.14)(25)$

$A = 78.5 \text{ mm}^2$

Rectangle

$A = h \times \pi d$

$A = 10 \times (3.14)(10)$

314 mm^2

$SA = 78.5 \text{ mm}^2 + 314 \text{ mm}^2 = 392.5 \text{ mm}^2$

Total surface area is prism + cylinder

$SA = 3221.5 \text{ mm}^2 + 392.5 \text{ mm}^2 = 3614 \text{ mm}^2$

Volume = rectangular prism + cylinder prism

V = area of the base $\times$ height of object

$V = (l \times w) \times$ height

$V = (40 \times 25) \times 10$

$V = 1000 \times 10$

$V = 10\ 000 \text{ mm}^3$

Cylinder

V = area of the base $\times$ height of object

$V = \pi r^2 \times$ height

$V = (3.14)(5)^2 \times 10$

$V = (3.14)(25) \times 10$

$V = 78.5 \times 10$

$V = 785 \text{ mm}^3$

$V = 10\ 000 \text{ mm}^3 + 785 \text{ mm}^3 = 10\ 785 \text{ mm}^3$

Practice Quiz 2

Answers and Solutions

1. **a)** Name: Cube

Net:

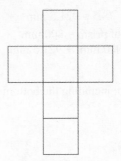

Edges: 12

Vertices: 8

b) Name: Square Pyramid

Net:

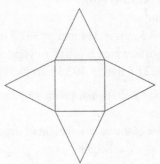

Edges: 8

Vertices: 5

c) Name: Triangular Prism

Net:

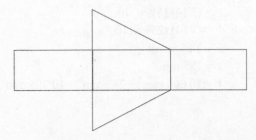

Edges: 9

Vertices: 6

2. **a)** $SA = 216 \text{ m}^2$

$A = l \times w$

$A = 6 \times 6$

$A = 36 \times 6$ because there are 6 equal squares

$SA = 216 \text{ m}^2$

b) $SA = 32.88 \text{ cm}^2$

Front and Back – 2 equal rectangles

$A = l \times w$

$A = 1.4 \times 3.2$

$A = 4.48 \times 2$

$A = 8.96 \text{ cm}^2$

Top and Bottom – 2 equal rectangles

$A = l \times w$

$A = 2.6 \times 3.2$

$A = 8.32 \times 2$

$A = 16.64 \text{ cm}^2$

Sides – 2 equal rectangles

$A = l \times w$

$A = 1.4 \times 2.6$

$A = 3.64 \times 2$

$A = 7.28 \text{ cm}^2$

Surface area = $8.96 \text{ cm}^2 + 16.64 \text{ cm}^2 + 7.28 \text{ cm}^2 = 32.88 \text{ cm}^2$

c) $SA = 72 \text{ m}^2$

Bottom – square

$A = l \times w$

$A = 4 \times 4$

$A = 16 \text{ m}^2$

Sides – 4 equal triangles

$A = \dfrac{b \times h}{2}$

$A = \dfrac{(4) \times (7)}{2}$

$= \dfrac{28}{2}$

$A = 14 \times 4$ (4 equal triangles)

$A = 56 \text{ m}^2$

$SA = 16 + 56 = 72 \text{ m}^2$

d) $SA = 336 \text{ m}^2$

Front, back, bottom – three equal rectangles
$A = l \times w$
$A = 8 \times 12$
$A = 96 \times 3$
$A = 288 \text{ m}^2$

Sides – two equal triangles
$A = \dfrac{b \times h}{2}$
$A = \dfrac{(8) \times (6)}{2}$
$\quad = \dfrac{48}{2}$
$A = 24 \times 2$
$A = 48 \text{m}^2$
$SA = 288 + 48 = 336 \text{ m}^2$

e) $SA = 673.53 \text{ mm}^2$

Circles – two equal
$A = \pi r^2$
$A = (3.14)(5.5)^2$
$A = (3.14)(30.25)$
$A = 94.985 \times 2$
$A = 189.97 \text{ mm}^2$

Rectangle
$A = h \times \pi d$
$A = 14 \times (3.14)(11)$
$A = 483.56 \text{ mm}^2$
$SA = 189.97 + 483.56 = 673.53 \text{ mm}^2$

3. a) $V = 216 \text{ m}^3$

$V = $ area of the base $\times$ height of object
$V = (l \times w) \times$ height
$V = (6 \times 6) \times 6$
$V = 216 \text{ m}^3$

b) $V = 11.6 \text{ cm}^3$

$V = $ area of the base $\times$ height of object
$V = (l \times w) \times$ height
$V = (3.2 \times 2.6) \times 1.4$
$V = 11.6 \text{ cm}^3$

c) $V = 288 \text{ m}^3$

$V = $ area of the base $\times$ height of object
$V = \dfrac{b \times h}{2} \times$ height
$V = \dfrac{8 \times 6}{2} \times 12$
$V = \dfrac{48}{2} \times 12$
$V = 24 \times 12$
$V = 288 \text{ m}^3$

d) $V = 1\,329.8 \text{ mm}^3$

$V = $ area of the base $\times$ height of object
$V = \pi r^2 \times$ height
$V = (3.14)(5.5)^2 \times 14$
$V = (3.14)(30.25) \times 14$
$V = 1\,329.8 \text{ mm}^3$

4. $SA = 1\,178 \text{ cm}^2$

Front and Back – 2 equal rectangles
$A = l \times w$
$A = 20 \times 23$
$A = 460 \times 2$
$A = 920 \text{ cm}^2$

Top and Bottom – 2 equal rectangles
$A = l \times w$
$A = 23 \times 3$
$A = 69 \times 2$
$A = 138 \text{ cm}^2$

Sides – 2 equal rectangles
$A = l \times w$
$A = 3 \times 20$
$A = 60 \times 2$
$A = 120 \text{ cm}^2$

Surface area =
$920 \text{ cm}^2 + 138 \text{ cm}^2 + 120 \text{ cm}^2 = 1\,178 \text{ cm}^2$
The surface area of the book is $1\,178 \text{ cm}^2$.

5. $SA = 37.1 \text{ m}^2$

This is a cylinder, but only include 1 circle.
Circle
$A = \pi r^2$
$A = (3.14)(0.75)^2$
$A = (3.14)(0.5625)$
$A = 1.766\,25 \text{ m}^2$

Rectangle

$A = h \times \pi d$

$A = 73.5 \times (3.14) \, (1.5)$

$A = 35.325 \text{ m}^2$

$SA = 1.766\ 25 + 35.325 = 37.1 \text{m}^2$

6. $V = 346.2 \text{ cm}^3$

Height is 9 cm. $(10 - 1$ because not completely full)

$V =$ area of the base $\times$ height of object

$V = \pi r^2 \times$ height

$V = (3.14) \, (3.5)^2 \times 9$

$V = (3.14) \, (12.25) \times 9$

$V = 346.2 \text{ cm}^3$

7. $V = 0.9 \text{ m}^3$

$V =$ area of the base $\times$ height of object

$V = (l \times w) \times$ height

$V = (1 \times 0.75) \times 1.25$

$V = 0.9 \text{ m}^3$

8. **a)** $SA = 631.4 \text{ m}^2$, $V = 881.2 \text{ m}^3$

Large Prism

Front and Back – 2 equal rectangles

$A = l \times w$

$A = 15 \times 10$

$A = 150 \times 2$

$A = 300 \text{ m}^2$

Top and Bottom – 2 equal rectangles

$A = l \times w$

$A = 10 \times 6$

$A = 60 \times 2$

$A = 120 \text{ m}^2$

Sides – 2 equal rectangles

$A = l \times w$

$A = 15 \times 6$

$A = 90 \times 2$

$A = 180 \text{ m}^2$

Surface area of large prism = 300 m^2 + 120 m^2 + 180 m^2 = 600 m^2

Cylinder

Circles – end pieces that will be subtracted

$A = \pi r^2$

$A = (3.14) \, (1)^2$

$A = (3.14) \, (1)$

$A = 3.14 \times 2$

$A = 6.3 \text{ m}^2$

Rectangle – middle that will be added

$A = h \times \pi d$

$A = 6 \times (3.14)(2)$

$A = 37.68 \text{ m}^2$

Total surface area = prism – end pieces of cylinder + middle of cylinder

$SA = 600 \text{ m}^2 - 6.28 \text{ m}^2 + 37.68 \text{ m}^2$
$= 631.4 \text{ m}^2$

Volume = rectangular prism – cylinder

Prism

$V =$ area of the base $\times$ height of object

$V = (l \times w) \times$ height

$V = (10 \times 6) \times 15$

$V = 60 \times 15$

$V = 900 \text{ m}^3$

Cylinder

$V =$ area of the base $\times$ height of object

$V = \pi r^2 \times$ height

$V = (3.14) \, (1)^2 \times 6$

$V = (3.14)(1) \times 6$

$V = 3.14 \times 6$

$V = 18.84 \text{ m}^3$

$V = 900 \text{ m}^3 - 18.84 \text{ m}^3 = 881.2 \text{ m}^3$

b) $SA = 136.5 \text{ m}^2$, $V = 90 \text{ m}^3$

Rectangular prism

Front and Back – 2 equal rectangles

$A = l \times w$

$A = 3 \times 4$

$A = 12 \times 2$

$A = 24 \text{ m}^2$

Top and Bottom – 2 equal rectangles

$A = l \times w$

$A = 3 \times 3$

$A = 9 \times 2$

$A = 18 \text{ m}^2$

Left side only

$A = l \times w$

$A = 3 \times 4$

$A = 12 \text{ m}^2$

Surface area = $24 \text{ m}^2 + 18 \text{ m}^2 + 12 \text{ m}^2$

$= 54 \text{ m}^2$

Triangular Prism

Bottom rectangle

$A = l \times w$

$A = 6 \times 3$

$A = 18 \text{ m}^2$

Left Rectangle – only the top part of the rectangle that is showing

$A = l \times w$

$A = 3 \times 2$

$A = 6 \text{ m}^2$

Diagonal Rectangle

$A = l \times w$

$A = 8.5 \times 3$

$A = 25.5 \text{ m}^2$

Sides – two equal triangles

$A = \dfrac{b \times h}{2}$

$A = \dfrac{(6) \times (6)}{2}$

$A = \dfrac{36}{2}$

$A = 18 \times 2$

$A = 36 \text{ m}^2$

$SA = 18 + 6 + 25.5 + 36 = 85.5 \text{ m}^2$

Total surface area = area of rectangular prism + area of triangular prism

$SA = 54 \text{ m}^2 + 85.5 \text{ m}^2 = 139.5 \text{ m}^2$

Volume = rectangular prism + triangular prism

Rectangular Prism

V = area of the base × height of object

$V = (l \times w) \times \text{height}$

$V = (3 \times 3) \times 4$

$V = 9 \times 4$

$V = 36 \text{ m}^3$

Triangular Prism

V = area of the base × height of object

$V = \dfrac{b \times h}{2} \times \text{height}$

$V = \dfrac{6 \times 6}{2} \times 3$

$V = \dfrac{36}{2} \times 3$

$V = 18 \times 3$

$V = 54 \text{ m}^3$

Total volume = $36 \text{ m}^3 + 54 \text{ m}^3 = 90 \text{ m}^3$

Lesson 9— Enlargements and Reductions

PRACTICE EXERCISE
Answers and Solutions

1. a) larger

    Scale factor is greater than 1, so image would be larger.

    b) smaller

    Scale factor is less than 1, so image would be smaller.

    c) larger

    Scale factor is greater than 1, so image would be larger.

2.

Original Length (cm)	New Length (cm)	Scale Factor
7	224	32
75	15	$\dfrac{1}{5}$
3	8.1	2.7
14.2	5.68	0.4
0.93	93	100

3. Images are labelled with the prime symbol: F becomes F'

4. Images are labeled with the prime symbol: H becomes H'

5. Scale Factor = New length ÷ original length

    Scale Factor = $1 \div 3 = \dfrac{1}{3}$

    $X'Z' = 1, (xz = 3)$

6. New length = Original length × scale factor
(which is 2 in this diagram)

$\overline{LM} \times 2 = 3 \times 2 = \overline{L'M'} = 6$

$\overline{MN} \times 2 = 2 \times 2 = \overline{M'N'} = 4$

$\overline{NL} \times 2 = 3.5 \times 2 = \overline{N'L'} = 7$

7. Scale factor = $\overline{A'E'} \div \overline{AE}$

$= 8 \div 2 = 4$

New length = original length × scale factor
(which is 4 in this diagram)

$\overline{AB} \times 4 = 1 \times 4 = \overline{A'B'} = 4$

$\overline{BC} \times 4 = 2 \times 4 = \overline{B'C'} = 8$

$\overline{CD} \times 4 = 1 \times 4 = \overline{C'D'} = 4$

$\overline{DE} \times 4 = 1 \times 4 = \overline{D'E'} = 4$

$\overline{AE} \times 4 = 2 \times 4 = \overline{A'E'} = 8$

8.

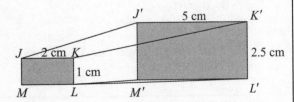

9. 2

Scale Factor = new size ÷ original size

Scale Factor = $\dfrac{0.75}{1.5} = \dfrac{3}{6} = \dfrac{1}{2}$

Lesson 10—Scale Diagrams

PRACTICE EXERCISE
Answers and Solutions

1. 2.5 m

$\dfrac{1}{125} = \dfrac{2\,\text{cm}}{x} = 125 \times 2 \div 1 = 250\ \text{cm} = 2.5\ \text{m}$

2. 3 cm

$\dfrac{1}{25} = \dfrac{d}{75\,\text{cm}} = 1 \times 75 \div 25 = 3\ \text{cm}$

3. $6\dfrac{2}{3}$

$\dfrac{100}{15} = 6\dfrac{10}{15} = 6\dfrac{2}{3}$

4. 2.52 m

$7 \times 360 = 2\,520\ \text{cm} = 25.2\ \text{m}$

5. 3 cm

$\dfrac{d}{0.75} = \dfrac{4}{1} = 0.75 \times 4 \div 1 = 3\ \text{cm}$

6. $\dfrac{3}{20}$

$\dfrac{6}{40} = \dfrac{3}{20}$

7. 5.2 cm

$\dfrac{1}{7\,000\,000} = \dfrac{m}{363}\ 1 \times 363 \div 7\,000\,000 = 5.2\ \text{cm}$

8. $\dfrac{1}{40\,000\,000}$

$\dfrac{2\,\text{cm}}{800\,\text{km}} = \dfrac{2\,\text{cm}}{80\,000\,000\,\text{cm}} = \dfrac{1}{40\,000\,000}$

9. 1 192 km

$\dfrac{1}{16\,000\,000} = \dfrac{7.45}{x} = 16\,000\,000 \times 7.45 \div 1$

$= 119\,200\,000\ \text{cm} = 1\,192\ \text{km}$

10. 10.5 cm

$\dfrac{1}{25\,000\,000} = \dfrac{d}{2\,626} = 1 \times 2\,626 \div 25\,000\,000 =$

10.5 cm

Lesson 11—Maps

PRACTICE EXERCISE
Answers and Solutions

1. **a)** 10

    b) 8

    c) 8

2. **a)** 3

    b) 3

    c) 4

3. **a)** checked or spiral

    b) gray or checked

    c) spiral

    d) checked or spiral

Lesson 12—Networks

PRACTICE EXERCISE
Answers and Solutions

1. **a)**

    i.

    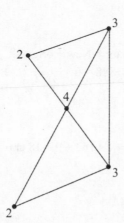

    ii. Odd = 2, Even = 3

    iii. Traceable

b)

i.

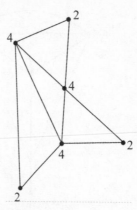

ii. Odd = 0, Even = 6

iii. Traceable

c)

i.

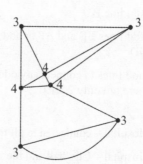

ii. Odd = 4, Even = 3

iii. Not traceable

d)

i.

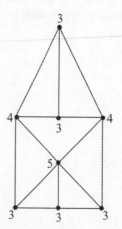

ii. Odd = 6, Even = 2

iii Not traceable

e)

i.

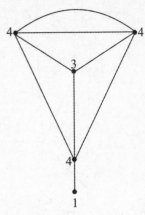

ii. Odd = 2, Even = 3

iii. Traceable

2. a) Add line BD

   b) Add lines EB and AF or add lines BH and GD

   (add lines to connect any odd vertices until there are only 2 left)

3. a) Hospital – connected to all the other vertices

   b) Hospital – City hall and the zoo are not connected, you have to go through the hospital first.

   c) Back at the park – There are only two roads out of the park, so if you go out one, and want to travel all the roads, the last road will be the other one coming back to the park.

Practice Quiz 3

Answers and Solutions

1.

	Original Length (cm)	New Length (cm)	Scale Factor
a)	10	30	3
b)	15	7.5	$\frac{1}{2}$
c)	6	15	$2\frac{1}{2}$

2. 2.25

Scale Factor = New ÷ original

$SF = 4.5 \div 2 = 2.25$

3. Triangle *CAT* has sides that are 6 cm long each. Draw the image of the triangle after a reduction of $\frac{1}{3}$.

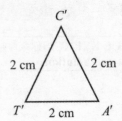

4. 6

Scale Factor = New ÷ original
$SF = 108 \div 18 = 6$

5. 18 cm

$\frac{1}{9} = \frac{x}{162} = 1 \times 162 \div 9 = 18$ cm

6. 8.925 m

$\frac{1}{255} = \frac{3.5}{x} = 3.5 \times 255 \div 1 = 892.5$ cm = 8.925 m

7. 3.68 cm

Change 1840 km into cm = 184 000 000

$$\frac{1}{50\,000\,000} = \frac{m}{184\,000\,000} = 1 \times 184\,000\,000 \div$$

50 000 000 = 3.68 cm

8. 1: 27 000 000

$$\frac{4\,cm}{1\,080\,km} = \frac{4\,cm}{108\,000\,000\,cm} = \frac{1}{27\,000\,000} =$$

1: 27 000 000

9. Start at one side of the map coloring so that no adjacent regions are the same colour. Do not add another colour until absolutely necessary.

a) 2

b) 3

c) 4

10. a) Yes

b) No

c) No

11. a) $A = 4, B = 2, C = 4, D = 2, E = 2$

Odd: 0, Even: 5
Traceable

b) $7 + 12 = 19$ m

c) Point A because a line goes out to each other vertex

d) An edge loops around, it begins at point C and ends at point C.

Practice Test

Answers and Solutions

1. a) $c = 36.1$ m

$$a^2 + b^2 = c^2$$
$$(20)^2 + (30)^2 = c^2$$
$$400 + 900 = c^2$$
$$1300 = c^2$$
$$\sqrt{1300} = \sqrt{c^2}$$
$$36.1\text{ m} = c$$

b) $b = 15.9$ m

$$a^2 + b^2 = c^2$$
$$(9.4)^2 + b^2 = (16.5)^2$$
$$88.36 + b^2 = 272.25$$
$$88.36 - 88.36 + b^2 = 272.25 - 88.36$$
$$b^2 = 184.14$$
$$\sqrt{b^2} = \sqrt{184.14}$$
$$b = 13.6\text{ m}$$

2. 82 km = c

$$a^2 + b^2 = c^2$$
$$(50)^2 + (65)^2 = c^2$$
$$2500 + 4225 = c^2$$
$$6725 = c^2$$
$$\sqrt{6725} = \sqrt{c^2}$$
$$82\text{ km} = c$$

3. 70 mm

$7 \times 10 = 70$ mm

4. $S = 38$ m

$S = 105 - 12 - 8 - 10 - 15 - 12 - 10 = 38$ m

5. a) $A = 104$ m^2

$$A = b \times h$$
$$A = (13) \times (8)$$
$$A = 104\text{ m}^2$$

b) $A = 32.1536$ mm^2

$A = \pi r^2$

$A = (3.14)(3.2)^2$

$A = (3.14)(10.24)$

$A = 32.1536$ mm^2

c) $A = 52.5$ m^2

$A = \dfrac{b \times h}{2}$

$A = \dfrac{(7) \times (15)}{2}$

$= \dfrac{105}{2}$

$A = 52.5$ m^2

d) $A = 108$ cm^2

If original length and width were 3 and 4 cm tripled, they are 9 and 12 cm.

$A = l \times w$

$A = (9) \times (12)$

$A = 108$ cm^2

6. a) $A = 79.5$ m^2

Area = Area of rectangle + trapezoid + triangle

$A = l \times w$

$A = (3) \times (2)$

$A = 6$ m^2

$A = \dfrac{h(a + b)}{2}$

$A = \dfrac{7(3 + 12)}{2}$

$A = \dfrac{7(15)}{2}$

$A = \dfrac{105}{2}$

$A = 52.5$ m^2

$A = \dfrac{b \times h}{2}$

$A = \dfrac{(6) \times (7)}{2}$

$= \dfrac{42}{2}$

$A = 21$ m^2

Area = 6 + 52.5 + 21 = 79.5 m^2

b) $A = 243.48$ mm^2

Area of parallelogram – area of half-circle

$A = b \times h$

$A = (20) \times (15)$

$A = 300$ mm^2

$A = \pi r^2$

$A = (3.14)(6)^2$

$A = (3.14)(36)$

$A = 113.04 \div 2$ because half-circle

$A = 56.52$ mm^2

Area = 300 – 56.52 = 243.48 mm^2

7. a) Name: Cube

Skeleton:

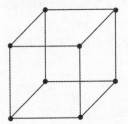

b) Name: Square Pyramid

Skeleton:

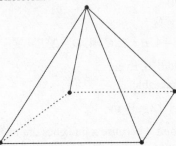

8. a) $SA = 120$ m^2, $V = 96$ m^3

Front, back, bottom – three equal rectangles

$A = l \times w$

$A = 4 \times 8$

$A = 32 \times 3$

$A = 96$ m^2

Sides – two equal triangles

$A = \dfrac{b \times h}{2}$

$A = \dfrac{(4) \times (6)}{2}$

$= \dfrac{24}{2}$

$A = 12 \times 2$

$A = 24 \text{ m}^2$

$SA = 96 + 24 = 120 \text{ m}^2$

$V = $ area of the base $\times$ height of object

$V = \dfrac{b \times h}{2} \times$ height

$V = \dfrac{4 \times 6}{2} \times 8$

$V = \dfrac{24}{2} \times 8$

$V = 12 \times 8$

$V = 96 \text{ m}^3$

b) $SA = 1\ 530.75 \text{ cm}^2, V = 4\ 451.625 \text{ cm}^3$

Circles – two equal

$A = \pi\, r^2$

$A = (3.14)\,(7.5)^2$

$A = (3.14)\,(56.25)$

$A = 176.625 \times 2$

$A = 353.25 \text{ cm}^2$

Rectangle

$A = h \times \pi\, d$

$A = 25 \times (3.14)\,(15)$

$A = 1\ 177.5 \text{ cm}^2$

$SA = 353.25 + 1\ 177.5 = 1\ 530.75 \text{ cm}^2$

$V = $ area of the base $\times$ height of object

$V = \pi r^2 \times$ height

$V = (3.14)\,(7.5)^2 \times 25$

$V = (3.14)(56.25) \times 25$

$V = 4451.625 \text{ cm}^3$

c) $SA = 36 \text{ cm}^2, V = 8 \text{ cm}^3$

Front and Back – 2 equal rectangles

$A = l \times w$

$A = 2 \times 4$

$A = 8 \times 2$

$A = 16 \text{ cm}^2$

Top and Bottom – 2 equal rectangles

$A = l \times w$

$A = 2 \times 4$

$A = 8 \times 2$

$A = 16 \text{ cm}^2$

Sides – 2 equal rectangles

$A = l \times w$

$A = 2 \times 1$

$A = 2 \times 2$

$A = 4 \text{ cm}^2$

Surface Area $= 16 \text{ cm}^2 + 16 \text{ cm}^2 + 4 \text{ cm}^2$

$= 36 \text{ cm}^2$

$V = $ area of the base $\times$ height of object

$V = (l \times w) \times$ height

$V = (4 \times 1) \times 2$

$V = 8 \text{ cm}^3$

9. $V = 0.48 \text{ m}^3$

$V = $ area of the base $\times$ height of object

$V = (l \times w) \times$ height

$V = (0.5 \times 0.8) \times 0.8 = 0.96 \div$ because half-full

$V = 0.48 \text{ m}^3$

10. a) $SA = 46 \text{ cm}^2, V = 60 \text{ cm}^3$

Right Rectangular Prism:

Front and back – 2 equal rectangles

$A = l \times w$

$A = 6 \times 3$

$A = 18 \times 2$

$A = 12 \times 2$

$A = 36 \text{ cm}^2$

Bottom and top – rectangles

$A = l \times w$

$A = 6 \times 2$

$A = 24 \text{ cm}^2$

Right side

$A = l \times w$

$A = 2 \times 3$

$A = 6 \text{ cm}^2$

Surface area of left rectangular prism $=$

$36 \text{ cm}^2 + 24 \text{ cm}^2 + 6 \text{ cm}^2 = 66 \text{ cm}^2$

Left Rectangular Prism:

Front and back – 2 equal rectangles

$A = l \times w$

$A = 3 \times 4$

$A = 12 \times 2$

$A = 24 \text{ cm}^2$

Bottom and top – rectangles

$A = l \times w$

$A = 3 \times 2$

$A = 6 \times 2$

$A = 12 \text{ cm}^2$

Left side

$A = l \times w$

$A = 4 \times 2$

$A = 8 \text{ cm}^2$

Right Side

$A = l \times w$

$A = 1 \times 2$

$A = 2 \text{ cm}^2$

Surface area of left rectangular prism = $24 \text{ cm}^2 + 12 \text{ cm}^2 + 8 \text{ cm}^2 + 2 \text{ cm}^2 = 46 \text{ cm}^2$

Surface area of composite figure = left prism + right prism

$= 66 \text{ cm}^2 + 46 \text{ cm}^2 = 112 \text{ cm}^2$

V = volume of right rectangular prism + volume of left rectangular prism

Right prism

V = area of the base $\times$ height of object

$V = (l \times w) \times$ height

$V = (6 \times 2) \times 3$

$V = 12 \times 3$

$V = 36 \text{ cm}^3$

Left prism

V = area of the base $\times$ height of object

$V = (l \times w) \times$ height

$V = (3 \times 2) \times 4$

$V = 6 \times 4$

$V = 24 \text{ cm}^3$

V = volume of left rectangular prism + volume of right rectangular prism

$V = 36 \text{ cm}^3 + 24 \text{ cm}^3 = 60 \text{ cm}^3$

b) $SA = 791.28 \text{ cm}^2$, $V = 1507.25 \text{ cm}^3$

Large Cylinder

Circles – two equal

$A = \pi r^2$

$A = (3.14) (6)^2$

$A = (3.14) (36)$

$A = 113.04 \times 2$

$A = 226.08 \text{ cm}^2$

Rectangle

$A = h \times \pi d$

$A = 15 \times (3.14) (12)$

$A = 565.2 \text{ cm}^2$

SA of large cylinder =

$226.08 \text{ cm}^2 + 565.2 \text{ cm}^2 = 791.28 \text{ cm}^2$

Small cylinder

Circles – end pieces that will be subtracted

$A = \pi r^2$

$A = (3.14) (2)^2$

$A = (3.14) (4)$

$A = 12.56 \times 2$

$A = 25.12 \text{ cm}^2$

Rectangle – middle that will be added

$A = h \times \pi d$

$A = 15 \times (3.14) (4)$

$A = 188.4 \text{ cm}^2$

Total surface area is large cylinder – end pieces of small + middle of small

$SA = 791.28 \text{ cm}^2 - 25.12 \text{ cm}^2 + 188.24 \text{ cm}^2$

$= 954.56 \text{ cm}^2$

V = volume of large cylinder – volume of small cylinder

Large Cylinder

V = area of the base $\times$ height of object

$V = \pi r^2 \times$ height

$V = (3.14) (6)^2 \times 15$

$V = (3.14)(36) \times 15$

$V = 113.04 \times 15$

$V = 1695.6 \text{ cm}^3$

Small Cylinder

V = area of the base $\times$ height of object

$V = \pi r^2 \times$ height

$V = (3.14) (2)^2 \times 15$

$V = (3.14)(4) \times 15$

$V = 12.56 \times 15$

$V = 188.4 \text{ cm}^3$

V = volume of large cylinder – volume of small cylinder

$V = 1695.6 \text{ cm}^3 - 188.4 \text{ cm}^3$

$V = 1507.25 \text{ cm}^3$

11. Original = new $\times$ scale factor

New = Original $\times$ scale factor

Scale Factor = New $\div$ original

Original Length (cm)	New Length (cm)	Scale Factor
5	32.5	6.5
18	6	$\frac{1}{3}$
7	7	1

12. Because the scale factor is 7, multiply each dimension by 7

$6 \times 8 \times 1$ becomes $42 \times 56 \times 7$ inches

13. $\dfrac{2}{10} = \dfrac{1}{5} = 1{:}5$

14. 5.6 cm

Change 280 km into cm = 28 000 000

$$\frac{1}{5\,000\,000} = \frac{x}{28\,000\,000}$$

$= 1 \times 28\,000\,000 \div 5\,000\,000 = 5.6$ cm

15. a) 4

b) 3

16. $3 + 2 + 4 + 6 = 15$

17. a) Cities and roads in the Okanagan of B.C.

b) No, because this network is not traceable. There are 3 odd vertices.

STATISTICS AND PROBABILITY

Lesson 1—Surveys

PRACTICE EXERCISE
Answers and Solutions

1. Here, you are looking for information about busy roads that lots of people use each day, which do not have a lot of restaurants. To collect these data, you could check city records to see which roads have the most traffic, or use a telephone survey or random people to see where they think something should be opened.

2. There are lots of different possibilities for this question, but the answer probably should be something done over the computer because it does not involve people asking questions.

3. Use something where people are interviewed to fill in detailed answers and give you more information. A survey with choices defined will not give you as much information.

4. No, this would not give accurate results. To give accurate results, you need to survey only students in Grade 12, not everyone in the school.

5. a) 100

Add all the numbers together for the total.

$22 + 26 + 34 + 18 = 100$

b) During playoff time, more people watch hockey so the occasionally category would probably get smaller and the often and always categories would likely increase.

c) Various answers are possible for this. Mainly, anyone who sponsors hockey teams, or the TV station advertisers.

6. a) Since all the answers are types of pop, the question could have been: What is your favourite type of pop?

b) Various answers are possible for this. For example, what type of pop should organizers purchase for the school dance?

c) There are lots of ways to choose a random sample of people. Use any situation where each choice has an equal chance of being selected. An example could include, every tenth person with a drink at a food court where various types of pops are served.

d) Ask any type of question that would give you biased results. An example could be: I think Coke is the best type of pop. Do you agree with me, or do you like something else? What? Here, someone is more likely to list Coke as their favourite drink because they are just going to agree with you.

or

Ask people who are drinking cola what type of pop they prefer.

7. They are biased because almost every farmer has a truck. To fix it, randomly ask people who own a vehicle, not specifically city people or farmers.

8. Parents are looking for certain qualities in a restaurant: atmosphere, price, quality of food. Kids would be interested in other aspects: entertainment, quick service, "kid-friendly" food.

9. **a)** This is stating an opinion: that they should all go to jail. You would have to change it to ask something about what do you think is a fair punishment for stealing?

   b) This is stating an opinion: that newscasts are boring and sitcoms are funny. An unbiased question would be just asking what type of TV program do you like to watch?

Lesson 2—Survey Results

PRACTICE EXERCISE
Answers and Solutions

1.

Types of Flowers in a Garden

	Flower	Tally	Frequency	Fraction	Percent
a)	Rose	⊞⊞ IIII	9	$\frac{9}{50}$	18%
b)	Petunia	⊞⊞ II ⊞⊞	12	$\frac{12}{50}$	24%
c)	Tulip	⊞⊞ III	8	$\frac{8}{50}$	16%
d)	Marigold	⊞⊞ ⊞⊞ ⊞⊞ IIII	19	$\frac{19}{50}$	38%
e)	Other	II	2	$\frac{2}{50}$	4%

Fill in the chart by using 50 as the total number of flowers.

Looking at the fraction for marigolds, you know that the survey is out of 50 because the denominator is 50.

Roses take up 9 so fill in the tally column, the fraction with 9 out of 50, and convert the fraction to a percentage.

To calculate the petunia row, count up the tally marks to give a frequency of 12. Write this as a fraction out of 50 and find the percentage.

16% are tulips. To find the fraction, put the percentage over 100 and reduce to something over 50 because that is what the survey is out of. $\frac{16}{100} = \frac{8}{50}$ This tells you the frequency is 8, then draw the tally.

The numerator for the fraction for marigolds tells you that the frequency is 19. Write the tally, and then convert the fraction to a percentage.

To calculate the other row, count up the tally marks to give a frequency of 2. Write this as a fraction out of 50 and find the percent.

2. a) marigolds

   Find category with the highest frequency, which is marigolds

   b) 10

   19 marigolds – 9 roses = 10 more

   c) 8% less

   24% petunias – 16% tulips = 8% less

3. **a)** Add up the numbers for each food to find the total for the table.

Total = 19 + 12 + 9 + 6 + 4 = 50

Favourite Breakfast Foods				
Food	Tally	Frequency	Fraction	Percent
Eggs	HHH HHH HHH IIII	19	$\dfrac{19}{50}$	38%
Bacon	HHH II HHH	12	$\dfrac{12}{50}$	24%
Hash browns	HHH IIII	9	$\dfrac{9}{50}$	18%
Toast	HHH I	6	$\dfrac{6}{50}$	12%
Cereal	IIII	4	$\dfrac{4}{50}$	8%

b) 31

Add bacon 12 + eggs 19 = 31

c) 10%

18% hash browns – 8% cereal = 10% more

d) Tally for eggs – tally for toast = difference

HHH HHH HHH IIII – HHH I =
HHH HHH III
= 13

e) 7

Calculate 24% of 30 = 0.24 × 30 = 7.2 or about 7 people

f) 12 boxes

Calculate 8% of 850 = 0.08 × 850 = 68

68 ÷ 6 because that is how many people each box can serve.

68 ÷ 6 = 11.3 → Therefore, 12 boxes of cereal will be needed.

4. **a)** Add up the numbers for each day to find the total for the table.

Total = 1 + 3 + 3 + 5 + 7 + 12 + 9 = 40

Use the frequency of each part to fill in the tally section. For the fraction, put the frequency (the given number) over 40. Use the fraction to find the percentage. (numerator divided by denominator times 100).

Days of the Week				
Day	Tally	Frequency	Fraction	Percent
Mon	I	1	$\dfrac{1}{40}$	2.5%
Tues	III	3	$\dfrac{3}{40}$	7.5%
Wed	III	3	$\dfrac{3}{40}$	7.5%
Thurs	HHH	5	$\dfrac{5}{40}$	12.5%
Fri	HHH II	7	$\dfrac{7}{40}$	17.5%
Sat	HHH HHH II	12	$\dfrac{12}{40}$	30%
Sun	HHH IIII	9	$\dfrac{9}{40}$	22.5%

b) Saturday and Sunday

Look for the days with the highest frequency. They are Saturday and Sunday. These are probably the highest because they are the weekends and lots of people do not have to work.

c) 76

Add to see how many people like a week day = 2.5% + 7.5% + 7.5% + 12.5% + 17.5% = 47.5%

Calculate 47.5% of 160 because 47.5% of the people like weekdays = 0.475 × 160 = 76 people

d) 10 500

Calculate 17.5 % of 60 000 because 17.5% of the people like
Fridays = $0.175 \times 60\ 000 = 10\ 500$ people

e) Answers may vary.

Here, you need a question where the most common answers would be Saturday and Sunday. There are many possible questions you could write. One could be "on which day of the week do you get the most sleep?"

Lesson 3—Graphing

PRACTICE EXERCISE
Answers and Solutions

1. a) Bar graph

Here, a bar graph would be best because it is a comparison of numbers of people's favourite colours.

b) Circle graph

Here, a circle graph would be best because the information is given in percentages.

c) Pictograph

This is looking for approximate numbers, so a pictograph is best because it shows pictures in an approximation.

d) Bar graph

A bar graph because you are comparing the amount of precipitation in different cities with each other.

e) Line graph

This is best with a line graph because it shows sleep needed over time, which is a trend during a person's lifespan.

2. a) This graph is showing a team's win/loss record. You can tell this by the title that describes the graph.

b) 94°

Central angle is degrees of the section. Calculate this by using the percentage of 360 that is being used.

26% of 360 = $0.26 \times 360 = 93.6 \rightarrow$ rounds to 94° for the angle

c) 2

Since the team tie 8% of its games, calculate 8% of the 25 games for the number of ties.
$0.08 \times 25 = 2$ games

3. a) Winter

To see which has the most snow, look at the graph and see which point is the highest: winter.

b) 15 cm more

28 cm in fall – 13 cm in spring = 15 cm more in fall

c) 93 cm

$55 + 12 + 0 + 26 = 98$ cm

4. a) 45 schools

Here, each picture represents 10 actual schools. Since there are 4 and a half pictures, that is 45 schools.

b) Pictographs give you an approximation, so you just round the 32 schools to 30 and draw three pictures.

c) 130

Count all the schools. There are 12 full schools and 2 halves, which equal 13 full schools. Since each picture represents 10, there are 130 schools in total.

5. a) Bar graph

Use a bar graph because the information is given in the number of people who answered each choice in the survey and you can compare between each column.

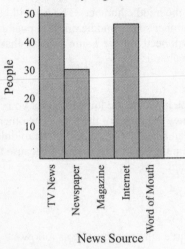

Where you get your news

b) Circle graph

Use a circle graph because the information is given as a percentage

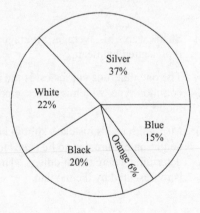

What Colour is your Car

c) Line graph

Use a line graph because the information is given over five years. A line graph is used for anything that shows trends over a certain period of time.

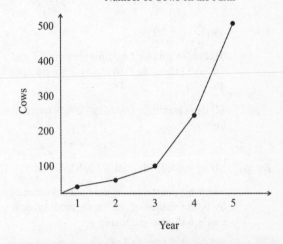

Number of Cows on the Farm

Lesson 4—Data Sets

PRACTICE EXERCISE
Answers and Solutions

1. a) Mean = 4.125, Medium = 3.5, Mode = 3

Put all the numbers in order first, and then calculate. 2, 3, 3, 3, 4, 5, 6, 7

Mean = add all the numbers and divide by the total.
$2 + 3 + 3 + 3 + 4 + 5 + 6 + 7 = 33$
$33 ÷ 8 = 4.125$

Median = there are two numbers in the middle: 3 and 4. Add up and divide by 2.
$3 + 4 = 7.$ $7 ÷ 2 = 3.5$

Mode = number that occurs most often is 3

b) Mean = 19.1, Median = 18, Mode = 12, 18

Put all the numbers in order first, and then calculate. 12, 12, 17, 18, 18, 21, 23, 24, 27

Mean = add all the numbers and divide by the total.
$12 + 12 + 17 + 18 + 18 + 21 + 23 + 24 + 27$
$= 172$
$172 ÷ 9 = 19.\overline{1}$

Median = middle number is 18

Mode = 12, 18 (both these numbers occur the same number of times)

c) Mean = 8, Median = 48.5, Mode = no mode

Put all the numbers in order first, and then calculate.
30, 32, 35, 44, 47, 50, 51, 56, 62, 73

Mean = add and divide by the total.
$30 + 32 + 35 + 44 + 47 + 50 + 51 + 56 + 62 + 73 = 480$
$480 \div 10 = 48$

Median = middle two numbers are 47 and 50. Add them and divide by 2 for median.
$47 + 50 = 97 \div 2 = 48.5$

Mode = no mode (nothing occurs more than once)

2. a) Mean = 14.2, Median = 12, Mode = 10

Since all the values in the data set increase by 6, the values of the mean, median, and mode will also increase by 6.

Mean: $8.2 + 6 = 14.2$

Median: $6 + 6 = 12$

Mode: $4 + 6 = 10$

b) Mean = 4.1, Median = 3, Mode = 2

Since all the values in the data set are divided by 2, the values of the mean, median, and mode will also be divided by 2.

Mean: $8.2 \div 2 = 4.1$

Median: $6 \div 2 = 3$

Mode: $4 \div 2 = 2$

c) Mean = 24.2, Median = 18, Mode = 12

Since all the values in the data set are multiplied by 3, the values of the mean, median, and mode will also be multiplied by 3.

Mean: $8.2 \times 3 = 24.2$

Median: $6 \times 3 = 18$

Mode: $4 \times 3 = 12$

3. Answers may vary.

The mode is the most common number. List any 5 numbers where 3 occurs most often.

e g., 3 3 3 3 3
1 2 3 3 4

4. Mean is the average: the sum of the numbers divided by the total. With there being 6 numbers, the sum will have to be 72 because $6 \times 12 = 72$ and dividing will give you a mean of 12.

5. Median is the middle number. The list will have an even number so the middle ones (in positions 4 and 5) will need to have a sum of 70 so that the average of them is 35.

6. Because the high and the low are given, you already know the range of the data. The other 4 numbers can be anything as long as the middle (the fourth number) has a value of 4 because that is the median.

e g., 1 _ _ 4 _ _ 18

7. The first three numbers must be as follows: 3, 3, 5 ___, ___. This is because for there to be a mode of 3 and a median of 5, the 5 has to be the middle number, and there must be more than one 3. There are a variety of different numbers that the last two can be, so long as their sum is 19 to give a total sum of 30 for the data set, and hence a mean of 6.

8. a) Shane wants his average. Average is represented by mean.

b) The one that runs out fastest is the most common type, which is represented by the mode.

c) Mr. Smith needs his class split in half by height on picture day so he needs to determine where the middle is. The middle is represented by the median.

9. a) Mean = 17.6, Median = 17, Mode = 17

To calculate the measures of central tendency, put all the numbers in order first, and then calculate. 10, 13, 17, 17, 18, 22, 26

Mean = average. Add all the numbers and divide by the total.
$10 + 13 + 17 + 17 + 18 + 22 + 26 = 123$

$123 \div 7 = 17.\overline{571428}$

Median = find the middle number. Because there is an odd number of numbers, the median is 17

Mode = number that occurs most often is 17

b) If 3 more 18s were added, the new set would be 10, 13, 17, 17, 18, 18, 18, 18, 22, 26. Here, the mode would change because there are now more 18s than 17s.

c) If 56 was added to the end, the new set would be 10, 13, 17, 17, 18, 22, 26, 56. This would change the mean the most because the sum would increase from 123 to 179. Therefore, the mean would go up by 4.8, from $17.\overline{571428}$ to 22.375.

Lesson 5—Stem-and-Leaf Plots and Box-and-Whisker Plots

PRACTICE EXERCISE
Answers and Solutions

1. a) Determine the smallest and largest numbers from the data set.

Smallest number = 30
Largest number = 64

Stem goes from 3 to 6 because the smallest number is 30 and the highest is 64. The stem represents all the digits but the last one. The digits from the ones place are filled in on the leaf part. Make sure that all the digits in the leaf are in ascending order.

Stem	Leaf
3	0, 2, 5, 7, 7, 7
4	4, 9
5	2, 5, 7
6	4

b) Determine the smallest and largest number from the data set.

Smallest number = 443

Largest number = 473

Stem goes from 44 to 47 because the smallest number is 443 and the highest is 473. The stem represents all the digits but the last one, and the digits from the ones place are filled in on the leaf part. Make sure that all the digits in the leaf are in ascending order.

Stem	Leaf
44	3,4,6
45	0,7
46	2,6,9
47	1,2,3

2. Put together the stem for the digits in the hundreds and tens place. Then look at the leaf and the value of the ones place. Put them together for each number. The boxed ones are 790, 806, 825, 832

3. Put together the stem for the digits in the hundreds and tens place. Then look at the leaf and the value of the ones place. Put them together for each number. The data set is 790, 792, 793, 801, 806, 806, 807, 823, 824, 825, 832, 832, 835, 838, 839

4. a) To make a box-and-whisker plot, find the five-number summary.

Lowest value – 10
Highest value – 22

Median – the middle number is 18

Lower quartile – the median of the numbers below 18. Using 10, 10, 14, 16, 16, you find that the median is 14.

Upper quartile – the median of the numbers above 18. Using 18, 19, 20, 20, 22, you find that the middle number is 20.

Draw a number line, plot the points above the line, then draw the whiskers and the box.

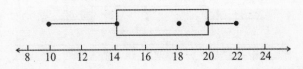

b) With this set of data, the first thing you need to do is put the numbers in ascending order. You will get the following. 4, 16, 18, 19, 20, 23, 25, 26, 26, 26, 31, 31,

To make a box-and-whisker plot, find the 5 number summary

Lowest value – 4

Highest value – 31

Median – the middle number is
$$\frac{23+25}{2}=24$$

Lower quartile – the median of the numbers below 24. Using 4, 16, 18, 19, 20, 23, you find that the median is 18.5.

Upper quartile – the median of the numbers above 24. Using 25, 26, 26, 31, 31, you find that the middle number is 26.

Draw a number line, plot the points above the line, then draw the whiskers and the box.

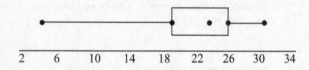

| 2 | 6 | 10 | 14 | 18 | 22 | 26 | 30 | 34 |

c) To make a box-and-whisker plot from the stem-and-leaf plot, write out the set of data in ascending order.

33, 38, 39, 42, 42, 46, 47, 53, 55, 58, 61, 62, 64, 70, 70, 72

Lowest value – 33

Highest value – 72

Median – is the middle number. Since there is an even set of numbers, take the middle two, add, and divide by two.
53 + 55 = 104 ÷ 2 = 54

Lower quartile – median of the numbers below 54. Use 33, 38, 39, 42, 42, 46, 47, 53. Lower quartile is 42.

Upper quartile – median of the numbers above 54. Use 55, 58, 61, 62, 64, 70, 70, 72. Upper quartile is 63.

Draw a number line, plot the points above the line, then draw the whiskers and the box

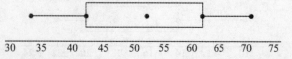

| 30 | 35 | 40 | 45 | 50 | 55 | 60 | 65 | 70 | 75 |

5. a) Highest number = 514, Lowest number = 502

Look on plot and find points that correspond with the highest and lowest value. The high value is the upper point, which is 514, and the lowest value is the first point, which is 502.

b) 507

The median is shown with the middle dot. That is at 507.

c) 75%

Determine where 505 is on the number line. From there, look at the portion of the box-and-whisker plot that is above. What you see is that there is the complete box, which represents 50% of the data, and a whisker, which represents 25% of the data. So 75% (50 + 25) of the data are above 505.

d) 65%

Find the numbers 504 and 512. You see that there is the complete box in between them (50%) and you would estimate that there is another 7% or 8% on each side. The approximate amount in between is 50 + 7 + 8 = 65%

6. a) 13

Upper quartile starts at the 4th dot (104), and the lower quartile ends at the 2nd dot (91). Subtract to find the difference. 104 – 91 = 13

b) By including 125 in the data set the highest value would change from 107 to 125. This would make the second whisker become much longer.

c) In a box-and-whisker plot, the middle number is the median. It is the centre of the set of data, but if the data are not evenly distributed, it will not necessarily be in the middle of the box. There may be a larger range of numbers on either side of the median.

d) 86

If the lowest value is 62 and the range is 24, add them together to find the highest mark. 62 + 24 = 86

418

Practice Quiz 1

Answers and Solutions

1. a)

Chore	Tally	Frequency	Fraction	Percent
Favourite Household Chore				
Vacuuming	⊮⊮ IIII	9	$\frac{9}{50}$	18%
Laundry	⊮⊮ II ⊮⊮	12	$\frac{12}{50}$	24%
Washing Dishes	⊮⊮ ⊮⊮ ⊮⊮	15	$\frac{15}{50}$	30%
Garbage	⊮⊮ I	6	$\frac{6}{50}$	12%
Dusting	⊮⊮ III	8	$\frac{8}{50}$	16%

Make a chart based on a sample of 50 people. Add up the frequency for each chore. $(9 + 12 + 15 + 6 + 8 = 50)$

Fill in the frequency column first based on the given numbers.

Draw the tally for each frequency.

Make the fraction with the frequency over the total, which is 50.

Calculate the percentage by dividing the numerator by the denominator or by doubling the numerator and denominator to obtain a fractio out of 100.

b) Base the bar graph on the frequency column.

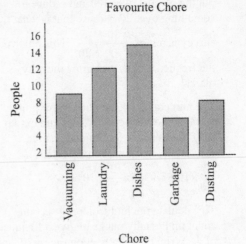

Favourite Chore

c) Pick a picture to represent the people who like each chore, and draw the graph.

People's Favourite Chore					
Chore					
Vacuuming	☺	☺	☺		
Laundry	☺	☺	☺	☺	
Dishes	☺	☺	☺	☺	☺
Garbage	☺	☺			
Dusting	☺	☺	☺		

Each ☺ = 2 people

2. a) Fill in the chart based on a sample of 20 people because looking at the fraction for pink, you know that the survey is out of 20 people.

The freguency of blue is 3 so fill in 3 tally marks. The fraction will be 3 out of 20, and convert the fraction to a percentage.

$$3 \times 5 = \underline{15}$$
$$20 \times 5 = 100$$

or

$$\frac{3}{20} \times 100$$

To calculate the white section, count up the tally marks to give a frequency of 5. Write this as a fraction out of 20, and find the percentage.

$$\frac{5}{20} \times 100 = \quad \text{or} \quad 5 \times \frac{5}{20} = \frac{25}{100}$$

30% use a green towel. To find the fraction, put the percent over 100 and reduce to something over 20 because that is what the survey is out of. $\dfrac{30}{100} = \dfrac{6}{20}$ This tells you the frequency is 6, then draw the tally marks.

The numerator for the fraction for pink tells you that the frequency is 2. Write in two tally marks and 2 for frequency, then convert the fraction to a percentage.

$\dfrac{2}{20} \times 100$ or $5 \times \dfrac{2}{20} = 10\%$

To calculate the multicoloured section, count up the tally marks to give a frequency of 4. Write this as a fraction out of 20, and find the percentage.

$\dfrac{4}{20}$; $\dfrac{4}{20} \times 100$ or $5 \times \dfrac{4}{20} = 20\%$

Colour of Towel Used				
Colour	**Tally**	**Frequency**	**Fraction**	**Percent**
White	⊞⊞⊞	5	$\dfrac{5}{20}$	25%
Blue	|||	3	$\dfrac{3}{15}$	15%
Green	⊞⊞⊞	6	$\dfrac{6}{20}$	30%
Pink	||	2	$\dfrac{2}{20}$	10%
Mulicoloured	||||	4	$\dfrac{4}{20}$	20%

b) 1 person

Pink = 10%. Calculate 10% of 10
$= 0.1 \times 10 = 1$ person

c) 21 people

Green = 30%. Calculate 30% of 70
$= 0.3 \times 70 = 21$ people

d) 140 people

Blue and white = 15 + 25 = 40%
Calculate 40% of 350 = 0.4 × 350 = 140 people

3. a) Since all the choices seem to be about skiing, a good question would be: What type of skiing do you prefer?

b) 32°

Water = 9%. Find 9% of 360
$= 0.09 \times 360 = 32.4° \rightarrow 32°$

c) 10

Do not ski = 13%. Calculate 13% of 75 = $0.13 \times 75 = 9.75 =$ about 10 people

4. This is not a fair survey because the people are more likely to be thinking about the movie they just saw and not thinking about all movies they have ever seen when deciding on their favourite one.

5. a) Something random could be every 10th person entering the cafeteria, because if the surevy asked every 10th student in the school, the results would be biased because some students do not eat in the cafeteria.

b) A verbal interview of students in the cafeteria would be the easiest because they are already in the cafeteria and you could get the information right away. They may not take time to answer a questionnaire.

c) The people who want to change the menu, (staff of the cafeteria and students).

d) See what the cost is, and adjust so the cafeteria makes a small profit.

6. a) Approximately 132 beats per minute

Look for the highest point on the graph, which that is the peak heart rate. It is at 130 – 132 beats per minute.

b) Here, the graph levels out, which means that the heart rate is constant.

c) The person started exercising from rest and at the end of 20 min, the rate is still dropping, but not back to the same rate that it was at before exercise.

d) Because it is continuous information over a certain period of time.

7. Mean = 54.54, Median = 56, Mode = 47.58

Numbers are already in order so just calculate. Add them to find that the sum is 600.

Mean = is average. Total sum divided by amount of numbers = $600 \div 11 = 54.\overline{54}$
Median = is middle number = 56
Mode = 47, 58 because they both occur twice.

8. a) Mean = 50.9, Median = 50, Mode = 50

Put numbers in order, then calculate

35, 40, 45, 45, 50, 50, 50, 55, 60, 65, 65.
Sum = 560

b) Mean = 10.2, Median = 10, Mode = 10

Divide the values in previous question by 5 because the values of each set of data is divided by 5.
Mean = $50.9 \div 5 = 10.\overline{18}$,
Median = $50 \div 5 = 10$,
Mode = $50 \div 5 = 10$

9. a) Mean = 61, Median = 63, Mode = 67

Add 7 to each value because each data point was increased by 7.
Mean = 54 + 7 = 61,
Median = 56 + 7 = 63
Mode = 60 + 7 = 67

b) Mean = 13.5, Median = 14, Mode = 15

Divide each value by 4 for the new mean, median and mode.
Mean = $54 \div 4 = 13.5$
Median = $56 \div 4 = 14$
Mode = $60 \div 4 = 15$

10. a) Since the mean has to be 30, you need any 5 numbers with a sum of 150 because $30 \times 5 = 150$.

b) Any 6 numbers where 120 is the most common.

c) Any 8 numbers where the middle two have a sum of 41 so they can be added up and divided by 2 to give a median of 20.5

d) Any 7 numbers with the middle one being 12 and 8 being the most common.

11. The Numbers are already in ascending order. Smallest value is 123, and the largest value is 157. The stem goes from 12 to 15. Fill in the leaf part.

Stem	Leaf
12	3, 6
13	5, 9
14	0, 2, 2
15	3, 7

Find the five-number summary.

Lowest value – 123

Highest value – 157

Median – 140 (the middle number)

Lower quartile – 130.5 The median of 123, 126, 135, 139

Upper quartile – 147.5

Plot the points, and make the box-and-whisker plot.

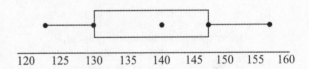

12. To make a box-and-whisker plot from the stem-and-leaf plot, write out the set of data in ascending order.

132, 132, 133, 135, 140, 141, 147, 152, 159, 161, 168, 177, 178, 178

Lowest value – 132

Highest value – 178

Median – the middle number. Since there is an even set of numbers, take the middle two, add and divide by two. $147 + 152 = 229 \div 2 = 149.5$

Lower quartile – median of the numbers below 149.5. Use 132, 132, 133, 135, 140, 141, 147. Lower quartile is 135.

Upper quartile – median of the numbers above 149.5. Use 152, 159, 161, 168, 177, 178, 178. Upper quartile is 168.

Draw a number line, plot the points above the line, and then draw the whiskers and the box.

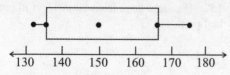

a) 132 and 149.5

The numbers between the lowest value and the median, which are 132 and 149.5, represent the lower half of the data.

b) 33

The upper quartile starts at 168, and the lower quartile ends at 135. Subtract to find range. $168 - 135 = 33$

c) 35%

Between 140 and 160 there is just over half the box (which represents 50%) so the percentage is about 35%.

13. a) 55 %

40 is just a little bit above the median, which is half the data, so it is approximately 55%

b) 46

Upper quartile is the fourth point at 46.

c) 24

Highest value – lowest value = $50 - 26 = 24$

Lesson 6—Probability

PRACTICE EXERCISE
Answers and Solutions

1. a) On a standard die, there are 6 possibilities. They are 1 to 6, and they are all equally likely.

b) Flipping a coin has two possibilities, H or T, that are equally likely.

c) There is not an even number of each colour of marble, so the outcomes are not equally likely – blue is most likely because there are more of them.

d) The outcomes are not equally likely: gray is most likely because one-half of the spinner is gray but only one-quarter is white and one-quarter is black.

2. a) Flip a coin with heads representing true and tails representing false or vice versa. The outcomes are equally likely and would represent guessing at a question.

b) Let the 1 on the die represent the candidate winning. Let the 2, 3, 4, 5, 6 represent the candidate losing.
Calculate the probabilities of each number to see the candidates chance of winning or losing.

$P(1) = \dfrac{1}{6}$ chance of winning

$P(2, 3, 4, 5, 6) = \dfrac{5}{6}$ chance of losing.

3. a) There is one 2 on a regular die and 6 possible numbers. Set up the fraction with P $(2) = \dfrac{1}{6}$

b) Even numbers are 2, 4, 6, so there are 3 favourable outcomes, and 6 possible outcomes. Set up the fraction and reduce.

$P \text{ (even number)} = \dfrac{3}{6} = \dfrac{1}{2}$

c) 1, 2, 3, 4, are less than 5. There are 4 favourable outcomes, and 6 total outcomes. Set up fraction and reduce.

$P \text{ (a number less than 5)} = \dfrac{4}{6} = \dfrac{2}{3}$

d) There is no number 8 on a regular die. Set up the fraction with 0 being the favourable outcome. There are 6 possible outcomes.

$P \text{ (8)} = \dfrac{0}{6} = 0$

e) 1, 2, 4, 5, 6 are not 3. There are 5 favourable outcomes, and 6 total outcomes.

$P \text{ (not a three)} = \dfrac{5}{6}$

f) Four 7s in a deck of cards. There are 4 favourable outcomes and 52 total outcomes. Set up fraction and reduce.

$P \text{ (7)} = \dfrac{4}{52} = \dfrac{1}{13}$

g) 12 face cards in a deck. There are 12 favourable outcomes and 52 total outcomes. Set up fraction and reduce.

$$P \text{ (face card)} = \frac{12}{52} = \frac{3}{13}$$

h) The numbers found in a deck of cards include 2, 3, 4, 5, 6, 7, 8, 9, 10 of each suit. (there are 4 different suits) . So there are 36 favourable outcomes and 52 total outcomes. Set up fraction and reduce.

$$P \text{ (a number)} = \frac{36}{52} = \frac{9}{13}$$

i) Half the cards in a regular deck are black. There are 26 favourable outcomes and 52 total outcomes. Set up fraction and reduce.

$$P \text{ (black)} = \frac{26}{52} = \frac{1}{2}$$

4. a) There are 2 Ms in the word *mathematics*. There are 2 favourable outcomes and 11 total outcomes. Set up fraction.

$$P \text{ (M)} = \frac{2}{11}$$

b) There are 4 vowels in the word *mathematics*. There are 4 favourable outcomes and 11 total outcomes. Set up fraction and reduce.

$$P \text{ (vowel)} = \frac{4}{11}$$

c) There are 7 consonants in the word *mathematics*. There are 7 favourable outcomes and 11 total outcomes. Set up fraction and reduce.

$$P \text{ (consonant)} = \frac{7}{11}$$

d) There are 4 letters that are M or T in the word *mathematics*. There are 4 favourable outcomes and 11 total outcomes. Set up fraction and reduce.

$$P \text{ (M or T)} = \frac{4}{11}$$

5. The spinner will need to have 4 parts because you have two parts that are broken down into quarters and the half can be represented by two quarters. Make a spinner and divide is up as follows. You will need two parts black, one part gray, and one part that is white.

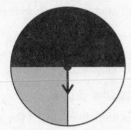

6. a) There are 4 odd numbers on the spinner: 1, 3, 5, and 7. There are 4 favourable outcomes and 8 total outcomes. Set up fraction, reduce, then calculate the percentage.

$$P \text{ (odd number)} = \frac{4}{8} = \frac{1}{2} = 50\%$$

b) There is one 4 on the spinner. There is 1 favourable outcome and 8 total outcomes. Set up fraction, reduce, then calculate the percentage.

$$P \text{ (4)} = \frac{1}{8} = 12.5\%$$

c) The numbers greater than 2 are 3, 4, 5, 6, 7, and 8. There are 6 favourable outcomes and 8 total outcomes. Set up fraction, reduce, then calculate the percentage.

$$P \text{ (more than 2)} = \frac{6}{8} = \frac{3}{4} = 75\%$$

d) 1, 2, 4, 5, 6, 7, 8 are not 3. There are 7 favourable outcomes and 8 total outcomes. Set up fraction, reduce, then calculate the percentage.

$$P \text{ (not 3)} = \frac{7}{8} = 87.5\%$$

7. There are 7 days of the week, 1 is a Monday. Probability that February 21 will be a Monday is the 1 Monday out of 7 total days in the week. Set up fraction and reduce if possible.

$$P \text{ (Monday)} = \frac{1}{7}$$

8. *P* (favourable outcome) = 0 means that outcome will never occur.

9. 16.7 %

Man's likelihood is $\frac{5}{12}$ because there are 5 men out of 12 people.

Woman's likelihood is $\frac{7}{12}$ because there are 7 women out of the 12 people

A woman is more likely to get the job by $\frac{2}{12} = \frac{1}{6} = 16.7\%$ because there are (7 – 5 =) 2 more women than men.

Lesson 7—Independent Events

PRACTICE EXERCISE
Answers and Solutions

1. **a)**

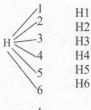
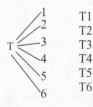

Tree diagram:

H — 1, 2, 3, 4, 5, 6 → H1, H2, H3, H4, H5, H6

T — 1, 2, 3, 4, 5, 6 → T1, T2, T3, T4, T5, T6

b)

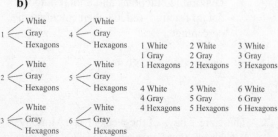

1 White	2 White	3 White
1 Gray	2 Gray	3 Gray
1 Hexagons	2 Hexagons	3 Hexagons
4 White	5 White	6 White
4 Gray	5 Gray	6 Gray
4 Hexagons	5 Hexagons	6 Hexagons

c)

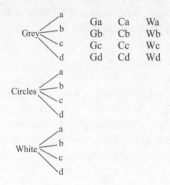

Grey — a, b, c, d : Ga, Ca, Wa / Gb, Cb, Wb / Gc, Cc, Wc / Gd, Cd, Wd

Circles — a, b, c, d

White — a, b, c, d

2. a) Using the spinner and the die $\frac{1}{3} \times \frac{1}{6} = 18$.

There are 18 probable outcomes. Possibility of getting a white and a 1 is 1 out of the 18. Write the fraction and reduce if possible.

P (White, 1) $= \frac{1}{18}$

b) You know that there are 18 probable outcomes. Possibility of getting a black and an even is 3: black and 2, 4, or 6. Write the fraction and reduce if possible.

P (Black, even number) $= \frac{3}{18} = \frac{1}{6}$

c) You know that there are 18 probable outcomes. Possibility of getting a gray and a number is 6 out of the 18: gray and 1, 2, 3, 4, 5, or 6. Write the fraction and reduce if possible.

P (Gray, a number) $= \frac{6}{18} = \frac{1}{3}$

d) You know that there are 18 probable outcomes. Possibility of getting a white or gray and a 2 or 6 is 4 out of the 18: white and 2 or 6 or gray and 2 or 6. Write the fraction and reduce if possible.

P (White or Gray, 2 or 6) $= \frac{4}{18} = \frac{2}{9}$

e) You know that there are 18 probable outcomes. Possibility of getting a colour and a number less than three is 6 out of the 18: any colour (white, black, or gray) and 1 or 2. Write the fraction and reduce if possible.

P (a colour, a number less than 3) $= \frac{6}{18} = \frac{1}{3}$

3. a) With the two spinners, there are 12 outcomes. Probability of a 1 and a 1 is 1 outcome out of the 12. Set up the fraction and reduce.

$$P(1, 1) = \frac{1}{12}$$

b) With the two spinners, there are 12 outcomes. Probability of a 1 and a 4 is 1 outcome out of the 12. Set up the fraction and reduce.

$$P(1, 4) = \frac{1}{12}$$

c) With the two spinners, there are 12 outcomes. Probability of a 3 and an odd is 2 outcomes out of the 12: (3, 1 or 3, 3). Set up the fraction and reduce.

$$P(3, \text{odd}) = \frac{2}{12} = \frac{1}{6}$$

d) For a sum of 6, both numbers must add up to 6. Possible combinations are 4, 2 and 3, 3. There are 2 possibilities out of 12. Set up the fraction and reduce.

$$P(\text{sum of 6}) = \frac{2}{12} = \frac{1}{6}$$

e) Combinations for a sum of 4 are, 1,3 or 2,2 or 3,1. There are 3 possible outcomes out of 12. Set up the fraction and reduce.

$$P(\text{sum of 4}) = \frac{3}{12} = \frac{1}{4}$$

4. There are four possible outcomes for this situation: G,G G,B B,G and B,B..

a) Possibility of boy, boy is 1 in 4.

$$P(B, B) = \frac{1}{4} = 25\%$$

b) Possibility of a girl, boy is 1 in 4.

$$P(G, B) = \frac{1}{4} = 25\%$$

c) Possibility of at least 1 girl, is G,G G,B B,G, which is 3 in 4.

$$P(\text{at least 1 girl}) = \frac{3}{4} = 75\%$$

d) Only G, G has no boys, so possibility is 1 in 4 chance.

$$P(\text{no boys}) = \frac{1}{4} = 25\%$$

5. a) 11 quarters out of 20 coins, 6 loonies out of 20 coins

$$P(\text{quarter, loonie}) = \frac{11}{20} \times \frac{6}{20} = \frac{66}{400} = \frac{33}{200}$$

b) 6 loonies out of 20 coins, 3 toonies out of 20 coins

$$P(\text{loonie, toonie}) = \frac{6}{20} \times \frac{3}{20} = \frac{18}{400} = \frac{9}{200}$$

c) 3 toonies out of 20 coins, 11 quarters out of 20 coins

$$P(\text{toonie, quarter}) = \frac{3}{20} \times \frac{11}{20} = \frac{33}{400}$$

d) 11 quarters out of 20 coins, 11 quarters out of 20 coins

$$P(\text{quarter, quarter}) = \frac{11}{20} \times \frac{11}{20} = \frac{121}{400}$$

e) 9 loonies or toonies (11 + 2) out of 20 coins and 11 quarters out of 20 coins

$$P(\text{loonie or toonie, quarter}) = \frac{9}{20} \times \frac{11}{20} = \frac{99}{400}$$

6. a) H is 1 out of 2, red is 26 out of 52

$$P(H, \text{red}) = \frac{1}{2} \times \frac{26}{52} = \frac{26}{104} = \frac{1}{4}$$

b) T is 1 out of 2, face card is jack, queen, or king in 4 different suits = 12 face cards out of 52

$$P(T, \text{face card}) = \frac{1}{2} \times \frac{12}{52} = \frac{12}{104} = \frac{3}{26}$$

c) T is 1 out of 2, 4 aces in a deck out of 52

$$P(T, \text{ace}) = \frac{1}{2} \times \frac{4}{52} = \frac{4}{104} = \frac{1}{26}$$

d) H is 1 out of 2, a number is 2, 3, 4, 5, 6, 7, 8, 9, 10 in each suit is 36 numbers out of 52

$$P(H, \text{a number}) = \frac{1}{2} \times \frac{36}{52} = \frac{36}{104} = \frac{9}{26}$$

e) T is 1 out of 2, four 6s in a deck out of 52

$$P(T, 6) = \frac{1}{2} \times \frac{4}{52} = \frac{4}{104} = \frac{1}{26}$$

f) H or T is guaranteed so 1 out of 1. There are four 7s in a deck out of 52

$$P(H \text{ or } T, 7) = \frac{1}{1} \times \frac{4}{52} = \frac{4}{52} = \frac{1}{13}$$

7. Rolling 2 dice gives 36 possible outcomes (6×6)

Meredith's possibilities for 11 are: 5, 6 or 6, 5

Her probability is $\frac{2}{36} = \frac{1}{18} = 5.6\%$

Cathy's possibilities for 6 are: 1,5 or 2,4 or 3,3 or 4,2 or 5,1

Her probability is $\frac{5}{36} = 13.8\%$

$13.8 - 5.6 = 8.2\%$

Cathy has a better chance of winning by just over 8%.

Practice Quiz 2

Answers and Solutions

1. a) On a coin the possibilities are heads or tails; both equally likely

b) The outcomes for rolling a die with sides 1, 1, 2, 2, 3, 4 are not equally likely, 1 and 2 more common than 3 and 4

c) The outcomes on the spinner are not equally likely. Stars is more likely because it is larger than the others

d) In a regular deck of cards, all the outcomes for drawing a random card are equally likely

e) A pocket of coins with 8 dimes, 6 quarters, and 4 pennies does not have equally likely outcomes because there are more dimes than others.

2. a) Roll a die where each number represents a different contestant. The number that comes up represents the winner.

b) Make a spinner with 8 sections where each section represents a different company. Spin and see which is being represented.

c) Flip a coin where heads is one possibility, and tails is the other.

3. a) 2 white, 6 total. Set up fraction and reduce.

$$P(\text{white}) = \frac{2}{6} = \frac{1}{3}$$

b) 3 shaded, 6 total. Set up fraction and reduce.

$$P(\text{shaded}) = \frac{3}{6} = \frac{1}{2}$$

c) 1 stars, 6 total. Set up fraction and reduce.

$$P(\text{any design}) = \frac{1}{6}$$

d) 5 not stars, 6 total. Set up fraction and reduce.

$$P(\text{not stars}) = \frac{5}{6}$$

e) 4 stars or shaded, 6 total. Set up fraction and reduce.

$$P(\text{stars or shaded}) = \frac{4}{6} = \frac{2}{3}$$

4. a) Four 3s in a regular deck (one from each suit), 52 total. Set up fraction and reduce.

$$P(3) = \frac{4}{52} = \frac{1}{13}$$

b) 12 face cards (J, Q, K from each suit), 52 total. Set up fraction and reduce.

$$P(\text{face card}) = \frac{12}{52} = \frac{3}{13}$$

c) 2, 3, 4, 5, 6, 7, 8, 9, 10 from each suit, 52 total. Set up fraction and reduce.

$$P(\text{a number}) = \frac{36}{52} = \frac{9}{13}$$

d) 2 black 4s (spades and clubs), 52 total. Set up fraction and reduce.

$$P(\text{a black 4}) = \frac{2}{52} = \frac{1}{26}$$

5. 240 white jelly beans

$$\frac{3\,\text{white}}{10\,\text{total}} = \frac{x}{800} = \text{cross-multiply to solve for}$$

$x = 3 \times 800 \div 10 = 240$ white jelly beans

6. 17 medium out of 47 total $(22 + 17 + 8 = 47)$
Write fraction then convert to a percentage.

$$P\,(\text{medium}) = \frac{17}{47} = 36\%$$

7. List the outcomes from one event with each outcome from the other event.

a)

H — W   HW
  — B   HB
  — G   HG

T — W   TW
  — B   TB
  — G   TG

b)

1 — P   4 — P   1P   4P
  — N   — N   1N   4N
  — D   — D   1D   4D

2 — P   5 — P   2P   5P
  — N   — N   2N   5N
  — D   — D   2D   5D

3 — P   6 — P   3P   6P
  — N   — N   3N   6N
  — D   — D   3D   6D

8. **a)** Multiply the total outcomes together.
Card = 52, Die = 6. $52 \times 6 = 312$ outcomes

b) A letter from the alphabet is selected (26) and a card is drawn from a deck (52).
$26 \times 52 = 1\,352$ outcomes

9. **a)** Gray is 2 out of 5, 6 is 1 out of 6 Multiply probabilities of each.

$$P\,(\text{gray, 6}) = \frac{2}{5} \times \frac{1}{6} = \frac{2}{30} = \frac{1}{15}$$

b) Brick is 2 out of 5, even is 3 out of 6
Multiply probabilities of each.

$$P\,(\text{brick, even}) = \frac{2}{5} \times \frac{3}{6} = \frac{6}{30} = \frac{1}{5}$$

c) Swirl is 1 out of 5, not a 4 is 5 out of 6.
Multiply probabilities of each.

$$P\,(\text{Swirl, not a 4}) = \frac{1}{5} \times \frac{5}{6} = \frac{5}{30} = \frac{1}{6}$$

d) Any marble is 5 out of 5, odd is 3 out of 6.
Multiply probabilities of each.

$$P\,(\text{marble, odd}) = \frac{5}{5} \times \frac{3}{6} = \frac{15}{30} = \frac{1}{2}$$

e) Gray or brick is 4 out of 5, 3 is 1 out of 6.
Multiply probabilities of each.

$$P\,(\text{gray or brick, 3}) = \frac{4}{5} \times \frac{1}{6} = \frac{4}{30} = \frac{2}{15}$$

f) Swirl is 2 out of 5, a number is 6 out of 6.
Multiply probabilities of each.

$$P\,(\text{swirl, a number}) = \frac{1}{5} \times \frac{6}{6} = \frac{6}{30} = \frac{1}{5}$$

10. a) H is 1 out of 2, penny is 2 out of 10 $(2 + 1 + 7)$ Multiply the probabilities of each.

$$P\,(\text{H, penny}) = \frac{1}{2} \times \frac{2}{10} = \frac{2}{20} = \frac{1}{10}$$

b) H is 1 out of 2, nickel is 1 out of 10 $(2 + 1 + 7)$ Multiply the probabilities of each.

$$P\,(\text{H, nickel}) = \frac{1}{2} \times \frac{1}{10} = \frac{1}{20}$$

c) T is 1 out of 2, not a quarter is 3 out of 10 $(2 + 1 + 7)$ Multiply the probabilities of each.

$$P\,(\text{T, not a quarter}) = \frac{1}{2} \times \frac{3}{10} = \frac{3}{20}$$

d) T is 1 out of 2, not a nickel is 9 out of 10 $(2 + 1 + 7)$ Multiply the probabilities of each.

$$P\,(\text{T, not a nickel}) = \frac{1}{2} \times \frac{9}{10} = \frac{9}{20}$$

e) H or T is 2 out of 2, quarter is 7 out of 10 (2 + 1 + 7) Multiply the probabilities of each.

$$P \text{ (H or T, quarter)} = \frac{2}{2} \times \frac{7}{10} = \frac{14}{20} = \frac{7}{10}$$

f) T is 1 out of 2, there are no loonies, so loonie is 0 out of 10 multiply the probabilities of each.

$$P \text{ (T, loonie)} = \frac{1}{2} \times \frac{0}{10} = \frac{0}{20} = 0$$

11. He has a 1 in 10 chance of picking each digit, so find the probability of each (1 out of 10) and multiply that together for the total probability.

$$P \text{ (winning)} = \frac{1}{10} \times \frac{1}{10} \times \frac{1}{10} = \frac{1}{1000}$$

Practice Test

Answers and Solutions

1. a)

Favourite Types of Shows on TV				
Type	Tally	Frequency	Fraction	Percent
News	HHH IIII	9	$\frac{9}{40}$	22.5%
Soap Operas	HHH I	6	$\frac{6}{40}$	15%
Sitcoms	HHH HHH	10	$\frac{10}{40}$	25%
Educational Programs	II	2	$\frac{2}{40}$	5%
Sports	HHH HHH III	13	$\frac{13}{40}$	32.5%

Fill in the chart based on working with 40 people.

According to the frequency, 9 people chose news. Use this number to fill in the tally part and the fraction with 9 out of 40 (22.5%). Convert the fraction to a percentage.

The percentage of people who chose soap operas was 15%. To find the fraction, put the percentage over 100 and reduce to something over 40 because that is what the survey is out of. $\frac{15}{100} = \frac{6}{40}$ This tells you that the frequency is 6. Finally, using the frequency, work the tallies.

The numerator for the fraction for sitcoms tells you that the frequency is 10. Mark in the tally (10 marks), and then convert the fraction to a percentage (25%).

To calculate the educational programs section, the tally marks show that there is a frequency of 2. Write this as a fraction out of 40 $\left(\frac{2}{40}\right)$ and find the percentage (5%).

The percentage of people who chose sport was 32.5%. To find the fraction, put the percentage over 100 and reduce to something over 40 because that is what the survey is out of. $\frac{23.5}{100} = \frac{13}{40}$ This tells you that the frequency is 13. Finally, using the frequency, mark the tallies.

b) 4 people

Soaps (6) minus educational programs (2) = 6 − 2 = 4 people

c) 10 %

32.5% of the people like sports minus 22% of the people who like the news. 32.5% − 22.5% = 10%

d) 125 people

Sitcoms = 25% Calculate 25% of 500 = 0.25 × 500 = 125 people

2. **a)** Make the graph with the choices across the bottom, and the percentage going up the side.

Where Does Your Money Go?

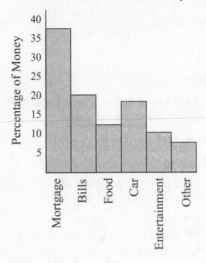

b) Bills = 20%, find 20% of 360 = 0.2 × 360 = 72°

c) 15% cars are cars. So, if each bill represents 10%, you need $1\frac{1}{2}$ bills.

3. **a)** This is biased because they are at a specific mall asking questions about any mall.

b) Not biased; the sample is random.

c) Biased because they are only asking lawyers about their fees.

4. **a)** Cookie Dough

b) Vanilla (30) – strawberry (15) = 30 – 15 = 15 people

5. **a)** Nothing in seen on the graph because there is no growth yet. The seed is not above the ground.

b) Day 5 = 0.5 cm, day 10 = 2 cm

Growth = 2 – 0.5 = 1.5 cm

6. **a)** Put numbers in order than add and divide by 8 for total scores. 58, 59, 62, 62, 63, 65, 67, 71

Mean: Sum ÷ total number = 507 ÷ 8 = 63.375

b) Median = 62 and 63, Mode = 62

median = middle number 62 and 63 are in the middle Add and divide by 2. 62 + 63 = 125 ÷ 2 = 62.5, mode = 62 (most often)

7. **a)** Numbers are already in order. Find the sum. 2 + 2 + 4 + 6 + 6 + 6 + 7 + 8 = 41 Mean = sum divided by total numbers = 41 ÷ 8 = 5.1, median = middle number = 6, mode = 5.125

b) Write the new set of data and find the measures of central tendency if all the values are decreased by 3.

Decrease the values of question 18 by 3.

–1, –1, 1, 3, 3, 3, 4, 5. Mean = – 1 + – 1 + 1 + 3 + 3 + 3 + 4 + 5 = 17 ÷ 8 = 2.125, median = 3, mode = 3.

8. Write any 5 numbers between 20 and 80 with 55 in the middle to give you the median.

9. **a)** Smallest value is 45, largest value is 76. The stem goes from 4 to 7. Fill in the leaf part with the digits in the ones place. Make sure the numbers in the leaf are in ascending order.

Stem	Leaf
4	5, 7, 9
5	0, 0, 5
6	
7	1, 3, 6

b) Find the five-number summary from 45, 47, 49, 50, 50, 55, 71, 73, 76

Lowest value – 45

Highest value – 76

Median – 50

Lower quartile – median of 45, 47, 49, 50 = 48

Upper quartile – median of 55, 71, 73, 76 = 72

Draw a number line, plot the points, and make the box-and-whisker plot.

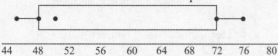

44   48   52   56   60   64   68   72   76   80

c) Almost a half of the box is between 55 and 70. Since the box represents 50%, you can estimate that 23% is represented.

d) The lower whisker would be much longer if 14 were added because it would drastically change the lower value of the set of data. The lower quartile would change from 48 to 46.

10. a) Randomly picking a letter of the word MISSISSIPPI out of a hat is not equally likely, S is most likely because there are more of them.

b) Not all sections are the same size. Shaded is most likely outcome because it is the largest section.

c) The outcomes for rolling a number are equally likely because each side is a different digit.

11. a) 1 B in 6 letters write as a fraction, then covert to a percentage. $P(B) = \dfrac{1}{6} = 16.\overline{6}\%$

b) 2 Ns in 6 letters write as a fraction, then covert to a percentage.

$P(N) = \dfrac{2}{6} = \dfrac{1}{3} = 33.\overline{3}\%$

c) 3 letters that are not A in 6 letters write as a fraction, then covert to a percentage.

$P(\text{not an A}) = \dfrac{3}{6} = \dfrac{1}{2} = 50\%$

d) 3 consonants (b, n, n) in 6 letters write as a fraction, then covert to a percentage.

$P(\text{consonant}) = \dfrac{3}{6} = \dfrac{1}{2} = 50\%$

e) 0 Ss in 6 letters write as a fraction, then covert to a percentage. $P(S) = \dfrac{0}{6} = 0\%$

12. 35 people out of the 150 in the office are allergic so $150 - 35 = 115$ people are not allergic. 115 out of 150 are not allergic. Write as a fraction then reduce.

$P(\text{not allergic}) = \dfrac{115}{150} = \dfrac{7}{30}$

13. Outcomes are H or T and 1, 2, 3, 4, 5 or 6

a) H is 1 out of 2, 3 is 1 out of 6 multiply the probabilities and then reduce.

$P(H, 3) = \dfrac{1}{2} \times \dfrac{1}{6} = \dfrac{1}{12}$

b) T is 1 out of 2, not 1 is 5 out of 6 multiply the probabilities and then reduce.

$P(T, \text{not } 1) = \dfrac{1}{2} \times \dfrac{5}{6} = \dfrac{5}{12}$

c) T is 1 out of 2, 9 is 0 out of 6 because there are no 9s. Multiply the probabilities and then reduce.

$P(T, 9) = \dfrac{1}{2} \times \dfrac{0}{6} = \dfrac{0}{12} = 0$

d) H is 1 out of 2, composite numbers (numbers that have factors) are 4 and 6; that is, 2 out of 6 multiply the probabilities and then reduce.

$P(H, \text{composite number}) = \dfrac{1}{2} \times \dfrac{2}{6} = \dfrac{2}{12} = \dfrac{1}{6}$

14. Outcomes are: 2 and 1, 2, 3, 4

4 and 1, 2, 3, 4

6 and 1, 2, 3, 4

a) 2 is 1 out of 3 and 3 is 1 out of 4 multiply the probabilities and then reduce.

$P(2, 3) = \dfrac{1}{3} \times \dfrac{1}{4} = \dfrac{1}{12}$

b) 1 is 0 out of 3 because there is no 1 on the spinner and 3 is 1 out of 4 multiply the probabilities and then reduce.

$P(1, 3) = \dfrac{0}{3} \times \dfrac{1}{4} = \dfrac{0}{12} = 0$

Nick Vandome

Laptops
for Seniors

7th edition
for all laptops with Windows 10

In easy steps is an imprint of In Easy Steps Limited
16 Hamilton Terrace · Holly Walk · Leamington Spa
Warwickshire · United Kingdom · CV32 4LY
www.ineasysteps.com

Seventh Edition

Notice of Liability
Every effort has been made to ensure that this book contains accurate
and current information. However, In Easy Steps Limited and the
author shall not be liable for any loss or damage suffered by readers
as a result of any information contained herein.

Trademarks
Microsoft® and Windows® are registered trademarks of Microsoft
Corporation. All other trademarks are acknowledged as belonging to
their respective companies.

In Easy Steps Limited supports The Forest Stewardship Council (FSC),
the leading international forest certification organization. All our titles
that are printed on Greenpeace approved FSC certified paper carry the
FSC logo.

MIX
Paper from
responsible sources
FSC® C020837

Printed and bound in the United Kingdom

ISBN 978-1-84078-842-6

Contents

1 Choosing a Laptop 7

A Brief History of Laptops 8
Laptops v. Desktops 10
Types of Laptops 11
Laptop Jargon Explained 12
Size and Weight 14
Getting Comfortable 15
Carrying a Laptop 18
Keyboard and Touch Pad 19
Using an External Mouse 20
Ports and Slots 21
The Wonder of Wireless 22
Cleaning a Laptop 23
Choosing a Carry Case 24
Spares and Accessories 25

2 Around a Laptop 27

Opening Up and Turning On 28
Touchscreen Laptops 29
About Windows 10 30
The Start Button 34
The Start Menu 36
Pinning Items 38
Using Live Tiles 39
Desktop, Taskbar and Task View 40
Shutting Down 43
Using a Microsoft Account 44
Personalization 46
Lock Screen Settings 48
Using Themes 50
Screen Resolution 52
Managing Storage 53
Adjusting Volume 54
Loading CDs and DVDs 55
USB Flashdrives 56

3 Getting Up and Running — 57

Sign-in Options — 58
Settings — 60
Searching — 62
Setting Up Cortana — 64
Using Cortana — 65
Viewing Notifications — 68
Dark Mode — 70
Snipping (Screenshots) — 71
Opening File Explorer — 72
Quick Access in File Explorer — 73
Scenic Ribbon — 75

4 Working with Apps — 77

Starting with Apps — 78
Windows 10 Apps — 80
Using Windows 10 Apps — 82
Closing Apps — 84
Viewing All Apps — 85
Searching for Apps — 86
Using the Microsoft Store — 87
Buying Apps — 89
Viewing Your Apps — 90
Installing and Uninstalling Apps — 91

5 The Online World — 93

Introducing the Edge Browser — 94
Smart Address Bar — 95
Setting a Homepage — 96
Using Tabs — 97
Bookmarking Web Pages — 100
Adding Notes to Web Pages — 101
Organizing with the Hub — 103
Reading List — 104

Reading View   105
Shopping Online   106
Booking a Vacation   108
Setting Up Mail   110
Working with Mail   112
Using OneDrive   114
OneDrive Settings   117
Finding People   118
Using the Calendar   120

6 A Digital Lifestyle — 123

Viewing Photos   124
Editing Photos   128
Groove Music App   130
Playing Music   131
Viewing Movies and TV   132
Books in Windows 10   133
Gaming with Windows 10   134

7 On Vacation — 135

Transporting Your Laptop   136
Keeping Your Laptop Safe   137
Temperature Extremes   138
Laptops at Sea   139
Power Sockets   140
Airport Security   141
Keeping in Touch   142

8 Sharing with Your Family — 143

About Multiple Users   144
Adding Users   146
Family Safety   148

9 Networking and Wireless 153

Network Components 154
Going Wireless 155
Connecting to a Network 156
Sharing Settings 157
Nearby Sharing 158
Saving Files for Sharing 160
Network Troubleshooting 162

10 Battery Issues 163

Types of Battery 164
Power Consumption 165
Battery Management 166
Charging the Battery 169
Removing the Battery 170
Dead and Spare Batteries 171
Battery Troubleshooting 172

11 System and Security 173

Privacy 174
Troubleshooting 175
System Properties 176
Clean Up Your Disk 178
Windows Update 180
Backing Up 181
System Restore 182
Security and Maintenance 184
Windows Defender Firewall 185
Malware Protection 186

Index 187

1 Choosing a Laptop

More and more computer users are now using laptops because of their convenience and portability. This chapter looks at some of the issues to consider when buying a laptop, and how to ensure you buy the right one for your needs. It also covers the elements of a laptop and some of the accessories you will need.

8   A Brief History of Laptops

10 Laptops v. Desktops

11 Types of Laptops

12 Laptop Jargon Explained

14 Size and Weight

15 Getting Comfortable

18 Carrying a Laptop

19 Keyboard and Touch Pad

20 Using an External Mouse

21 Ports and Slots

22 The Wonder of Wireless

23 Cleaning a Laptop

24 Choosing a Carry Case

25 Spares and Accessories

Don't forget

Apple has an excellent range of laptops, running its macOS operating system. However, the majority of this book deals with "IBM-compatible" laptops, as they are known. These types of laptops are the most common, and run on the Windows operating system.

A Brief History of Laptops

Modern computers have come a long way since the days of mainframe computers, which took up entire rooms and were generally only the domain of large educational establishments or government organizations. Before microprocessors (the chips that are used to run modern-day computers), these mainframe computers were usually operated by punchcards: the operators programmed instructions via holes in a punchcard and then waited for the results, which could take hours or days.

The first personal computers – i.e. ones in which all of the computing power was housed in a single box – started to appear in the early 1970s, and the first machine that bore any resemblance to modern personal computers was called the Datapoint 2200. The real breakthrough for personal computers came with the introduction of microprocessors – small chips that contained all of the necessary processing power for the computer. After this, the industry expanded at a phenomenal rate with the emergence of major worldwide companies such as Microsoft, Apple, IBM, Dell and Intel.

But even as personal computers were being developed for a mass-market audience, there was a concerted drive to try to create a portable computer so that people could take their own computer with them wherever they went. Even in the fast-moving world of technology, the timescale for shrinking a computer from the size of a large room to the size of a small briefcase was a dramatic one.

First portable computers

With most types of technology, we are obsessed with the idea of making the item as small as possible, whether it is a music player, a telephone or a computer. However, the first portable computers bore little resemblance to the machines that we now know as laptops. At the beginning of the 1980s there were a few portable computers released, but most of them were bulky, had very small screens and could not run on internal batteries. The most popular of these was called the Osborne 1, which was released in 1981. Although this was the size of a small suitcase and had a minuscule amount of computing power compared with modern machines, it proved a big success as it enabled people to carry their computers around with them for the first time.

The machine that first used the term "laptop" was called the Gavilan SC, which was developed in 1983 and introduced in 1984. This had the big advantage of being able to run on an internal battery, and it was also one of the first portable computers that appeared with the now-universal "clamshell" design, where the monitor folded down over the keyboard.

In the late 1980s, companies such as Kyocera, Tandy, Olivetti, NEC, IBM, Toshiba, Compaq and Zenith Data Systems began developing faster and more powerful laptops, and it is in this period that the growth of laptops really began to take off.

In 1991, Apple introduced its PowerBook range of laptops, and in 1995 the introduction of Windows 95 provided a widely-used operating system for IBM-compatible laptops.

Laptops have now become an integral part of the computer market, and in many areas sales have outstripped those of desktop computers. Also, they are more than capable of comfortably meeting the computing needs of most computer users. Add to this their portability (which has reached a stage where you no longer need to worry about causing yourself an injury in order to carry one around), and it is clear why laptops have become so popular.

Mobility is now an essential part of computing, and when Windows 8 was released it was aimed firmly at the mobile world. However, this caused some issues, particularly with users of desktop and laptop computers. Windows 10 has gone a long way to addressing these issues, partly by reinstalling a number of features that are aimed more at users with a traditional keyboard and mouse. This shows that laptops still have an important role to play, and will continue to do so.

Don't forget

Because of their size and weight, the first portable computers, such as the Osborne 1, were known rather unflatteringly as "luggables".

Laptops v. Desktops

When considering buying a laptop computer, one of the first considerations is how it will perform in comparison with a desktop computer. In general, you will pay more for a laptop with similar specifications to a desktop. The reason for this is purely down to size: it is more expensive to fit the required hardware into a laptop than the more generous physical capacity of a desktop computer. However, with modern computing technology and power, even laptops with lower specifications than their desktop cousins will be able to handle all but the most intensive computing needs of most home users. The one situation where laptops will need to have as high a specification as possible is if you are going to be doing a lot of video downloading and editing, such as converting and editing old family movies.

Some of the issues to consider when looking at the differences between laptops and desktops are:

Another issue with laptops is battery power, which is required to keep them operating when they are removed from a mains electrical source. Obviously, this is not an issue that affects desktops.

- **Portability**. Laptops easily win over desktops in this respect, but when looking at this area it is worth thinking about how portable you actually want your computer to be. If you want to mainly use it in the home, then you may think that a desktop is the answer. However, a laptop gives you portability in the home too, which means that you can use your computer in a variety of locations within the home and even in the garden, if desired.

- **Power**. Even the most inexpensive laptops have enough computing power to perform most of the tasks that the majority of users require. However, if you want to have the same computing power as the most powerful desktops, then you will have to pay a comparatively higher price.

- **Functionality**. Again, because of their size, desktops have more room for items such as DVD writers, multi-card readers and webcams. These can be included with laptops, but this can also increase the price and the weight of the laptop.

Types of Laptops

To meet the needs of the different types of people who use laptops there are several variations that are available:

- **Netbooks**. These are the ultimate in small laptops, but have less power and functionality than larger options. They generally have screens that are approximately 10 inches (measured diagonally from corner to corner) and are best suited for surfing the web and sending email, although they can also do productivity tasks.

- **Ultrabooks**. These are very light and slim laptops that still have significant power and functionality. They have screens of approximately 13 inches, and weigh as little as 1.2 kg. They are an excellent option if you are going to be using your laptop a lot while traveling.

- **Notebooks**. These are the most common types of laptops as they have a good combination of size, weight and power. They generally have screens that are approximately 13-17 inches and weigh approximately 2-3.5 kg. Notebooks are an excellent option for using in the home and also while traveling.

- **Desktop replacements**. These are larger, heavier laptops that can be used in the home instead of a desktop computer. They are more powerful than other types of laptops, but they are not as portable. They generally have screens that are up to approximately 17-19 inches, and weigh approximately 4-6 kg.

- **Hybrids**. With the proliferation of touchscreen mobile computing devices such as smartphones and tablet computers, manufacturers have been looking at ways to incorporate this functionality into laptops. This has resulted in the development of touchscreen laptops and hybrid devices, which can be used both as a laptop and a tablet. This is done by including a keyboard that can be hidden (by having a sliding, detachable or revolving screen) so that the device can quickly be converted into a touchscreen tablet. These devices are becoming increasingly popular.

Beware

Netbooks usually have a slimmed-down version of the full Windows operating system, due to limits of their memory and architecture.

Don't forget

A lot of the weight in a laptop is taken up by peripherals such as DVD writers, card readers and webcams. The more of these that a laptop has, the heavier it is likely to be.

Laptop Jargon Explained

Since laptops are essentially portable computers, much of the jargon is the same as for a desktop computer. However, it is worth looking at some of this jargon and the significance it has in terms of laptops:

- **Processor**. Also known as the central processing unit, or CPU, this refers to the processing of digital data as it is provided by programs on the computer. The more powerful the processor, the quicker the data is interpreted.

- **Memory**. This closely relates to the processor and is also known as random-access memory, or RAM. Essentially, this type of memory manages the programs that are being run and the commands that are being executed. The more memory there is, the quicker programs will run. With more RAM, they will also be more stable and less likely to crash. In the current range of laptops, memory is measured in megabytes (MB) or gigabytes (GB).

- **Storage**. This refers to the amount of digital information that the laptop can store. In the current range of laptops, storage is measured in gigabytes. There are no external signs of processor or memory on a laptop but the details are available from within the This PC option, which is accessed from the File Explorer (see page 72).

Memory can be thought of as a temporary storage device, as it only keeps information about the currently-open programs. Storage is more permanent, as it keeps the information even when the laptop has been turned off.

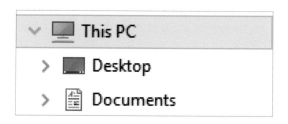

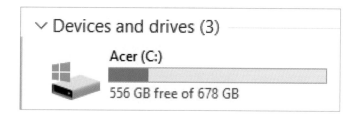

- **Optical drive**. This is a drive on the laptop that is capable of reading information from, and copying it to, a disc such as a CD or a DVD. Some modern laptops have internal optical drives such as CD writers or DVD writers.

- **Connectivity**. This refers to the different types of media device to which the laptop can be connected. These include card readers for memory cards from digital cameras, USB devices such as music players, and USB flashdrives for backing up files or storing items.

- **Graphics card**. This is a device that enables images, video and animations to be displayed on the laptop. It is also sometimes known as a video card. The faster the graphics card, the better the quality the relevant media will be displayed at. In general, very fast graphics cards are really only needed for intensive multimedia applications such as video games or videos.

- **Wireless**. This refers to a laptop's ability to connect wirelessly to a network – i.e. another computer or an internet connection. In order to be able to do this, the laptop must have a wireless card, which enables it to connect to a network or high-speed internet connection.

- **Ports**. These are the parts of a laptop into which external devices can be plugged, using a cable such as a USB. They are usually located on the side of the laptop, and there can be two or three of each.

- **Pointing device**. This is the part of the laptop that replaces the traditional mouse as a means of moving the cursor on the screen. Most pointing devices are in the form of a touch pad, where a finger on a pad is used to move the cursor. An external mouse can also be connected to the laptop and used in the conventional way.

- **Webcam**. This is a type of camera that is fitted into the laptop, and can be used to take still photographs, or communicate via video with other people.

Hot tip

External optical drives can also be connected to a laptop through a USB cable.

Don't forget

For more on using wireless technology, see page 155.

13

Don't forget

USB stands for Universal Serial Bus, and is a popular way of connecting external devices to computers.

Size and Weight

The issues of size and weight are integral to the decision to buy a laptop. In addition to getting a machine with enough computing power, it is also important to ensure that the screen is large enough for your needs and that it is light enough for you to carry around comfortably.

Size

The main issue with the size of a laptop is the dimensions of the screen. This is usually measured in inches, diagonally from corner to corner. The range for the majority of laptops currently on the market is approximately 12-17 inches, with some more powerful models going up to 19 inches.

When considering the size of screen it is important to think about how you are going to use your laptop:

Beware

Looking at material on a smaller screen can be more tiring on the eyes as, by default, it is displayed proportionally smaller than on a larger screen. It is possible to change the size of the screen display, but this will lead to less material being displayed on the screen. See page 52 to see how to change the screen resolution.

- If you are going to use it mainly for functions such as letter writing and sending email, then a smaller screen might suffice.

- If you are going to use it mainly for functions such as surfing the web or editing and looking at photographs, then you may feel more comfortable with a larger screen.

- If you, or anyone else, is going to be using it for playing games and watching videos, then the larger the screen, the better.

Weight

Unless you are buying a laptop to replace a desktop, weight should not be too much of an issue, as most models are similar in this respect. However, make sure you physically feel the laptop before you buy it.

If you are going to be traveling a lot with your laptop, then a lighter, ultrabook type may be the best option. When considering this, take into account the weight of any type of case that you will use to carry the laptop, as this will add to the overall weight.

Getting Comfortable

Since you will probably be using your laptop in more than one location, the issue of finding a comfortable working position can be vital, particularly as you cannot put the keyboard and monitor in different positions as you can with a desktop computer. Whenever you are using your laptop try to make sure that you are sitting in a comfortable position, with your back well supported, and that the laptop is in a position where you can reach the keyboard easily and also see the screen without straining.

Despite the possible temptation to do so, avoid using your laptop in bed, on your lap, or where you have to slouch or strain to reach the laptop properly:

Don't forget

Working comfortably at a laptop involves a combination of a good chair, good posture and good positioning of the laptop.

Hot tip

If possible, the best place to work at a laptop is at a dedicated desk or workstation.

15

Seating position

The ideal way to sit at a laptop is with an office-type chair that offers good support for your back. Even with these types of chairs it is important to maintain a good body position so that your back is straight and your head is pointing forwards.

If you do not have an office-type chair, use a chair with a straight back and place a cushion behind you for extra support and comfort, as required.

Hot tip

One of the advantages of office-type chairs is that the height can usually be adjusted, and this can be a great help in achieving a comfortable position.

...cont'd

Laptop position

When working at your laptop it is important to have it positioned so that both the keyboard and the screen are in a comfortable position. If the keyboard is too low, then you will have to slouch or strain to reach it:

Beware

Take regular breaks when working with a laptop, and stop working if you experience aches or pins and needles in your arms or legs.

If the keyboard is too high, your arms will be stretching. This could lead to pain in your tendons:

The ideal setup is to have the laptop in a position where you can sit with your forearms and wrists as level as possible while you are typing on the keyboard:

Adjusting the screen

Another factor in working comfortably at a laptop is the position of the screen. Unlike with a desktop computer, it is not feasible to have a laptop screen at eye level, as this would result in the keyboard being in too high a position. Instead, once you have achieved a comfortable seating position, open the screen so that it is approximately 90 degrees from your eyeline:

Find a comfortable body position and adjust your laptop's position to this, rather than vice versa.

One problem with laptop screens is that they can reflect glare from sunlight or indoor lighting:

Most modern laptops have screens with an anti-glare coating. However, even this will not be very effective against bright sunlight that is shining directly onto the screen.

If this happens, either change your position or block out the light source, using some form of blind or shade. Avoid squinting at a screen that is reflecting glare as this will quickly give you a headache.

Carrying a Laptop

As laptops are designed for mobility, it is safe to assume that they will have to be carried around at some point. Because of the weight of even the lightest laptops, it can be uncomfortable to carry a laptop for an extended period of time. To try to minimize this, it is important to follow a few rules:

- Carry the laptop with a carry case that is designed for this task (or a double-strapped backpack).

- Carry the laptop on one side of your body and move it from side to side if necessary.

- Do not cross the strap over your shoulders, and try not to carry too many other items at the same time.

If you are traveling with your laptop you might be able to incorporate it into your luggage, particularly if it can be moved on wheels.

If you are carrying your laptop for a long period of time make sure that you take regular breaks, otherwise you may cause yourself a strain or an injury.

If you place your laptop with another piece of luggage, make sure that you keep it with you at all times, so as to minimize the chance of theft.

Keyboard and Touch Pad

Laptops have the same basic data input devices as desktop computers; i.e. a keyboard and a mouse. A laptop keyboard is very similar to a desktop one, although it is best to try the action of the keys before you buy a particular laptop, to ensure that they are not too "soft"; i.e. that there is enough resistance when they are pressed.

One of the main differences between a laptop and a desktop computer is the mouse (or pointing device) that controls the on-screen cursor. In the early days of laptops, some of them had a small control stick to move the cursor. However, these have been almost universally replaced by touch pads, which are small, sensitive, square or rectangular pads that are activated by stroking a finger over them to move the cursor. It sometimes takes a bit of practice to get used to them, but after a little experience they can be as effective as a traditional mouse. When using a keyboard or touch pad, avoid having your fingers too high:

Instead, keep your hands and fingers as flat as possible over the keyboard and the touch pad:

Don't forget

Laptop keyboards contain the same functionality as any standard computer keyboard. However, most manufacturers have keyboards with functions that are specific to their own laptops.

Using an External Mouse

Not everyone likes touch pads as a means of moving the cursor on a laptop, and it is true they can sometimes be slightly fiddly and prone to erratic movement if the control is too jerky. The good news is that it is possible to use a conventional mouse with a laptop to move the cursor.

A mouse can be connected to a laptop via one of the suitable sockets (ports) at the back or side of the laptop. These are usually in the form of USB ports:

Once the mouse has been connected to the laptop it can be used in exactly the same way as with a desktop computer. In some cases it is possible to add a wireless mouse, which can be used without the need for a cable:

Don't forget

It is certainly worth persevering with a laptop's touch pad, even if it seems very frustrating at first. Once you have found the correct pressure to apply, it will become much easier to control.

Ports and Slots

Most laptops have a slightly bewildering array of sockets and slots for connecting external devices. These sockets are known as ports, and they come in a variety of shapes and sizes for different devices and uses:

- **USB**. This is a method for connecting a variety of external devices such as digital cameras, digital music players, scanners and printers. The latest standard in widespread use is USB 3.0, and this has largely replaced parallel and serial ports in terms of connecting devices such as printers or an external mouse.

- **USB Type-C**. This is the latest type of USB port, for devices with a USB Type-C cable. The port is thinner than a standard USB one and is reversible, so that the end of the cable can be inserted both ways, rather than a single way as for standard USB ports.

- **Ethernet**. This can be used as a cable connection to your internet router, rather than using a Wi-Fi connection.

- **HDMI (High-Definition Multimedia Interface)**. This can be used to connect to compatible digital devices, including high-definition TVs. This enables you to view whatever is on your laptop screen on a television, and is a good option for watching movies or displaying photos.

- **Memory card readers**. These are used for downloading photos from memory cards from digital cameras or smartphones. Some laptops only have an SD card slot, since these are most commonly used. If you need to attach a multi-card reader for different types of memory card, this can be done using a USB port.

The main slot on some laptops is:

- **CD/DVD players or re-writers**. These can be used to play music CDs or watch videos on a DVD. They can also be used to copy data to blank CDs or DVDs. This is a good option for backing up items that you want to keep, such as photos.

Laptops with USB 3.0 ports can still be used with USB 2.0 (or earlier) devices, but they will also work with any USB 3.0 devices.

Not all laptops have a CD/DVD player, although external CD/DVD drives can be connected.

The Wonder of Wireless

For anyone who has struggled with a tangle of computer cables and wires, the advent of wireless technology has been one of the great computing breakthroughs of recent years.

Wireless technology does exactly what the name suggests: it allows a wireless-enabled computer to communicate with other similarly-enabled devices such as other computers, printers, or an internet connection. First of all, the devices have to be set up as a network; i.e. they have to be linked together so that they know they should be communicating with each other. Once this has been done, files can be shared or sent to the printer, and the internet browsed, all without the need to connect the devices using a cable.

In order to be part of a wireless network, a laptop must have a wireless capability. Most modern laptops come with wireless cards already installed; otherwise, they can be installed in any available expansion slot.

Hotspots

One of the great growth areas of wireless technology is hotspots. These are public areas that have been set up to distribute the internet wirelessly. This means that anyone with a wireless card in their laptop can, if they are within a certain range, access the internet in a variety of public places. These include:

- Coffee shops
- Airports
- Hotels
- Libraries
- Supermarkets

Hotspots operate using Wi-Fi technology, which is the method by which the signal from the network is transferred to individual users. Most hotspots have a limited range of approximately 100 yards. Some are free to use, while others charge a fee, depending on usage.

One concern about hotspots is security. This is because if you can access a network wirelessly, someone else could then also access your laptop and data. Many hotspots have software in place to try to stop this.

For more details about Wi-Fi and networks, see Chapter 9.

Cleaning a Laptop

Like most things, laptops benefit greatly from a little care and attention. The two most important areas to keep clean are the screen and the keyboard.

Cleaning the screen

All computer screens quickly collect dust and fingerprints, and laptops are no different. If this is left too long it can make the screen harder to read, causing eye strain and headaches. Clean the screen regularly with the following cleaning materials:

- A lint-free cloth, similar to the type used to clean camera lenses (it is important not to scratch the screen in any way).

- An alcohol-free cleaning fluid that is recommended for computer screens.

- Screen wipes, again that are recommended for use on computer screens.

Cleaning the keyboard

Keyboards are notorious for accumulating dust, fluff and crumbs. One way to solve this problem is to turn the laptop upside down and very gently shake it to loosen any foreign objects. Failing this, a can of condensed air can be used with a narrow nozzle to blow out any stubborn items that remain lodged in the keys.

Don't forget

The outer casing of a laptop can be cleaned with the same fluid as used for the screen. Equally effective can be a duster or a damp (but not wet) cloth and warm water. Keep soap away from laptops if possible.

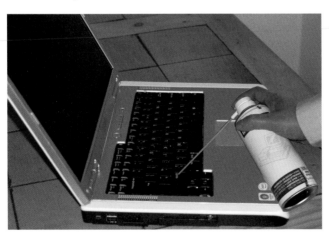

Choosing a Carry Case

When you are transporting your laptop it could be placed in any convenient bag such as a backpack, a duffle bag, or even a large handbag. However, there are several advantages to using a proper laptop carry case:

- It will probably be more comfortable when you are carrying it, as it is designed specifically for this job.

- The laptop will be more secure, as it should fit properly in the case.

- You should be able to keep all of your laptop accessories together in one case.

When choosing a carry case, look for one that fits your laptop well and has a strap to keep it secure inside:

Also, make sure that there are enough additional spaces and pockets for accessories such as cables and an external mouse. Finally, choosing a case with a padded shoulder strap will be of considerable benefit if you have to carry your laptop for any length of time.

Beware

A laptop case should also be lockable, either with its own internal lock or with a fastening through which a padlock can be put.

Spares and Accessories

Whenever you are going anywhere with your laptop, there are always spares and accessories to consider. Some of these are just nice things to have, while others could be essential to ensure that you can still use your laptop if anything goes wrong while you are on your travels. Items to consider for putting in your laptop case include:

- **Spare battery**. This is probably the most important spare if you are going to be away from home for any length of time, and particularly if you think you may be unable to access a power supply for a period of time and so be unable to charge your laptop battery. Like all batteries, laptop batteries slowly lose power over time and do not keep their charge for as long as when they are new. It is a good idea to always keep an eye on how much battery power you have left and, if you are running low, try to conserve as much energy as possible. Although laptop batteries are bulky and heavy, carrying a spare could mean the difference between frustration and relief if you are left with no battery power and no charging options.

- **Power cable**. This is the cable that can be used to power the laptop when it is not being run on battery power. It usually consists of a cable and a power adapter, which makes it rather bulky and heavy. Whenever possible, this should be used rather than the internal battery, and it should be kept with the laptop at all times.

Don't forget

For more information on batteries, see Chapter 10.

...cont'd

Hot tip

It is important that headphones are comfortable to wear for an extended period of time. In general, the types that fit over the ears are more comfortable than the "bud" variety that is inserted into the ear.

- **External mouse**. This can be used instead of the laptop's touch pad. Some people prefer a traditional mouse, particularly if they are going to be working on their laptop for an extended period of time.

- **Multi-card reader**. If you do not have a built-in multi-card reader (see page 21), an external one can be used to download photos from a digital camera memory card. This will connect via a USB port.

- **Headphones**. These can be used to listen to music or films if you are in the company of other people and you do not want to disturb them. They can also be very useful if there are distracting noises coming from other people.

- **USB flashdrive**. This is a small device that can be used to copy data to and from your laptop. It connects via a USB port and is about the size of a packet of chewing gum. It is an excellent way of backing up files from your laptop when you are away from home.

Don't forget

Backing up (see page 181) is the process of copying folders and files from your laptop onto an external device for safekeeping in case the folders and files on the laptop are deleted or corrupted.

- **Cleaning material**. The materials described on page 23 can be taken to ensure your laptop is always in tip-top condition for use.

- **DVDs/CDs**. Video or music DVDs and CDs can be taken to provide mobile entertainment, and blank ones can be taken to copy data onto, similar to using a USB flash drive.

2 Around a Laptop

This chapter shows how to quickly become familiar with your laptop and Windows 10. It gives an overview of Windows 10 so that you can become comfortable with this new environment and confidently use the Start menu, the Start button, the Taskbar, and the Desktop. It also looks at personalizing Windows 10 to exactly the way you want it.

28   Opening Up and Turning On

29   Touchscreen Laptops

30   About Windows 10

34   The Start Button

36   The Start Menu

38   Pinning Items

39   Using Live Tiles

40   Desktop, Taskbar and Task View

43   Shutting Down

44   Using a Microsoft Account

46   Personalization

48   Lock Screen Settings

50   Using Themes

52   Screen Resolution

53   Managing Storage

54   Adjusting Volume

55   Loading CDs and DVDs

56   USB Flashdrives

Opening Up and Turning On

The first step towards getting started with a new laptop is to open it ready for use. The traditional clamshell design keeps the screen and keyboard together through the use of an internal clip or connector. This can be released by a button on the exterior of the laptop, which is usually positioned at the front or side. Some laptops have a magnetic connection between the screen and the main body.

Beware

Open the screen of your laptop carefully, so as not to put any unnecessary pressure on the connection between the screen and the main body of the laptop.

Once the screen has been opened, it can then be positioned ready for use. The screen should stay in any position in which it is placed:

Beware

Press the Power button with one firm, definite motion. If you accidentally press it twice in quick succession, the laptop may turn on and then shut down immediately afterwards.

The Power button for turning on a laptop, ready for use, is usually located near to the keyboard:

The laptop can be turned on by pushing this button firmly. The laptop will then probably make a sound, to indicate that it has been turned on, and begin loading the operating system (the software that is used to run and manage all of the laptop's apps, folders and files). Once the laptop has completed its startup procedure, the opening screen should be displayed. At this point the laptop is ready for use.

Don't forget

Most laptops will take a couple of minutes to start up and be fully ready to use.

Touchscreen Laptops

Windows 10 is the latest operating system from Microsoft, and this will be installed on most new laptops. It is optimized for touchscreen use, so it is ideal for using with laptops with touchscreen capability and also with Windows 10 tablets.

Touchscreen laptops still have a traditional keyboard but navigation can also be done by tapping, swiping and pinching on the screen. Some of the functions that can be performed on a touchscreen laptop are:

- Activate a button, such as Done or OK, by tapping on it. Apps on the Windows 10 interface can also be accessed by tapping on them from the Start menu.

- Move up and down long pages by swiping in the required direction; e.g. to navigate around web pages.

- Zoom in and out of pages by pinching inwards or outwards with thumb and forefinger (if the open app has this functionality). It is most commonly used for zooming in and out of web pages.

Touchscreen laptops are a realistic option for users who want to get the most out of the functionality of Windows 10. Some laptop manufacturers to look at are:

- Acer

- Dell

- HP

- Lenovo

- Sony

- Toshiba

A number of touchscreen models can also be converted into tablet mode, either by revolving the screen or by detaching the keyboard. There are also some hybrid models with a detachable screen that can be used as either a tablet, or a traditional laptop with the keyboard attached.

The latest version of Windows 10 is the October 2018 Update version. This is the version used in this book but, in general, it will be referred to as Windows 10.

The Microsoft Surface Pro tablet also runs on Windows 10, and it is a realistic option in terms of replacing a regular laptop.

About Windows 10

The latest version of Windows (*at the time of printing*) was released in October 2018:

- 2018 – Windows 10 October 2018 Update, which can be used to upgrade any existing version of Windows 10.

All major computer operating systems (OS) undergo regular upgrades to new versions. In terms of Microsoft Windows, Windows 8 was one of the most radical updates to the user interface (UI), and introduced a number of new features for both desktop and mobile versions of Windows. However, it was not met with universal approval as it did not fully meet the needs of desktop users and those with mobile devices.

With Windows 10, a lot of the problems with Windows 8 were addressed: the familiar Start menu was reinstated to return to a similar UI to earlier versions of Windows; there was a greater consolidation between desktop and mobile devices running Windows 10; and the operation of apps was standardized. In a sense, this was a case of going back one step in order to go forwards two steps, and Windows 10 has succeeded in creating a familiar environment, coupled with a range of innovative and useful features.

Windows 10 October 2018 Update

The intention for Windows 10 has always been to produce incremental updates, rather than waiting a period of time for the next major update. This is the reason why it is unlikely that there will be a Windows 11: instead, there will be regular online updates to Windows 10. The Windows 10 October 2018 Update marks the third anniversary of the release of the software. It contains a number of improvements and refinements but, in keeping with the Windows 10 ethos, it is an incremental update rather than a major new operating system. The October 2018 Update is delivered online through the Windows Update function in the Settings app (see page 180). A registered version of Windows 10 has to be installed in order for the October 2018 Update to be downloaded (or a license can be bought when downloading the October 2018 Update).

Don't forget

It is possible to synchronize Windows 10 so that all of your settings and apps will be available over multiple devices through an online Microsoft Account (see pages 44-45).

Obtaining Windows 10

Windows 10 is a departure by Microsoft in that it is promoted as an online service, rather than just a stand-alone operating system. This means that by default, Windows 10 is obtained and downloaded online, with subsequent updates and upgrades provided on a regular basis.

The original version of Windows 10 was a free upgrade if it was downloaded and installed by July 2016. Windows 10 can now be bought from the Microsoft website, or through software retailers. A registered version of Windows 10 has to been installed before the free October 2018 Update can be downloaded.

The three main options for obtaining the Windows 10 October 2018 Update are:

- **Use Windows Update** – Replace an older version of Windows 10, retaining the installed applications and settings. This can be done through the **Settings** app (select **Update & Security** > **Windows Update** and click on the **Check for updates** button).

- **Microsoft website** – Visit the software download page on the Microsoft website (**microsoft.com/en-us/software-download/windows10**) to use the **Update Assistant** to download the Windows 10 October 2018 Update.

- **Pre-install** – Buy a new laptop with the Windows 10 October 2018 Update already installed.

Some of the steps that the installation will go through are:

- **Personalize**. These are settings that will be applied to your version of Windows 10.

- **Microsoft Account**. You can set up a Microsoft Account during installation.

- **Privacy**. Certain privacy settings can be applied during the setup process for the Windows 10 October 2018 Update.

Don't forget

If a laptop is running Windows 7 or 8, it can be upgraded to the October 2018 Update if a Windows 10 license is bought.

...cont'd

About the October 2018 Update

Although the October 2018 Update is still under the Windows 10 banner, there are a range of significant additions and enhancements from the early versions of the operating system. Some of these include:

- **Dark Mode**. This is a new setting that can be used to turn the background of compatible Windows apps to black, with white text.

Hot tip

In the Clipboard settings there is also an option for copying multiple items to the clipboard, for use at a later time. If this is turned **On**, the clipboard history can be viewed, and pasted from, by pressing the **Windows key** (**WinKey**) + **V**.

- **Cloud clipboard**. This can be used if you are using other Windows 10 devices, in addition to your laptop. This could be another Windows 10 computer or a mobile device such as the Surface Pro tablet. Items copied on one device are stored in the clipboard on all other devices, so that they can be pasted into files or documents. The Cloud clipboard can be set up within **Settings** > **System** > **Clipboard**. Click on the Get started button under the **Sync across devices** heading to set up the Cloud clipboard.

Sync across devices

Paste text on your other devices. When this is on, Microsoft receives your clipboard data to sync it across your devices.

Get started

- **Snip & Sketch app**. This can be used to create screenshots, i.e. an image of 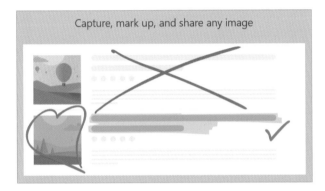 the screen being viewed, and also annotate them once they have been captured. This is done with the **Snip & Sketch** app, which can be used to capture rectangular areas of the screen, freehand areas of the screen, or the full screen area. Once a screenshot has been captured, it can be annotated within the Snip & Sketch app.

- **Cortana updates**. Cortana, the Windows 10 search and digital voice assistant function, has been updated so that there is an improved interface when you are searching with Cortana. These include displaying options for apps, settings, documents and photos on your laptop, and also searching over the web.

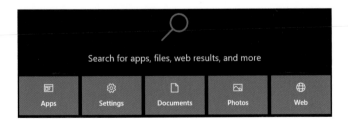

- **Updated apps**. These include: the News app, which makes it easier to collate news storied from different sources; the Photos app, which has improved albums that are created automatically; and the Calendar app can now be used to search for specific calendar events.

The Start Button

In the Windows 10 October 2018 Update, the Start button works in a similar way to most early versions of Windows, with some enhancements.

Using the Start button

The Start button provides access to the apps on your Windows 10 PC and also to the enhanced Start menu:

1 Click on the **Start** button in the bottom left-hand corner of the screen

2 The **Start** menu is displayed

3 The left-hand side of the Start menu contains links to frequently-used apps, a list of quick links to items such as the Power button, and an alphabetic list of all of the apps on the computer

4 The right-hand side of the Start menu is where apps can be pinned so that they are always available. This is displayed as a collection of large colored tiles

5 Other items can also be accessed from the Start button by right-clicking on it

Hot tip

The items on the Start menu can be customized from the **Personalization** > **Start** section of the Settings app.

Hot tip

Click on the **Power** button on the Start menu to access options for Sleep, Shut down or Restart.

Start button functionality

In addition to accessing the Start menu, the Start button can also be used to access the Power User menu, by right-clicking on it:

1 Right-click on the **Start** button to view the Power User menu

2 Click on the relevant buttons to view items including the **Desktop** and other popular locations such as the **File Explorer**

The Power User menu in Step 1 has a number of options for accessing system functions such as Windows PowerShell, and Disk Management.

35

3 Click on the **Shut down or sign out** button to access the options

The Start Menu

The Start menu in Windows 10 is where you can access areas within your computer, perform certain functions, and also access apps from a variety of locations. Some of the default items on the Start menu can be customized to a certain extent (under **Settings** > **Personalization** > **Start**), and there is considerable functionality here:

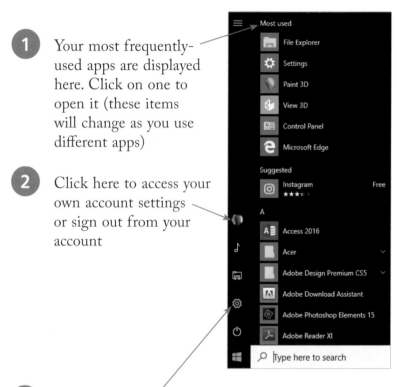

1 Your most frequently-used apps are displayed here. Click on one to open it (these items will change as you use different apps)

2 Click here to access your own account settings or sign out from your account

3 Click here to access items including the **File Explorer**, your **Documents** library within File Explorer, and the Windows 10 **Settings**

4 Click on the **Power** button for options to **Sleep** your computer, **Shut down** or **Restart**

5 Use the scroll bar at the right-hand side to move through the list of apps

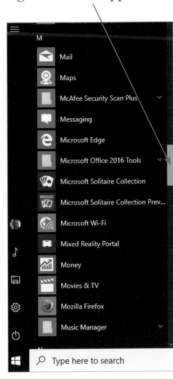

Hot tip

Click on a letter at the top of a section of apps to view an alphabetic grid. Click on a letter to move to that section.

6 If there is a down-pointing arrow next to an app, this means that there are additional items that can be accessed. Click on the arrow to view these

37

Pinning Items

In most cases, you will want to have quick access to a variety of apps on the Start menu and also the Taskbar at the bottom of the screen. To do this:

1 Click on the **Start** button

Hot tip

Tiles on the Start menu can be resized by right-clicking on them and clicking on the **Resize** button. The resizing options are **Small**, **Medium**, **Wide** and **Large**, although not all options can be applied to all apps.

2 Right-click on an app and click on the **Pin to Start** button

3 The app's tile is added to the **Start** menu

4 Right-click on an app and click on **More** > **Pin to taskbar**

5 The app's icon is added to the Taskbar and it can be opened directly from here

Using Live Tiles

Before any of the Windows 10 apps have been used, some of them are depicted on the Start menu with tiles of solid color. However, once you open an app it activates the Live Tile feature (if it is supported by that app). This enables the tile to display real-time information from the app, even when it is not the app currently being used. This means that you can view information from your apps directly from the Start menu. To use Live Tiles:

The apps with Live Tile functionality include: Mail, People, Calendar, Photos, Groove Music, News, Sport, and Money. Some of these, such as Mail, require you to first set up an account before Live Tiles can be fully activated.

1 Right-click on a tile to select it. If it has Live Tile functionality, click on the **Turn Live Tile on** button to activate this feature

2 Live Tiles display real-time text and images from the selected apps. These are updated when there is new information available via the app

Beware

If you have too many Live Tiles activated at the same time it can become distracting and annoying, with a lot of movement on the Start menu.

3 To turn off a Live Tile, right-click on a tile to select it, and click on the **Turn Live Tile off** button

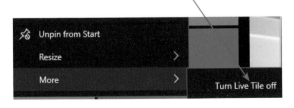

39

Desktop, Taskbar and Task View

The Windows Desktop is an integral part of Windows, and is visible when you turn on your laptop. This also displays the Taskbar at the bottom of the screen.

Hot tip

The Desktop can also be accessed by pressing the **WinKey** + **D** or by right-clicking on the Start button and selecting **Desktop**.
The WinKey can be used to access the Start menu at any time and also perform a number of tasks in conjunction with other keys.

Shortcut icons   Search box   Desktop background

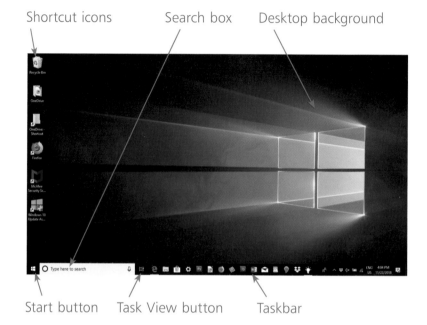

Start button   Task View button   Taskbar

1
Move the cursor over items on the Taskbar to see open windows for that item. Click on a window to make that the active one

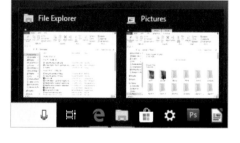

Don't forget

If an app has two or more windows open, each of them will be displayed when you move the cursor over the app's icon on the Taskbar.

2
The Notifications area at the right-hand side of the Taskbar has speaker, network and other system tools. Click on one to see more information about each item

Task View

Task View is an option for viewing thumbnail versions of all open items on your laptop. To use it:

1 Click on this button on the Taskbar to access Task View, which displays minimized versions of the currently-open apps

2 To show and hide the Task View button, right-click on the button and check On or Off the **Show Task View button** option

3 The Task View displays minimized versions of the currently-open apps and windows

4 As more windows are opened, the format is arranged accordingly. Click on a window in Task View to make it the active window

Different desktops can be added from within Task View. This can enable different apps to be opened on different desktops. To add new desktops, click on this button in the top left-hand corner of the screen.

+ New desktop

Apps can only be open on one desktop at a time. So if an app is open on one desktop and you try to open it on another, you will be taken to the already-open app.

To delete a desktop, click on the Task View button and click on the cross that appears when you hover your mouse over the desktop to be removed.

41

...cont'd

Timeline

Another feature within Task View is the Timeline. This displays a chronological list of items, for the past 30 days, that you have accessed on your laptop. The Timeline enables you to return to items that were accessed on a specific date, without having to open them or search for them in File Explorer. To use the Timeline:

1 Open Task View as shown on page 41 and drag on the sidebar to move through items that have been accessed on specific dates

2 The content is displayed for each date. Click on an item to access it within its own app

3 For each date, click on the **See all activities** option to see all of the items that were accessed on that date

April 29   See all 16 activities

Shutting Down

Options for shutting down Windows have been amended with some versions of the operating system. In the Windows 10 October 2018 Update, this functionality can be accessed from the Start menu.

Shutting down from the Start menu

1 Click on the **Start** button

2 Right-click on the **Power** button

3 Click on either the **Sleep**, **Shut down** or **Restart** buttons; or

Hot tip

For some updates to Windows you will need to restart your computer for them to take effect.

4 Right-click on the **Start** button and select either **Sign out**, **Sleep**, **Shut down** or **Restart** from the **Shut down or sign out** option

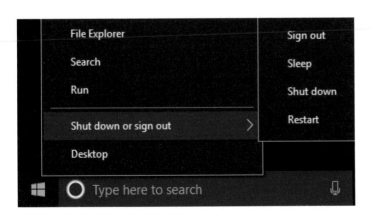

Using a Microsoft Account

We live in a world of ever-increasing computer connectivity, where users expect to be able to access and share their content wherever they are. This is known as Cloud computing, with content being stored on online servers, from where it can be accessed by authorized users.

In Windows 10, this type of connectivity is achieved with a Microsoft Account. This is a registration system (which can be set up with most email addresses and a password) that provides access to a number of services via the Windows 10 apps. These include:

Beware

Without a Microsoft Account you will not be able to access the full functionality of the apps listed here.

- **Mail**. This is the Windows 10 email app that can be used to access and manage your different email accounts.

- **People**. This is the address book app.

- **Calendar**. This is the calendar and organizer app.

- **Microsoft Store**. This is the online store for previewing and downloading additional apps.

- **OneDrive**. This is the online backup and sharing service.

Creating a Microsoft Account

It is free to create a Microsoft Account – this can be done with an email address and, together with a password, provides a unique identifier for logging into your Microsoft Account and the related apps. There are several ways in which you can create and set up a Microsoft Account:

- During the initial setup process when you install Windows 10. You will be asked if you want to create a Microsoft Account at this point. If you do not, you can always do so at a later time.

- When you first open an app that requires access to a Microsoft Account. When you do this you will be prompted to create a new account.

- From the **Accounts** section of the **Settings** app (for more information about the Settings app, see pages 60-61).

44

Whichever way you use to create a Microsoft Account, the
process is similar:

1 When you are first
prompted to sign in with
a Microsoft Account you
can enter your account
details, if you have one, or

2 Click on the **No
account?
Create one!** link

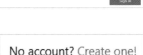

Microsoft Account
details can also be
used as your sign-in
for Windows 10 (see
pages 58-59).

45

3 Enter your name, an
email address and a
password for your
Microsoft Account

4 Click on the **Next** button to move
through the registration process

5 Enter your password
again to confirm your
account

6 Click on the **Finish**
button in the final
window to complete
setting up your Microsoft
Account

Lock Screen Settings

The Settings app enables you to set the appearance of the Lock screen, including selecting your own photo for the Lock screen background. To do this:

1 Open the **Settings** app and click on the **Personalization** button

2 Click on the **Lock screen** button

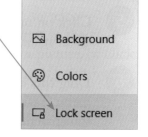

3 The current Lock screen background is shown here

Don't forget

If **Slideshow** is selected in Step 5, you will then have the option to choose an album of photos to use as the slideshow for the Lock screen background.

4 Click here to select options for the Lock screen background

5 Select one of the background options from **Windows spotlight**, **Picture**, or **Slideshow**

6 For the Picture option, click on the **Browse** button to select your own picture

7 Select an image and click on **Choose picture** to add this to the background options for the Lock screen

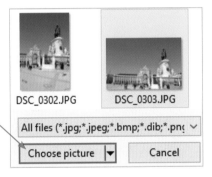

8 Other options for the Lock screen include selecting apps that display their detailed or quick status; options for screen timeout when not in use; and Screen saver settings

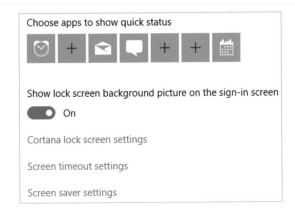

If you use your own images for the Lock screen background, these will remain available on the thumbnail row even if you switch to another image for the background.

49

Using Themes

Themes in the Windows 10 can be used to customize several items for the look and feel of Windows:

1 Open **Settings** and click on the **Personalization** button

2 Click on the **Themes** button

3 The current theme is displayed

4 Make a selection for a customized theme, using **Background**, **Color**, **Sounds** and **Mouse cursor**

5 The selections for the customized theme are shown in the **Current theme** preview window

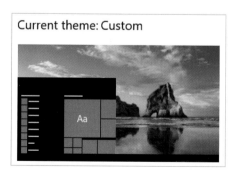

6 Click on the **Save theme** button to use it for the current theme

Save theme

7 Click on one of the preset themes to select it rather than customizing one

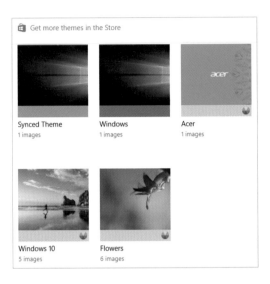

8 All of the elements of the preset theme are displayed in the preview window

9 Click on **Get more themes in the Store** to download more themes that can be used on your PC

Screen Resolution

If you have a high-resolution screen, you may find that the text, as well as the icons, is too small. You can increase the effective size by reducing the screen resolution.

1 Open the **Settings** app, select **System** and then click on the **Display** button

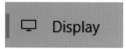

2 Drag this slider to change the overall brightness of items on your screen

3 Click here to change the screen resolution. Select a new resolution value from the list

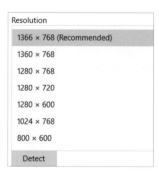

4 Click on the **Keep changes** button to change the screen resolution

Managing Storage

Computer storage is sometimes a feature that is taken for granted and left untouched. However, with the Windows 10 October 2018 Update there are options for customizing how storage functions on your computer. To use these:

1 Open the **Settings** app, select **System** and then click on the **Storage** button

2 At the top of the window, the current storage is displayed,
with the amount used shown by a colored bar

3 Drag the **Storage sense** button to **On** to enable Windows to free up storage space by deleting redundant files and items in the Recycle Bin

4 Under the **More storage settings** heading, click on **Change where new content is saved**

More storage settings

Change where new content is saved

5 Select options for where new items will be saved (this can be used if you are using more than one drive)

Adjusting Volume

There are different sources of sounds on a laptop. The main two are:

- Sounds from the speakers
- Sounds from the Windows system

The volume for each of these can be adjusted independently of the other. To do this:

Beware

If you are going to be using your laptop near other people, and without headphones, make sure the volume controls are set at a reasonable level, so as not to annoy people.

54

Hot tip

You can adjust the volume of your laptop's speakers, or mute them, by clicking on this icon in the Notifications area at the right-hand side of the Taskbar.

1 Open the **Settings** app, select **System** and then click on the **Sound** button

◁») Sound

2 In the Sound section, click here to choose the speakers to use and drag the slider to specify the volume

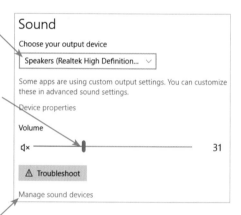

Sound

Choose your output device

Speakers (Realtek High Definition... ⌄

Some apps are using custom output settings. You can customize these in advanced sound settings.

Device properties

Volume

◁× ─────────●────────── 31

⚠ Troubleshoot

Manage sound devices

3 Click on the **Manage sound devices** option in Step 2 to access the available sound devices. Click on one to see its details

⌂ Manage sound devices

Below is a list of all your devices. Select a device you want to disable or enable.

Output devices

🔊 Speakers
Realtek High Definition Audio

Disabled

Input devices

🎤 Microphone
Realtek High Definition Audio

Loading CDs and DVDs

CDs and DVDs can be an important aspect of life with a laptop. They can be used to store information and also for playing music or movies, particularly when traveling. To load CDs or DVDs:

1 Locate the CD or DVD drive. This will be a slot that is located at the side or front of the laptop

2 Press the button on the front of the drive once, to eject the tray

3 Insert the CD or DVD into the tray and press the button again to close it, or push it in gently

Not all laptops have a CD or DVD drive, but external CD/DVD drives can be purchased and connected separately.

4 To view the location of the CD or DVD, click the **This PC** button in the File Explorer (see page 72). The CD or DVD will be shown as a separate drive

> ✔ 🖥 This PC
> > 🖵 Desktop
> > 📄 Documents
> > ⬇ Downloads
> > 🎵 Music
> > 🖼 Pictures
> > 🎞 Videos
> > 💾 Acer (C:)
> > 💿 DVD RW Drive (D:) Audio CD

USB Flashdrives

USB flashdrives are small devices that can be used for copying files and then transferring them between computers. To connect a flashdrive to a laptop and use it:

Hot tip

Because of their size, USB flashdrives can be lost quite easily. When traveling, attach them to something like a keyring or keep them in a small pocket in your laptop case.

1 Connect the flashdrive to one of the laptop's USB ports

2 The flashdrive should be recognized automatically and the necessary software installed so that it is ready to use

3 Access the Desktop and click on the **File Explorer** button on the Taskbar

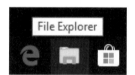

4 The flashdrive should appear as a removable drive under This PC. (Flashdrives can be renamed in File Explorer by right-clicking on the name and selecting **Rename**)

Hot tip

The File Explorer can also be accessed from the All Apps list on the Start screen (**Windows System > File Explorer**).

5 Double-click on the flashdrive to view its contents. The files can then be used in the same way as any others on your laptop

3 Getting Up and Running

This chapter looks at some of the features of Windows 10, including the settings, using the search facility Cortana, and the new features for Dark Mode and capturing screenshots. It also shows how to use the File Explorer.

58 Sign-in Options

60 Settings

62 Searching

64 Setting Up Cortana

65 Using Cortana

68 Viewing Notifications

70 Dark Mode

71 Snipping (Screenshots)

72 Opening File Explorer

73 Quick Access in File Explorer

75 Scenic Ribbon

Sign-in Options

Each time you start up your laptop you will need to sign in. This is a security feature so that no-one else can gain unauthorized access to your account on your laptop. The sign-in process starts with the Lock screen, and then you have to enter your password.

Hot tip

You can lock your laptop at any point by pressing the **WinKey** + **L**.

Don't forget

You will get an error message if you enter the wrong password, or if you simply mis-key and cause an incorrect character to be added.

1 When you start your laptop the **Lock screen** will be showing. This is linked to the sign-in screen

2 Click on the **Lock screen**, or press any key, to move to the **Sign-in** screen. Enter your Microsoft Account password (see page 45) and press **Enter**, or click on this arrow

3 On the sign-in screen, click on this button to select **Ease of Access** options

4 Click on this button to select **Power off** options, including Shut down and Restart

5 If there are other users with an account on the same laptop, their names will be displayed here

6 Click on another user to access their own sign-in screen

Sign-in settings
Settings for how you sign in can be accessed from the Accounts section in the Settings app:

1 Access the **Settings** app and click on the **Accounts** button

2 Under **Sign-in options**, select options to change your password, create a picture password, or create a PIN instead of a password

3 The **Picture** password option is designed primarily for touchscreen devices but can also be used with a mouse. Select a picture and draw a pattern to use as your sign-in

Don't forget

You can sign in with a Local Account or a Microsoft Account. If you sign in with the latter you will have full access to the related services, such as Mail and People. Also, you will be able to sync your settings and use them on another computer with your Microsoft Account.

59

Hot tip

Windows Hello is a function that uses biometric authentication for signing in to Windows 10. This is either done by scanning your face or with a fingerprint reader. However, specialist hardware is required, and this is not available on many devices at present.

Settings

Accessing Settings

The Settings in Windows 10 provide options for how you set up your computer and how it operates. There are 13 main categories of Settings, each of which have a number of sub-categories. The Settings app can be accessed in various ways:

Hot tip

Add the **Settings** app to the Taskbar for quick access. To do this, access it from the Start menu, right-click on it and click on **More** > **Pin to taskbar**.

60

1 Click on the **Start** button

2 Click on the **Settings** button on the Start menu or the **Settings** tile on the Start menu; or

3 Click on the **Notifications** button on the Taskbar

4 Click on the **All settings** button; or

5 Enter **Settings** into the **Search** box and click on the **Settings** button

6 In the **Settings** app, click on one of the main categories to view the options within that category

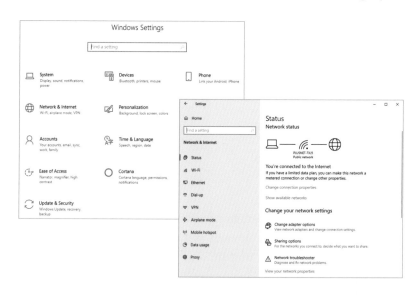

Settings categories

- **System.** These are settings for how your laptop operates, including options for the display, notifications, power and sleep, battery and storage.

- **Devices.** These are settings for how devices connect to your laptop, including Bluetooth devices, printers, touchpad and USB devices.

- **Phone.** This can be used to link an Android smartphone to your Windows Account.

- **Network & Internet.** These are settings for connecting to networks, including connecting to the internet by Wi-Fi, Ethernet cable or dial-up modem.

- **Personalization.** These are settings for personalizing a range of options for your laptop, including background, colors, Lock screen, themes, Start menu and the Taskbar.

- **Apps.** These are settings for managing your apps including viewing details and setting default apps.

- **Accounts.** These are settings for viewing and changing account settings and also setting up new accounts.

- **Time & Language.** These are settings for the time, language and region used on your laptop.

- **Gaming.** These are settings for managing gamer options, including activating Game Mode and using the Game Bar.

- **Ease of Access.** These are settings for accessibility options, covering sight and hearing issues.

- **Cortana.** This can be used to manage Cortana, the digital search and voice assistant.

- **Privacy.** These are settings for general privacy options and also location settings for apps using your location.

- **Update & Security.** These are settings for updating Windows and a range of security options.

Computer screens emit a blue light that can be disruptive in terms of maintaining good sleeping routines at night. The amount of blue light can be decreased in the evening, in the **System** > **Display** settings. Click on the **Night light settings** button in the main panel and apply the required settings (the default is to enable the Night Light settings from **Sunset to sunrise**).

System text can be made bigger within **Ease of Access** > **Display** and drag the **Make text bigger** slider. Click on the **Apply** button to apply any changes.

Searching

Searching for items and information on computers and the internet has come a long way since the first search engines on the web. Most computer operating systems now have sophisticated search facilities for finding things on your own computer as well as searching over the web. They also now have personal digital assistants, which are voice-activated search functions, that can be used instead of typing search requests.

Windows 10 has a Search box built in to the Taskbar, which also includes the personal digital assistant, Cortana. This can also be used for a wide range of voice-activated tasks.

Using the Search box for text searching

To use the Search box for text-only searches, over either your laptop or the web:

Hot tip

The Cortana Search box in Step 1 can be displayed as an icon by right-clicking in it and selecting **Cortana** > **Show Cortana icon** (or **Show search box**, to revert).

1 Click in the Search box

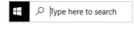

2 Enter a search term (or website address)

3 Click on one of the results, or on the **See web results** button, to view the search results page in the Microsoft Edge browser

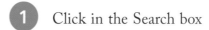

Hot tip

The top search result is displayed at the top of the window in Step 3.

Asking a question

The Search box can also be used to ask specific questions:

1 Enter a question in the Search box

2 Click on the **See web results** button at the top of the Search box to view the results in the Microsoft Edge browser (in some

instances, the answer will be displayed at the top of the Cortana Search box too)

Searching over your laptop

As well as searching over the web, the Search box can also be used to find items on your laptop:

1 Enter a search query into the Search box and click on one of the results to open the item on your computer

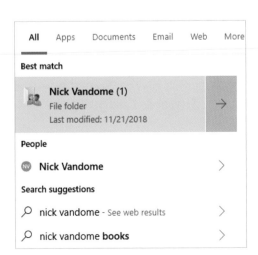

Hot tip

If you are searching for a keyword over files on your computer, the search will be conducted over the text in documents and folders, not just the document titles. It will also search over the online backup and storage facility, OneDrive, if you have this set up.

Setting Up Cortana

To ensure that you can use Cortana to perform voice searches and queries, the language settings on your Windows 10 laptop have to be set up correctly. To do this:

1 Open the **Settings** app and click on the **Time & Language** button

Time & Language
Speech, region, date

2 Click on the **Region** button

⊕ Region

3 Click here to select a country or region

Region

Country or region

United Kingdom ∨

Windows and apps might use your country or region to give you local content.

Regional format

Current format: English (United States)

Recommended [English (United States)] ∨

Windows formats dates and times based on your language and regional preferences.

The country or region, display language and speech language should be the same in order for Cortana to work.

4 Click on the **Language** button

A⅌ Language

5 Click here to select a language to use

Languages

Windows display language

English (United States) ∨

Windows features like Settings and File Explorer will appear in this language.

6 Click on the required display language and click on the **Set as default** button

7 Click on the **Speech** button under **Time & Language**

🎤 Speech

If the Cortana Search box is not displayed once the languages have been set, restart your computer to apply the changes.

8 Select the same **Speech language** as the one used as the display language in Step 5

Speech language

Choose the language you speak with your device

English (United States) ∨

64

Using Cortana

Once the correct languages have been selected for Cortana, you have to ensure that your microphone is working properly since it will be used for voice queries with Cortana.

Setting up the microphone
To set up your laptop's microphone:

1 Open the **Settings** app and click on the **Time & Language** button

2 Click on the **Speech** button

3 Under the **Microphone** section, click on the **Get started** button

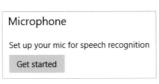

4 In the microphone wizard, click on the **Next** button

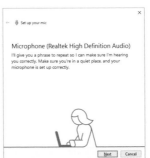

Most modern laptop computers have built-in microphones, but an external one may need to be attached to a desktop computer.

5 Repeat the phrase in the wizard window to complete setting up your microphone. (If the setup is successful, the wizard will move to the completion page automatically)

It can take Cortana a bit of time to fully recognize your voice and style of speech. Make sure that there is no loud background noise when you are using Cortana.

6 Click on the **Finish** button

...cont'd

Voice searching with Cortana

As with text searches, Cortana can be used to search over various places and for different items:

1 Click on the microphone button in the Search box to begin a voice search

2 The Cortana symbol is displayed in the Search window with the word **Listening...** in the Search box. Say what you want to find

3 If Cortana cannot understand what you said, you are asked to try again

4 Cortana can be used to open specific apps; e.g. by saying **Open Mail**. Click on the required items from the options

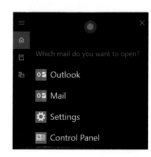

5 The selected app will open, ready for use

6 For a specific request, e.g. **Open Microsoft Edge**, the required app will be opened

Cortana voice commands can be used to turn off, restart or put your PC to sleep. They can also be used to change the system volume. Also, an increasing range of apps support Cortana so can be used in conjunction with it; e.g. for playing movies with Netflix.

Text searches with Cortana

Once Cortana has been set up, text searches can be performed and a range of other information can be displayed by Cortana.

1 Click in the Search box to start a text search

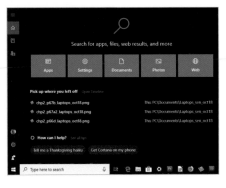

2 Before a search is started, Cortana displays a range of options over which you can search, including apps, settings, documents, photos, and the web. Click on an item to perform the search over this

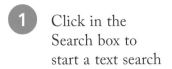
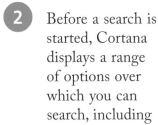

The Cortana interface has been updated in the Windows 10 October 2018 Update, with the options for searching apps, settings, documents, photos, and over the web, at the top of the Search panel.

67

Viewing Notifications

In the modern digital world there is an increasing desire to keep updated about what is happening in our online world. With Windows 10, the Action Center (containing the Notifications panel) can be used to display information from a variety of sources, so that you never miss a notification from one of your apps. To view your notifications:

Hot tip

Click on a notification to open it and view its full contents.

1 Click on the **Notifications** button on the Taskbar

2 New notifications appear at the top of the panel. For selecting what appears, see the next page

Don't forget

Notifications for certain apps also appear onscreen for a short period of time in a small banner, to alert you to the fact that there is a new notification.

3 Quick action buttons appear at the bottom of the panel. Click on an item to activate or deactivate it (when a button is blue, the item is active)

Settings for notifications

To change settings for the Action Center:

1 Click on the **Settings** app and access **System** > **Notifications & actions**

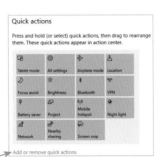

2 Under the **Quick actions** heading, click on the items and drag them into a new position to change where they appear in the Notifications panel

The Notifications area on the Taskbar on the previous page can be customized by right-clicking on the Taskbar and selecting **Taskbar settings** > **Select which icons appear on the taskbar**.

3 Click on the **Add or remove quick actions** link to turn **On** or **Off** the default items on the Taskbar

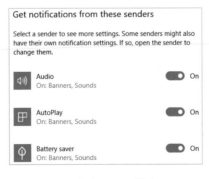

If notification icons are added to the Taskbar, their options can be selected by right-clicking on them.

4 Under the **Get notifications from these senders** heading on the notifications page in Step 2, drag the buttons **On** or **Off** to specify the items that appear in the Action Center. For instance, if the **Mail** button is **On**, you will be notified whenever you receive a new email

Notifications can also be shown on the Lock screen by dragging the **Show notifications on the lock screen** button to **On** in the **Notifications & actions** settings.

69

Dark Mode

By default, computer operating systems and the apps within them use dark text on a white background. However, in the Windows 10 October 2018 update it is possible to invert this, so that white text appears on a black background, known as Dark Mode. This can make text easier to read for some people and also make apps stand out more against the Windows 10 background. Dark Mode is generally a matter of personal taste but it can be a useful option. To use this:

1 Open the **Settings** app and click on the **Personalization** button

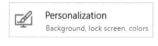

2 Click on the **Colors** button

3 By default, **Light** is selected below the **Choose your default app mode** heading. Click on the **Dark** button to apply Dark Mode

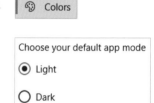

4 Dark Mode is applied to all compatible Windows 10 apps, including the Settings app and the File Explorer

Snipping (Screenshots)

Being able to capture what appears on the screen (screenshot) of a computing device is becoming increasingly popular, to send examples of what you are looking at to other people. In Windows 10 this is done with the Snip & Sketch app. To use this:

1 Click on the **Start** button

2 Navigate to the **Snip & Sketch** button on the Start menu and click on it to open it

3 Open the item to be captured and click on **New > Snip now** on the Snip & Sketch top toolbar

4 Click on one of these buttons to select the type of screenshot to be captured – from left to right: a rectangular selection; a freehand selection; full screen capture; or close the screen capture

5 Drag the cursor around the required area to capture it (the full screen option will automatically capture the whole screen)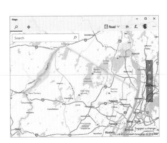

6 The selected area is opened in the Snip & Sketch app. Click on the **Save** button to save it

In Step 3 there are also options to perform the snip after 3 and 10 seconds. This gives you time to access the required item.

Click on the folder button on the top toolbar to select a location into which screenshots are saved.

Once a screenshot has been captured, it can be annotated in the Snip & Sketch app, using the tools on the top toolbar.

Opening File Explorer

Although File Explorer (formerly called Windows Explorer) is not necessarily one of the first apps that you will use with Windows 10, it still plays an important role in organizing your folders and files. To access File Explorer:

1 From the Desktop, click on this icon on the Taskbar, or

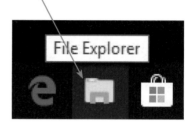

This PC displays files from different locations as a single collection, without actually moving any files.

2 Press **WinKey** + **E**, and File Explorer opens at the **Quick access** folder

3 When File Explorer is opened, click on the **This PC** option to view the top-level items on your laptop, including the main folders, your hard drive and any removable devices that are connected

You can click on the **Start** button and access File Explorer from here too (**Windows System > File Explorer**).

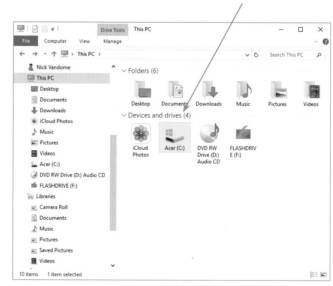

Quick Access in File Explorer

When working with files and folders there will probably be items that you access on a regular basis. The Quick access section of the File Explorer can be used to view the items that you have most recently accessed, and also to pin your most frequently-used and favorite items. To use the Quick access section:

1 Click on the **Quick access** button in the File Explorer Navigation pane so that the right-pointing arrow becomes downwards-pointing

The items displayed under Quick access are not physically located here; the links are just shortcuts to the actual location within your file structure.

2 In the main window, your frequently-used folders and most recently-used files are displayed

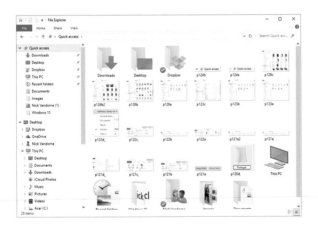

3 The folders are also listed underneath the **Quick access** button in the Navigation pane

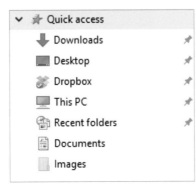

...cont'd

Adding items to Quick access

The folders that you access and use most frequently can be pinned to the Quick access section. This does not physically move them; it just creates a shortcut within Quick access. To do this:

Windows 10

1 Right-click on the folder you want to pin, and click on **Pin to Quick access**

> **Open**
> Open in new window
> Pin to Quick access

2 The folder is pinned to the Quick access section, which is denoted by the pin symbol; or

- Quick access
- Downloads
- Desktop
- Dropbox
- This PC
- Recent folders
- Windows 10

3 Drag the folder over the Quick access button until the **Pin to Quick access** option appears, and then release

Don't forget

To unpin an item from Quick access, right-click on it and click on **Unpin from Quick access**.

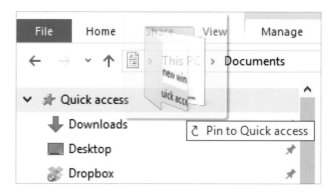

File   Home   Share   View   Manage

This PC › Documents

new win
uick acc

- Quick access
  - Downloads
  - Desktop
  - Dropbox

↻ Pin to Quick access

Scenic Ribbon

The navigation and functionality in the Libraries (where content within File Explorer is stored) is provided by the Scenic Ribbon at the top of the window. This has options for the Library itself and also the type of content that is being viewed.

The Scenic Ribbon is also referred to as just the Ribbon.

1 Click on the tabs at the top of the Library window to view associated tools

2 Click on the Library Tools tab to view the menus for the whole Library (see below)

3 Click on the content tab (Picture Tools in this example) to view menus for the selected content

Library File menu
This contains options for opening a new window; closing the current window; or moving to a frequently-visited location in the Library.

Library Home menu
This contains options for copying and pasting; moving; deleting; and renaming selected items. You can also create new folders; view properties; and select all items in a folder.

The **File** button in the Ribbon remains highlighted in blue, regardless of which other menu is accessed.

...cont'd

Library Share menu

This contains options for sharing selected items, by sending them to another user on the computer; burning them to a CD or DVD; creating a compressed Zip file; or sending the items to a printer.

Library View menu

This contains options for how you view the items in the current active folder.

Hot tip

Click on the **Options** button on the View menu to set additional options for the operation of a folder and how items are displayed within it.

Library Manage menu

This contains options for managing specific libraries. Click on the **Manage library** button to add additional folders to the one currently being viewed.

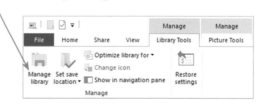

Library menu options

If there is a down-pointing arrow next to an item on a Library menu, click it to see additional options such as the **Optimize library for** button, which optimizes the folder for specific types of content.

4 Working with Apps

In Windows 10, some apps are pre-installed, while hundreds more can be downloaded from the Microsoft Store. This chapter shows how to work with and organize apps in Windows 10.

78 Starting with Apps

80 Windows 10 Apps

82 Using Windows 10 Apps

84 Closing Apps

85 Viewing All Apps

86 Searching for Apps

87 Using the Microsoft Store

89 Buying Apps

90 Viewing Your Apps

91 Installing and Uninstalling Apps

Starting with Apps

The word "app" is now widely used to cover any computer program. So, in Windows 10, most programs are referred to as "apps", although some legacy ones may still be referred to as "programs".

There are three clear types of apps within Windows 10:

- **Windows 10 apps**. These are the built-in apps that can be accessed from the Start menu. They cover the areas of communication, entertainment and information, and several of them are linked together through the online sharing service: OneDrive. In Windows 10 they open in their own window on the Desktop, in the same way as the older-style Windows apps (see below).

- **Windows classic apps**. These are the older-style Windows apps that people may be familiar with from previous versions of Windows. These open in the Desktop environment.

- **Microsoft Store apps**. These are apps that can be downloaded from the online Microsoft Store, and cover a wide range of subjects and functionality. Some Microsoft Store apps are free, while others have to be paid for.

Windows 10 apps

Windows 10 apps are accessed from the brightly-colored tiles on the Start menu (or listed on the left-hand side). Click on a tile to open the relevant app:

In Windows 10, all apps open directly on the Desktop and their operation is more consistent, regardless of the type of app.

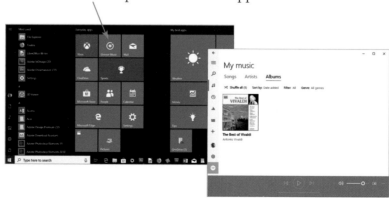

Windows classic apps

The Windows classic apps are generally the ones that appeared as default with previous versions of Windows, and would have been accessed from the Start button. The Windows classic apps can be accessed from the Start menu by using the alphabetic list, or searched for via the Taskbar Search box. Windows classic apps have the traditional Windows look and functionality, and they also open on the Desktop.

Some older Windows apps, such as Notepad and Paint, can be found in the Windows Accessories folder in the All Apps alphabetic list. Alternatively, they can be searched for using the Cortana Search box.

Microsoft Store apps

The Microsoft Store apps are accessed and downloaded from the online Microsoft Store. Apps can be browsed and searched for in the Store, and when they are downloaded they are added to the All Apps alphabetic list on the Start menu.

The Microsoft Store is accessed by clicking on the **Store** tile on the Start menu or on the Taskbar.

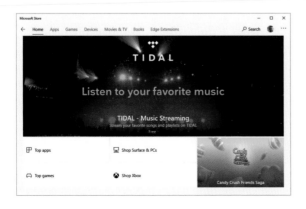

Windows 10 Apps

The Windows 10 apps that are accessed from the All Apps alphabetic list on the Start menu include:

If some of the apps listed here are not pre-installed on your Windows 10 laptop, they can be downloaded from the Microsoft Store, where some of them are prefixed with MSN; e.g. MSN Money.

See pages 94-105 for more information about working with the Microsoft Edge browser.

Don't forget

The Movies & TV app is named Films & TV in some regions.

 Alarms & Clock. This provides alarms; clocks around the world; a timer; and a stopwatch function.

 Calculator. This is a standard calculator that also has an option for using it as a scientific calculator.

 Calendar. This is a calendar that you can use to add appointments and important dates.

 Camera. This can be used to take photos directly onto your laptop, but only if it has a built-in camera.

 Connect. This can be used to connect a PC so that it can be used as a wireless projector.

 Cortana. This is the personal digital assistant for Windows 10 that can be used to search for items.

 Groove Music. This can be used to access the online Music Store, where music can be downloaded.

 Mail. This is the online Mail facility. You can use it to connect to a selection of email accounts.

 Maps. This provides online access to maps from around the world. It also shows traffic issues.

 Messaging. This can be used to send text messages to other users, using a Microsoft Account.

 Microsoft Edge. This is the default browser in Windows 10.

 Money. This is an information app that provides real-time financial news, based on your location.

 Movies & TV. This is where you will see the movies and TV shows you buy in the Microsoft Store.

 News. This is an information app that provides real-time news information, based on your location.

OneDrive. This is an online facility for storing and sharing content from your computer. This includes photos and documents.

 OneNote. This is a Microsoft note-taking app; part of the Office suite of apps.

 Paint 3D. This is an app that can be used to create, view and share 3D objects.

 People. This is the address book app for adding contacts. Your contacts from sites such as Gmail and iCloud can also be imported into the People app.

 Photos. This can be used to view and organize your photos. You can also share and print photos directly from the Photos app.

 Reader. This can be used to open and view documents in different file formats, such as PDF and TIFF.

 Sports. This is one of the information apps that provide real-time sports news, based on your location.

 Sticky Notes. This is an app for creating short notes that can be "stuck" to the screen, so that they are readily visible.

 Store. This provides access to the online Microsoft Store for buying and downloading apps.

 Tips. This can be used to view the latest tips and hints about using Windows 10.

 Weather. This provides real-time weather forecasts for locations around the world. By default, it will provide the nearest forecast to your location.

 Xbox. This can be used to download and play games, and also play online Xbox games.

OneDrive can also be used to share your content such as photos and documents with other people. See pages 114-117 for details.

The **3D Viewer** app can be used to download and view 3D objects that have been created by you (using the Paint 3D app) or by other people.

Using Windows 10 Apps

In Windows 8 and 8.1, the newer-style Windows apps had a different look and functionality. However, in Windows 10 all of the apps have been created with a more consistent appearance, although there are still some differences.

Windows 10 apps

Windows 10 apps open in their own window on the Desktop (in Windows 8 and 8.1 they only opened in full screen) and they can be moved and resized in the same way as older-style apps:

In Windows 10 there has been a conscious effort to achieve a greater consistency between the newer-style apps and the old, classic-style apps.

1 Click and drag on the top toolbar to move the app's window

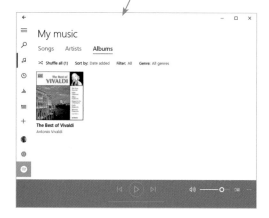

2 Drag on the bottom or right-hand border to resize the app's window (or the bottom right-hand corner to resize the height and width simultaneously)

Windows 10 app menus

Some Windows 10 apps have their own menus:

1 Click on this button (if available) within the app's window to access its menu

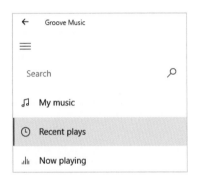

2 Click on the Menu button again to minimize the menu to just the icons, without text

Don't forget

Apps that are installed from a CD or DVD are automatically included on the alphabetical list on the Start menu.

3 Click here to move to previously-viewed pages within the app

Managing an app's window

As with older-style apps, the Windows 10 apps also have the same control buttons on the top toolbar:

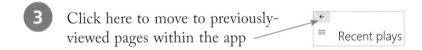

1 Click on this button to close the app

2 Click on this button to maximize the app's window

□

3 Click on this button to minimize the app's window (it will be minimized onto the Taskbar)

—

Closing Apps

There are several ways to close a Windows app:

- Click on the red **Close** button in the top-right of the window.

- Select **File** > **Exit** from the File menu (if available).

- Press **Alt** + **F4**.

It is always worth saving a new document as soon as it is created. It should also be saved at regular intervals as you are working on it.

- Right-click on the icon on the Taskbar and select **Close window**.

If any changes have been made to the document, you may receive a warning message advising you to save the associated file.

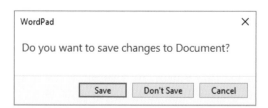

Viewing All Apps

There is a lot more to Windows 10 than the default Windows 10 apps. Most of the Windows apps that were available with previous versions of Windows are still there, and in Windows 10 they are all available directly from the Start button, on the Start menu. To access all of the apps:

1 Click on the **Start** button

2 All of the apps are displayed. Use the scroll bar to move through all of the apps, which are listed alphabetically

3 Click on a letter heading to view an alphabetic grid for finding apps. Click on a letter to move to that section

Searching for Apps

As you acquire more and more apps, it may become harder to find the ones you want. To help with this, you can use the Search box to search over all of the apps on your laptop. To do this:

1 Click in the Search box on the Taskbar

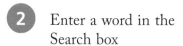

2 Enter a word in the Search box

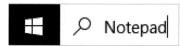

3 As you type, relevant apps are displayed. When the one you are seeking appears, click on it to start the app

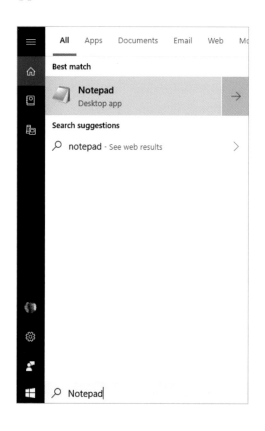

Hot tip

You just have to put in the first couple of letters of an app name, and the search will automatically suggest results based on this. The more that you type, the more specific the results become. Case does not matter when you are typing a search query.

Using the Microsoft Store

The third category of apps that can be used with Windows 10 are those that are downloaded from the Microsoft Store. These cover a wide range of topics and they provide an excellent way to add functionality to Windows 10. To use the Microsoft Store:

1 Click on the **Store** tile on the Taskbar

2 The currently-featured apps are displayed on the Home screen

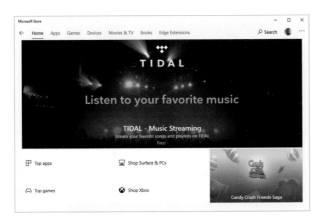

Windows 10 apps can all be downloaded from the Microsoft Store.

3 Scroll up and down to see additional featured apps

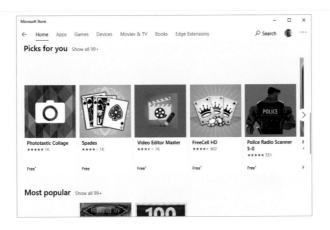

...cont'd

4 Click on the **Top apps** button on the Homepage and select apps under specific headings; e.g. **Best selling** apps

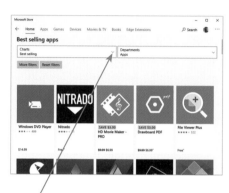

5 Click here to select options for viewing apps according to certain criteria; e.g. **Top free**

Scroll up and down in Step 6 to view ratings and reviews about the app and also any additional descriptions.

6 Click on an app to preview it, and for more details about the app

Buying Apps

When you find an app that you want to use, you can download it to your laptop. To do this:

1 Access the app and click on the **Get** (or price) button

If there is a fee for an app, this will be displayed instead of the **Get** button.

2 The app downloads from the Microsoft Store, and a **Downloading** message is displayed

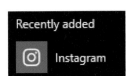

3 The app is added to the Start menu and has a **New** tag next to it. This disappears once the app has been opened

You need to have credit or debit card details registered on your Microsoft Account in order to buy paid-for apps.

4 Click on the app to open and use it (initially it will be available under the **Recently added** section of the Start menu, as well as its own alpha listing)

Viewing Your Apps

As you download more and more apps from the Microsoft Store you may lose track of which ones you have obtained, and when. To help with this, you can review all of the apps you have downloaded, from within the Microsoft Store. To do this:

1 Open the Microsoft Store and click on the Menu button, to the right of your account picture button at the top of the screen

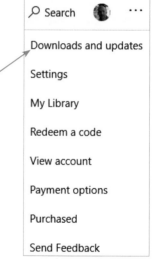

2 Click on the **Downloads and updates** button

Don't forget

You can reinstall apps from the Downloads and updates section, even if you have previously uninstalled them. If there was a fee for an app, you will not have to pay again to reinstall it.

3 All of the apps that have been downloaded are displayed. Click on the **Get updates** button to see if there are any updates for the listed apps

Installing and Uninstalling Apps

Installing apps from a CD or DVD

If the app you want to install is provided on a CD or DVD, you normally just insert the disc. The installation app starts up automatically, and you can follow the instructions to select features and complete the installation. If this does not happen automatically:

1 Insert the disc and click on this notification window

DVD RW Drive (D:) CS5 Design Prem1 ✕
Tap to choose what happens with this disc.

2 Double-click on the **Run Set-up.exe** file link to run it. Follow the on-screen prompts to install the app

DVD RW Drive (D:) CS5 Des...

Choose what to do with this disc.

Install or run program from your media

Run Set-up.exe
Published by Adobe Systems Incorporated

Other choices

Import pictures and videos
Dropbox

Open folder to view files
File Explorer

Take no action

3 Apps that are installed from a CD or DVD are added to the All Apps list on the Start menu

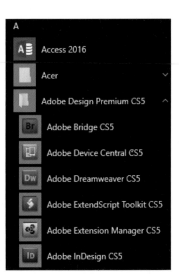

A

A☰ Access 2016

Acer

Adobe Design Premium CS5

Br Adobe Bridge CS5

Adobe Device Central CS5

Dw Adobe Dreamweaver CS5

Adobe ExtendScript Toolkit CS5

Adobe Extension Manager CS5

ID Adobe InDesign CS5

Hot tip

You can access the Run function in Windows 10 by right-clicking on the **Start** button and selecting **Run** from the contextual menu.

Hot tip

Apps can also be installed from discs from File Explorer. To do this, locate the **Set-up.exe** file double-click start the i process i way as

...cont'd

Uninstalling apps

In some previous versions of Windows, apps were uninstalled through the Control Panel. However, in Windows 10 they can also be uninstalled directly from the Start menu. To do this:

1 Right-click on an app to access its menu

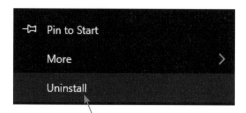

📌 Pin to Start

More   >

Uninstall

2 Click on the **Uninstall** button

3 A window alerts you to the fact that related information will be

> This app and its related info will be uninstalled.
>
> **Uninstall**

removed if the app is uninstalled. Click on the **Uninstall** button if you want to continue

4 If the app is a new Windows 10 one, or it has been pinned to the Start menu (or Taskbar), its tile will be removed from its pinned location(s). For other apps, they will no longer be available from the list of apps

If apps have been installed from a CD or DVD they can still be uninstalled from within the Control Panel (**Start > Windows system > Control Panel**). To do this, select the **Programs** section and click on the **Uninstall a program** link. The installed apps will be displayed. Select one of the apps and click on the **Uninstall/Change** link.

Don't forget

Some elements of Windows 10, such as the Control Panel, still refer to apps as ˈrograms, but they are ˈ same thing.

5 The Online World

This chapter looks at getting online so that you can make the most of the expanding online world. It covers the Microsoft Edge browser, for viewing and managing web pages; the Mail app for email; the online storage and backup facility, OneDrive; and the options for creating and viewing online address books and calendars.

94 Introducing the Edge Browser

95 Smart Address Bar

96 Setting a Homepage

97 Using Tabs

100 Bookmarking Web Pages

101 Adding Notes to Web Pages

103 Organizing with the Hub

104 Reading List

105 Reading View

106 Shopping Online

108 Booking a Vacation

110 Setting Up Mail

112 Working with Mail

114 Using OneDrive

117 OneDrive Settings

118 Finding People

120 Using the Calendar

Introducing the Edge Browser

The web browser Internet Explorer (IE) has been synonymous with Microsoft for almost as long as the Windows operating system. Introduced in 1995, shortly after Windows 95, it has been the default browser for a generation of web users. However, as with most technologies, the relentless march of time has caught up with IE and, although it is still included and can be used with Windows 10, the preferred browser is designed specifically for the digital mobile age. It is called Microsoft Edge, and adapts easily to whichever environment it is operating in: desktop, tablet or smartphone.

The Microsoft Edge browser has a number of performance and speed enhancements compared with IE, including a function for drawing on and annotating web pages, which can then be sent to other people as screenshots.

There is also a Hub where you can store all of your favorites, downloads and pages that you have selected to read at a later date (which can be when you are offline if required).

Click on this icon from the **Taskbar** or the **Start** menu to open the Microsoft Edge browser at the default Start page.

Before you can use the internet and browse the web, your laptop needs to be set up for connection to the internet. To do this you will require an Internet Service Provider (ISP) to provide an account that gives you access to the internet, either via Wi-Fi with a router; through a cable connection using an Ethernet cable; or through a fiber-optic connection.

Back/forward buttons   Refresh   Hub button   Toolbar buttons

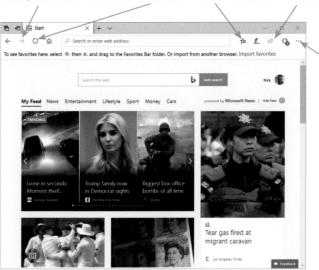

Menu options

The Start page can be replaced by your own specific Homepage. See page 96 for details.

Smart Address Bar

Smart address bars are now a familiar feature in a lot of modern browsers, and Microsoft Edge is no different. These can be used to enter a specific web address, to open that page or use it to search for a word or phrase. To use the smart address bar:

1 Click anywhere in the Start page address box or in the address box at the top of a web page

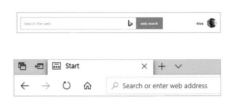

The personal digital assistant, Cortana, can also be used to open web pages, by asking it to open a specific page. The page will be opened in Microsoft Edge.

2 Start typing a word or website address. As you type, options appear below the address bar. Click on a web page address to open that website

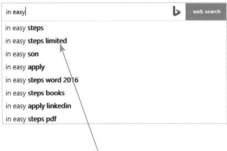

3 Click on one of the options to view the search result for that item

Search results are found through Microsoft's search engine, Bing. To change the default search engine, click on **...** (Menu Options) > **Settings**. Then, select the **Advanced** option and click on the **Change search provider** button at the bottom of the panel. Select a new default search engine and click on the **Set as default** button.

Setting a Homepage

By default, Microsoft Edge opens at its own Start page. This may not be ideal for most users, who will want to set their own Homepage that appears when Microsoft Edge is launched.

Hot tip

The Microsoft Edge browser has a Homepage button on the top toolbar. If the Homepage button is not showing, select **Settings** as in Step 2 and in the **General** section under **Show the home button**, click the button **On**.

Hot tip

Within the settings for Microsoft Edge there is an option for importing favorites from another web browser. To do this, click on the **Import or export** button in the **General** section, under the **Transfer favorites and other info** heading, then select the required browser, and click on the **Import** button.

1 Click on this button on the top toolbar to access the menu options

2 Click on the **Settings** button

3 The Settings open at the **General** section. By default, the Start page is selected as the opening page

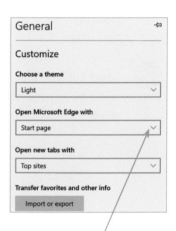

4 Click here and select **A specific page or pages**

5 Enter the website address you want to use as your Homepage, and click on the **Save** button

ineasysteps.com

Using Tabs

Being able to open several web pages at the same time in different tabs is now a common feature of web browsers. To do this with Microsoft Edge:

1 Click on this button at the top of the Microsoft Edge window

2 Pages can be opened in new tabs using the smart address bar or the list of **Top sites** that appears below it

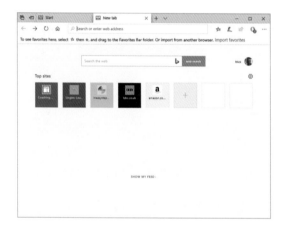

Hot tip

The Start page for new tabs, as displayed in Step 2, can be changed if required. To do this, open the Microsoft Edge **Settings** as shown on the previous page. In the **General** section change the selection under the **Open new tabs with** heading.

3 All open tabs are displayed at the top of the window. Click and hold on a tab to drag it into a new position

...cont'd

Tab previews

If there are a large number of tabs open it can be hard to remember exactly what is in each one. This is addressed in the Edge browser through the tab previews function.

1 All open tabs are shown at the top of the browser, with the current active tab colored light gray

2 Move the mouse cursor over one of the inactive tabs to view a preview of the content within it

3 Click on this button next to the New Tab button to view thumbnails of the current tabs

4 Thumbnails of all of the current tabs are displayed. Click on one to view it, or click on this button to close the preview panel

...cont'd

Set aside tabs
To avoid the Edge browser window becoming too cluttered with open tabs at the top of it, it is possible to set aside the current tabs so that they are stored together, but not along the top of the browser window. To do this:

1 All open tabs are shown at the top of the browser

2 Click on this button to set-aside the open tabs

3 The tabs are set aside, indicated by this button being colored
black and only the **New tab** window showing

4 Click on this button to view the set-aside tabs

5 Click on one of the set-aside tabs to open it

6 Click on the **Restore tabs** button to reopen all of the set-aside tabs

Restore tabs ··· ✕

7 Click on the **Menu** button to access the options for the set-aside tabs, including adding them to your favorites or sharing them

Bookmarking Web Pages

Your favorite web pages can be bookmarked so that you can access them with one click from the Hub area, rather than having to enter the web address each time. To do this:

1 Open the web page that you want to bookmark

2 Click on this button on the toolbar

3 Click on the **Favorites** button

4 Enter a name for the favorite and where you want it to be saved to

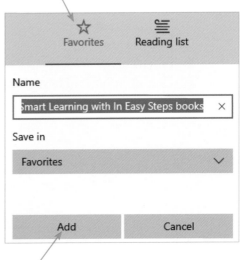

The Favorites bar can be displayed underneath the Address bar by opening the Microsoft Edge **Settings** and, in the **General** section, dragging the **Show the favorites bar** button to **On**.

5 Click on the **Add** button

6 The star button turns yellow, indicating that the web page has been added as a Favorite

7 Click on this button to access your Favorites (see page 103)

Adding Notes to Web Pages

One of the innovations in the Microsoft Edge browser is the ability to draw on and annotate web pages. This can be useful to highlight parts of a web page or add your own comments and views, which can then be sent to other people. To add notes:

1 Open a web page to which you want to add a note or draw on, and click on this button on the toolbar of the Microsoft Edge browser

2 Click on one of the pen options

3 Make selections for the pen style, including color and size

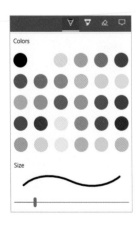

Don't forget

Click on this button on the Notes toolbar to create a web clipping. This is an area of a web page that is selected by dragging over it to make the selection.

Don't forget

Click on this button on the Notes toolbar to save a web note or clipping. These can then be accessed from the Favorites section of Microsoft Edge (see page 103).

...cont'd

4 Click and drag on the web page to draw over it

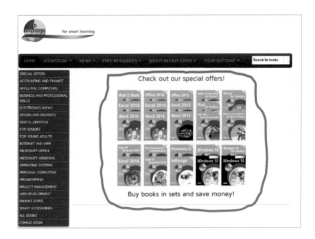

5 Click on the eraser icon and drag over any items that you have drawn to remove them, or part of them

6 Click on the text icon to add your own text

7 Drag over the web page to create a text box

8 Type the text that you want displayed on the web page

Look at some of these!

9 Click and drag here on a text box to move its position in the window

Organizing with the Hub

The Hub is the area where you can store a variety of items, from your favorite web pages to pages that you want to read offline at a later date. To use the Hub:

1 Click on this button to open the Hub

2 Click on this button to view your **Favorites**. Click on one to go to that page

3 Click on this button to view your **Reading list** of pages that you have saved to read offline, or at a later date (see page 104 for details)

4 Click on this button to view your web browsing **History**

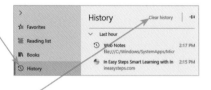

5 Click on **Clear history** to remove the items in the history

6 Click on this button to view **Downloads** that you have accessed from the web, such as PDF documents or apps (although not those from the Microsoft Store)

Hot tip

Click on the **Books** button within the Hub to view any books that have been downloaded from the Microsoft Store and read them in the Edge browser.

Reading List

With some web pages you may want to save the content so that you can read it at a later date. If you make the page a favorite, the content could change the next time you look at it. Instead, you can add the page to your Reading list to ensure that you can read the same content. Also, you have the advantage of being able to access the items in your Reading list when you are offline and not connected to the internet. To do this:

The Reading list is an excellent option if you are traveling and do not have internet access. You can save numerous articles in the Reading list and access them even when you are offline.

1 Open the web page to be added to the Reading list

2 Click on this button on the Edge toolbar

3 Click on the **Reading list** button

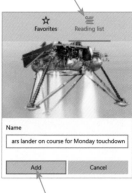

4 Enter a name for the item, and click on the **Add** button

5 Click on this button within the Hub to access and view your Reading list items

Reading View

Modern web pages contain a lot more items than just text and pictures: video clips, pop-up ads, banners, and more contribute to the multimedia effect on many web pages. At times this additional content can enhance the page, but a lot of the time it is a distraction. If you want to just concentrate on the main item on a web page, you can do this with the Reading view function:

1 Open the web page that you want to view in Reading view

Not all web pages support the Reading view functionality. If it is not supported, the button in Step 2 will be grayed out.

2 Click on this button on the Microsoft Edge toolbar

3 The text and pictures are presented on a new page, with any additional content removed

4 Click on this button again to return to the standard page view

Shopping Online

Some people love physically looking around shops, while for others it is a chore. For the latter group, online shopping is one of the great innovations of the web. With a laptop, it is possible to do your shopping in the comfort of your own home, while also avoiding the crowds.

When you are shopping online there are some guidelines that you should follow, to try to ensure you are in a safe online environment and do not spend too much money:

- Make a note of what you want to buy, and stick to this once you have found it. Online shopping sites are adept at displaying a lot of enticing offers, and it is a lot easier to buy something by clicking a button than it is to physically take it to a checkout.

- Never buy anything that is promoted to you via an email unless it is from a company who you have asked to send you promotional information.

- When paying for items, make sure that the online site has a secure area for accepting payment and credit card details. A lot of sites display information about this within their payment area, and another way to ascertain this is to check in the address bar of the payment page. If it is within a secure area, the address of the page will start with "https" rather than the standard "http".

Using online shopping

The majority of online shopping sites are similar in their operation:

- Goods are identified.

- Goods are placed in a shopping basket.

Don't forget

A lot of online shopping sites list recommendations for you based on what you have already looked at or bought on the site. This is done by using "cookies", which are small programs that are downloaded from the site and then track the items that you look at on the site (see the next page for further information on cookies).

- Once the shopping is completed, you proceed to the checkout.

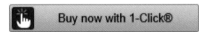

- For some sites you have to register before you can complete your purchase, while with others you do not.

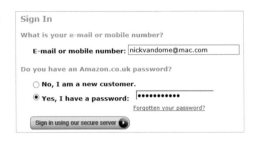

- You enter your shipping details and pay for the goods, usually with a credit or debit card.

In some cases, if you are registered on a site, you can complete your shopping by using a 1-Click system. This means that all of your billing, delivery and payment details are already stored on the site, and you can buy goods simply by clicking one button without having to re-enter your details. One of the most prominent sites to use this method is Amazon.

Using cookies

A lot of online shopping sites use cookies, which are small programs that store information about your browsing habits on the site. Sites have to tell you if they are using cookies, and they can be a good way to receive targeted information about products in which you are interested. This can be done on the sites when you are logged in, or via email.

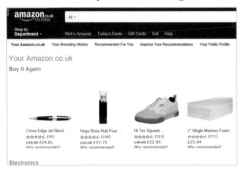

Beware

One-click shopping is an effective way to spend money very quickly. However, you usually have a period of time in which you can cancel your purchases after you have bought them in this way.

Booking a Vacation

Just as many retailers have created an online presence, the same is also true for vacation companies and travel agents. It is now possible to book almost any type of vacation on the web, from cruises to city breaks.

Several sites offer full travel services where they can deal with flights, hotels, insurance, car hire and excursions. These sites include:

- **www.expedia.com**
- **www.kayak.com**
- **www.orbitz.com**
- **www.travelocity.com**

These sites usually list special offers and last-minute deals on their Homepages, or if you sign up to an email newsletter. There is also a facility for specifying your precise requirements. To do this:

It is always worth searching different sites to get the best possible prices. In some cases it is cheapest to buy different elements of a vacation from different sites; e.g. flights from one and accommodation from another.

108

1 Select your vacation requirements. This can include flight or hotel only, or a combination of both, with or without car hire options

2 Enter flight details

3 Enter dates for your vacation

4 Click on the **Search** button

TripAdvisor

One of the best resources for travelers is TripAdvisor. Not only does the site provide a full range of opportunities for booking flights and hotels, it also has an extensive network of reviews from people who have visited the countries, hotels and restaurants on the site. These are independent, and usually very fair and honest. In a lot of cases, if there are

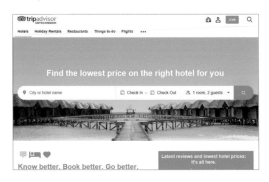

issues with a hotel or restaurant, the proprietor posts a reply to explain what is being done to address any problems.

Vacation and hotel websites usually have versions that are specific to your geographical location.

Cruises

There are also websites dedicated specifically to cruises:

- **www.carnival.com**
- **www.cruises.com**
- **www.princess.com**

The web is also excellent for researching family history and genealogy. Some sites to try are Ancestry; Genealogy; FamilySearch; and RootsWeb.

Hotels

There are a range of websites that specialize in hotel bookings, a lot of them at short notice to get the best price:

- **www.choicehotels.com**
- **www.hotels.com**
- **www.laterooms.com**
- **www.trivago.com**

Setting Up Mail

Email has become an essential part of our online lives, both socially and for official communication. Windows 10 accommodates this with the Mail app. This can be used to link to online services such as Gmail and Outlook (the renamed version of Hotmail), and also other email accounts. To set up an email account with Mail:

Hot tip

The **Other account** option in Step 4 can be used to add a non-webmail account. This is usually a POP3 account and you will need your email address, username, password, and usually the incoming and outgoing email servers. If you do not know these they should be supplied by your email provider. They should also be available in the account settings of the email account you want to add to the Mail app.

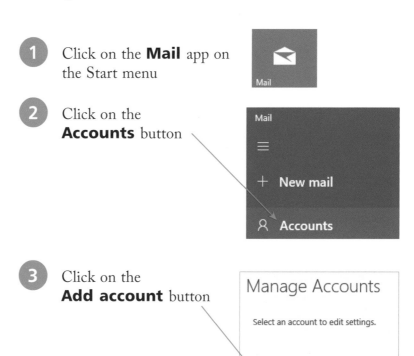

1 Click on the **Mail** app on the Start menu

2 Click on the **Accounts** button

3 Click on the **Add account** button

4 Select the type of account to which you want to link via the Mail app. This can be an online email account that you have already set up

5 Enter your current sign-in details for the selected email account and click on the **Sign in** button

You can add more than one account to the Mail app. If you do this you will be able to select the different accounts to view within Mail.

6 Once it has been connected, the details of the account are shown under the Mail heading, including the mailboxes within the account. Click on the **Inbox** to view the emails within it

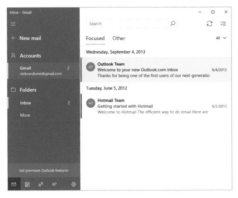

7 The list of emails appears in the main window. Double-click on an email to view it at full size

Working with Mail

Once you have set up an account in the Mail app you can then start creating and managing your emails with it.

1 On the Inbox page, open an email and click on the **Reply**, **Reply all** or **Forward** buttons

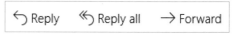

2 Open an email and click on the **Delete** button to remove it

To compose and send an email message:

Contacts that are added automatically as email recipients are taken from the People app, providing there is an email address connected to their entry.

1 Click on this button to create a new message

2 Click in the **To** field and enter an email address

3 Click on the **Cc & Bcc** link to access options for copying and blind copying

4 The email address can either be in the format of myname@email.com or enter the name of one of your contacts from the People app and the email address will be entered automatically

5 Enter a subject heading and body text to the email

6 Click on the **Insert** button on the top toolbar in the new email window and select one of the options, such as **Pictures**

7 Click on a folder from which you want to attach the file, and click on the **Insert** button

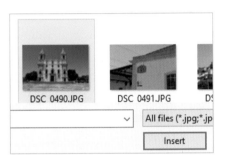

8 The file is shown in the body of the email

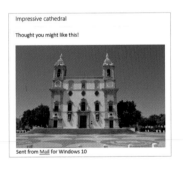

Social media is another popular way of keeping in touch with people and sharing a variety of content. Sites such as Facebook, Twitter, Snapchat, Instagram and Pinterest can be accessed through the Edge browser, and some have their own apps that can be downloaded from the Microsoft Store.

113

9 Select an item of text, and select the text formatting options from the top toolbar

10 Click on this button to send the email

Using OneDrive

Cloud computing is now a mainstream part of our online experience. This involves saving content to an online server connected to the service that you are using; i.e. through your Microsoft Account. You can then access this content from any computer, using your account login details, and also share it with other people by giving them access to your Cloud service. It can also be used to back up your files, in case they get corrupted or damaged on your PC.

The Cloud service with Windows 10 is known as OneDrive, and you can use it with a Microsoft Account. It consists of the OneDrive folder in the File Explorer; the OneDrive app; and the online OneDrive website. Content added to any of the elements will be available in the others. To use them:

Hot tip

Your OneDrive folder, and the OneDrive app, can be pinned to the Quick access section in File Explorer. To do this, right-click on the OneDrive icon in File Explorer and click on **Pin to Quick access**.

114

Don't forget

The OneDrive folder in File Explorer and the OneDrive app contain the same content, but they are accessed from different buttons on the Start menu. If the OneDrive app is not available, it can be downloaded from the Microsoft Store.

1 Click on the **OneDrive** folder in the File Explorer to view its contents. Or, click on this button on the Start menu

2 Download the OneDrive app from the Microsoft Store and click on this icon on the Start menu to open it. It should display the same items as in the OneDrive folder in the File Explorer

3 To view the
contents of
OneDrive online,
go to the website
at **onedrive.
live.com** and
sign in with
your Microsoft

Account details. Your OneDrive content is the same
as in your OneDrive folder on your computer

Files and folders can be added to OneDrive from any of the
three elements:

Adding items to OneDrive in File Explorer

1 In File Explorer, the
OneDrive folder is located
underneath Quick access
(and any other folders that
have been added)

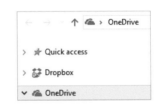

2 Click on the
OneDrive folder to
view its contents

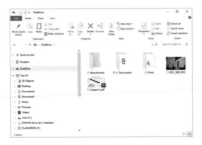

3 Add files to the
OneDrive folder
by dragging and
dropping them from
another folder, or by
using Copy and Paste

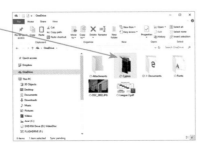

Files can also be saved
directly to OneDrive
when they are created.
To do this:

Open a new file in any
app and create the
required content.

Select **File** > **Save**
from the menu bar
and, in File Explorer,
select a OneDrive
folder into which you
want to save the file.

Click on the **Save**
button.

The file is saved into
the File Explorer
OneDrive folder and
will be available from
the OneDrive app, and
also online from your
OneDrive account.

115

...cont'd

Adding items to the OneDrive app

1 Open OneDrive app and click on this button

2 Click on the **Upload** button and navigate to the files that you want to upload from File Explorer

Adding items to OneDrive online

1 Access your online OneDrive account and click on the **Upload** button

Hot tip

You can share your **Public** folder from your online OneDrive account by opening it, and clicking or tapping on the **Share** button. You can then email the link to the Public folder to selected recipients.

2 Select whether to upload **Files** or a **Folder**

3 Navigate to the required item within File Explorer. Click on an item to select it and click on the **Open** button to add it to your online OneDrive site

OneDrive Settings

A range of settings can be applied to OneDrive, including adding and syncing folders. To do this:

1 Right-click on the OneDrive icon on the Notifications area of the Taskbar and click on **Settings**

> Open your OneDrive folder
>
> Settings
>
> View online

2 Click on the **Settings** tab for options for starting OneDrive when you sign in, and how notifications operate with OneDrive

3 Click on the **Account** tab and click on the **Choose folders** button to select the folder from your computer that you want to sync with your OneDrive account

4 Click on the **OK** button to apply any changes to the OneDrive settings

By default, you get 5GB of free OneDrive storage space with Windows 10 (the free allowance was reduced from 15GB in July 2016). This is an excellent way to back up your important documents, since they are stored away from your computer. For up-to-date information on plan allowances and pricing, visit **https://onedrive.live.com/about/plans/**

Finding People

An electronic address book is always a good feature to have on a computer, and with Windows 10 this function is provided by the People app. This can be used with a Microsoft Account so that your address book can be viewed online from any internet-enabled computer. You can also link to any of your online accounts, such as Gmail or iCloud, and import the contacts that you have there.

1 Click on the **People** app on the Start menu

2 The current contacts are displayed. By default, these will be linked to your Microsoft Account, if you have created one

3 Click on the **Settings** button to add new accounts from which you want to import contacts, such as a Google or an iCloud account (in the same way as setting up a new email account). Click on the **Add an account** button to add the required account: the contacts from the linked account are imported to the People app

Adding contacts manually

As well as importing contacts, it is also possible to enter them manually into the People app:

1 Click on this button at the top of the **People** app

2 Enter details for the new contact, including name, email address and phone number

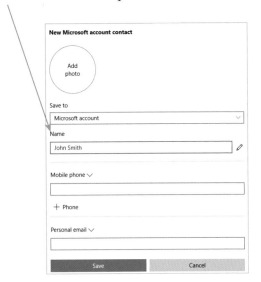

Hot tip

To delete a contact, right-click on their name in the Contacts list and click on the **Delete** button to remove it.

119

3 Click on the Down arrow next to a field to access additional options for that item

Hot tip

Once a contact has been added, select it from the list shown in Step 2 on the previous page and click on this button to edit the contact's details.

4 Click on the **Save** button at the bottom of the window to create the new contact

Using the Calendar

The Calendar app can be used to record important events and reminders. As with the People app, it can be connected to your Microsoft Account so that it can be viewed online from any internet-enabled computer. It can also be linked to other online accounts, so that you can import details from these. To use the calendar:

Don't forget

Accounts can be added to the Calendar app in the same way as for the Mail and People apps.

120

1 Click on the **Calendar** app on the Start menu, or access it from the All Apps list

2 Click on the **Settings** button (at the bottom-left of the screen)

3 Click on the **Manage Accounts** button to add or delete a calendar account

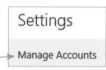

Settings

Manage Accounts

4 Click on the **Add account** button to add contacts from other online accounts, such as Google or iCloud

‹ Manage Accounts

Select an account to edit settings.

✉ Gmail
nickvandome@gmail.com

+ Add account

Hot tip

Events can be searched for in the Calendar app. To do this, type a keyword or phrase in the Search box at the top of the Calendar window.

5 The calendar is displayed in the main window (click on the **Menu** button to see this view)

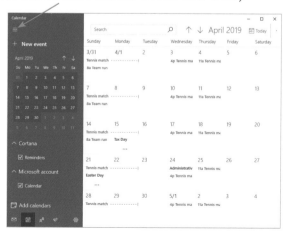

6 If the window is not maximized, click on the Menu button at the top of the window to view the calendar in **Day**, **Week**, **Month** or **Year** view, or print out the current calendar (if the window is maximized, these buttons appear at the top of the calendar)

Hot tip

Click on the **Today** button on the top toolbar to the left of the Menu button in Step 6 to access the current day, from any other calendar view.

7 If other accounts have been added they will be displayed in the left-hand panel. Click on one to display the items within it. Check items On or Off to show or hide them on the calendar

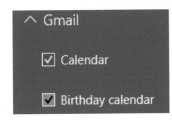

8 Click on these buttons to move between months (or swipe up or down on a touch pad)

9 Click on these buttons to move to **Mail** (left) or **People** (right)

...cont'd

Adding events

Events can be added to the calendar and various settings can be applied to them, such as recurrence and reminders.

Reminders can be set for calendar events, and these appear in the Notifications section. Click on this box on the top toolbar to set a time period for a reminder.

1 Click on a date to create a new event or click on the **New event** button

2 Enter an **Event name** and a **Location** at the top of the window

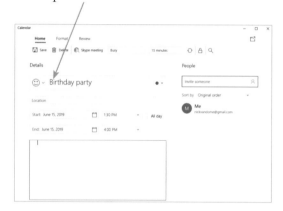

3 Click on the **Start** field, and enter a date and time for the event

4 If **All day** is selected, the time in the **Start** and **End** fields will be grayed out

6 A Digital Lifestyle

This chapter shows how to work with a range of apps for entertainment, so you can fully immerse yourself in the digital world.

124 Viewing Photos

128 Editing Photos

130 Groove Music App

131 Playing Music

132 Viewing Movies and TV

133 Books in Windows 10

134 Gaming with Windows 10

Viewing Photos

The Photos app can be used to manage and edit your photos, including those stored in your **Pictures** Library. To do this:

1 Click on the **Photos** app on the **Start** menu

2 The main categories are at the left-hand side of the main window

3 Other options are on the top toolbar, at the right-hand side of the window. This has options for creating a new album or automated displays, selecting items and importing new items

4 Click on the **Collection** button to view all of the photos in the Photos app, arranged by date. Scroll up and down to view the photos

5 Click on the **Albums** button to view photos from specific albums

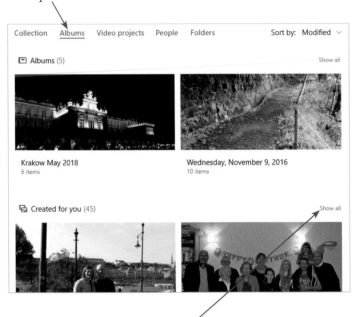

Beware

The albums displayed are taken from those stored in the specific folders in File Explorer (by default, the Pictures library). However, the Photos app displays what it thinks are the best photos in the folder, thus creating its own albums.

6 Click on the **Show all** button to display all of the albums that have been created by the Photos app

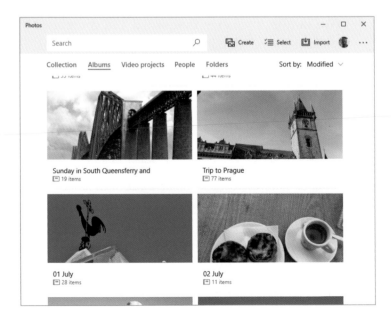

Don't forget

Click on the **Folders** button on the top toolbar to view photos that have been taken with your computer's camera (or copied into this folder from another location).

...cont'd

Don't forget

Albums can include photos and videos.

Hot tip

Click on the **Edit** button in Step 7 to access options for adding more photos to the slideshow; editing its duration; adding filters to the photos; and adding text to the photos.

7 Within the Albums section, double-click on an album to view its contents. This will play as an automated slideshow

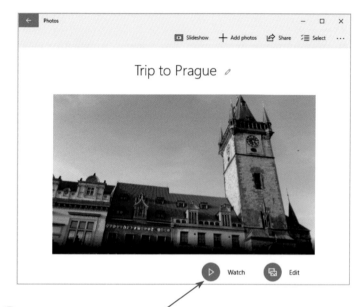

8 Click on the **Watch** button to view the slideshow with additional music. Click on the **Remix it for me** button to change the format and content of the slideshow; e.g. play it with different music

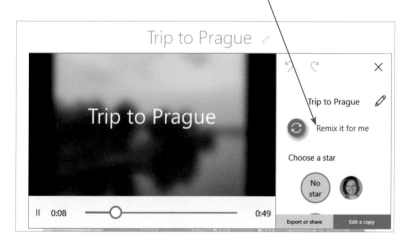

Sharing photos

Photos within either a collection or an album in the Photos app can be selected and then shared with other people in various ways, or deleted. To do this:

1 In Collections, or an open album, click on the **Select** button on the top toolbar

2 Click here to select a photo or photos

Hot tip

If an item is selected in the Collections section, click on the **Trash** icon on the top toolbar to delete it from the Photos app. If an item is selected in an album, click on the **Remove from album** button to remove it from the album (it will still remain within the Collections section).

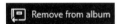

127

3 Click on the **Share** button to share the selected photo(s)

4 Click on one of your existing contacts to share the photo with, or click on an app to share the photo using this app

Hot tip

Click on the **Get apps in Store** button in Step 4 to access apps that are compatible for viewing and sharing photos.

5 Alternatively, click on the **Copy** button on the top toolbar so that the select image(s) can be pasted into another app

Editing Photos

In Windows 10, the Photos app has a range of editing functions so that you can improve and enhance your photos. To use these:

1 Open a photo at full size

2 Click on this button on the top toolbar to access the editing options. Click on the **Edit** button and scroll up and down in the right-hand panel to view the editing options

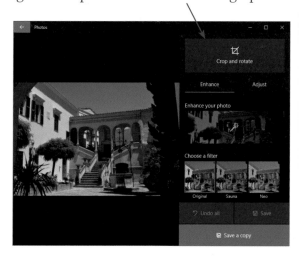

Hot tip

Click on the **Draw** button in Step 2 to access options for drawing directly on an image. Click on the **Save** button to save a copy of the image, or click on the cross to discard changes.

3 Click on the
**Crop and
rotate** button
in Step 2
to crop the
current photo
or rotate it in a
variety of ways,

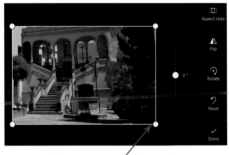

Hot tip

such as flipping horizontally or vertically or by a
specific amount, by dragging here

Most photos benefit
from some degree of
cropping, so that the
main subject is given
greater prominence
by removing
unwanted items in the
background.

4 Click on the **Enhance**
button in Step 2 to apply
filter effects. Click on the
Adjust button to adjust
elements in the photos by
dragging on these bars for
each element

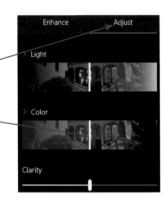

129

5 As the bar moves, so
the elements of the
photos are amended

6 Click here next to
one of the editing functions
to view additional items

7 Click on the **Save** button
to save the changes to the
original photo, or **Save a
copy** to create a new image

Groove Music App

The Groove Music app is used to access music that you have added to your laptop, and also the Spotify app, where you can stream music (play it from where it is stored on the Spotify app's central server/computer) directly to your laptop.

1 Click on the **Groove Music** app on the **Start** menu

2 Click on the **Menu** button to expand the menu so that the titles are visible, not just the icons

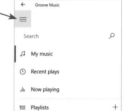

3 Click on a category to view those items

4 Click on the **Stream millions of songs free** button to access the Spotify app for listening to music

5 If you do not already have the Spotify app you will be redirected to the Microsoft Store to download it

6 Open the Spotify app to play music by streaming it via the app

To use Spotify you have to register with a username and password. The standard service is free (includes adverts) and there is also a monthly subscription Premium service that is advert-free, and offers improved streaming quality and options for downloading music rather than just streaming it from the Spotify app.

Playing Music

Playing your own music

Music that has been added to your laptop can be played through the Groove Music app. To do this:

1 Open the Groove Music app and click on the **My music** button

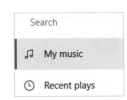

2 Click on the buttons at the top of the My music window to view your music according to Songs, Artists or Albums

3 Click on an item to access it

4 Click on a track or album to start playing it

5 Use these buttons above to, from left to right: shuffle the available tracks; go to the start of a track; pause/play a track; go to the end of a track; repeat a track

You can also add music to the Groove Music app from the Library that you have stored in your OneDrive folder.

When a folder is added to the Music library, any music that is copied here will be displayed by the Groove Music app.

Do not copy music and use it for commercial purposes as this will infringe the copyright of the artist.

Viewing Movies and TV

For movie and TV lovers, the Movies & TV app performs a similar function to the Groove Music app. It connects to the Microsoft Store, from where you can preview and buy your favorite movies and TV shows.

The Movies & TV app is named Films & TV in some regions.

1 Click on the **Movies & TV** app on the **Start** menu

Movies & TV

2 The Microsoft Store opens at the Movies & TV section. Click on these buttons to view the items in the **Movies & TV** section and items you have bought

Movies and TV shows can be streamed (viewed from the computer server where the item is stored, rather than downloading it) if you have a fast internet connection. They can also be downloaded to a single device so that they can be viewed while you are offline.

3 Click on the **Movies** button to view the available items (or **TV** for TV shows)

4 Click on an item to see more information; view a preview clip; or buy or rent and download the item

132

Books in Windows 10

Windows 10 caters for eBooks that can be downloaded from the Microsoft Store and read on your Windows 10 laptop:

1 Open the **Microsoft Store** and click on the **Books** button on the top toolbar

2 The range of books is displayed and can be navigated around in a similar way as for music or movies and TV

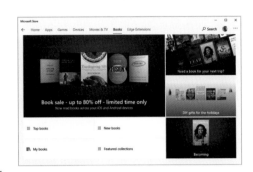

3 Click on a book to see details about it. Click on the **Buy** button to download the full text, or the **Read a sample** button to view a free sample

4 Books from the Microsoft Store are displayed within the Edge browser. Tap the spacebar to move forwards through the pages, or click on the left- and right-hand sides of the screen to move in those directions

Hot tip

In the Edge browser, click on the **Hub** button and click on the **Books** button to view books that you have downloaded, and also get more from the Microsoft Store.

Gaming with Windows 10

In Windows 10, the Xbox app can be used for playing games and interacting online with other gamers. To play games in Windows 10:

1 Click on the **Start** button and click on the **Xbox** app

2 Click on the **Home** button to view the Xbox Homepage. This contains the **Toolbar** (down the left-hand side), the **Activity feed** (in the left-hand panel) and the options for joining clubs and connecting with other gamers (in the right-hand panel)

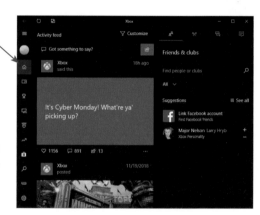

You have to be signed in with your Microsoft Account in order to use the Xbox app and all of its features.

3 Click on the **My games** button to view system games or those that you have downloaded from the Microsoft Store

4 Click on the **Achievements** button to view your scores from games you have played, and compare them with other gamers

5 Click on the **Clubs** button to view details of online game-playing clubs. This is where you can join up with other players, to compare scores and also play online games against other players (multiplayer games)

7 On Vacation

Due to their portability, laptops are ideal for taking on vacation. This chapter looks at the issues of taking your laptop with you and keeping it safe.

136 Transporting Your Laptop

137 Keeping Your Laptop Safe

138 Temperature Extremes

139 Laptops at Sea

140 Power Sockets

141 Airport Security

142 Keeping in Touch

Transporting Your Laptop

When you are going on vacation, your laptop can be a valuable companion. It can be used to download vacation photographs and home movies from a digital camera or a smartphone, keep a diary of your vacation, and keep a record of your itinerary and important documents. In many parts of the world, it can access the internet via wireless hotspots so that you can view the web and send emails. However, when you are traveling with your laptop it is sensible to transport this valuable asset as safely and securely as possible. Some of the options include:

Laptop case

A standard laptop case is a good option for when you are on vacation; it is compact, lightweight and designed to accommodate your laptop and its accessories.

Metal case

If you are concerned that your laptop may be in danger of physical damage on your vacation, you may want to consider a more robust metal case. These are similar to those used by photographers and, depending on the size and design, you may also be able to include your photographic equipment.

Backpacks

A serious option for transporting your laptop on vacation is a small backpack. This can either be a standard backpack or a backpack specifically designed for a laptop. The latter is clearly a better option as the laptop will fit more securely, and there are also pockets designed for accessories.

Don't forget

A backpack for carrying a laptop can be more comfortable than a shoulder bag as it distributes the weight more evenly.

Keeping Your Laptop Safe

By most measures, laptops are valuable items. However, in a lot of countries around the world their relative value can be a lot more than it is to their owners: in some countries the value of a laptop could easily equate to a month's, or even a year's, wages. Even in countries where their relative value is not so high, they can still be seen as a lucrative opportunity for thieves. Therefore, it is important to try to keep your laptop as safe as possible when you are on vacation. Some points to consider in relation to this are:

- If possible, try to keep your laptop with you at all times; i.e. transport it in a piece of luggage that you can carry rather than having to put it into a large case.

- Never hand over your laptop, or any other items of your belongings, to any local who promises to look after them.

- If you do have to detach yourself from your laptop, try to put it somewhere secure, such as a hotel safe.

- When you are traveling, try to keep your laptop as unobtrusive as possible. This is where a backpack carrying case can prove useful, as it is not immediately apparent that you are carrying a laptop.

- Do not use your laptop in areas where you think it may attract undue interest from the locals, particularly in obviously poor areas. For instance, if you are in a local café, the appearance of a laptop may create unwanted attention for you. If in doubt, wait until you get back to your hotel.

- If you are accosted by criminals who demand your laptop, then hand it over. No piece of equipment is worth suffering physical injury for.

- Make sure your laptop is covered by your vacation insurance. If not, get separate insurance for it.

- Trust your instincts with your laptop. If something doesn't feel right, then don't do it.

Hot tip

Save your important documents, such as vacation photos, onto a flashdrive on a daily basis when on vacation, and keep this away from your laptop. This way, you will still have these items if your laptop is lost or stolen.

Temperature Extremes

Traveling includes seeing different places and cultures, but it also invariably involves different extremes of temperature: a visit to the pyramids of Egypt can see the mercury in the upper reaches of the thermometer, while a cruise to Alaska would present much colder conditions. Whether it is hot or cold, looking after your laptop is an important consideration in extremes of temperature.

Heat

When traveling in hot countries, the best way of avoiding damage to your laptop is to prevent it from getting too hot in the first place:

- Do not place your laptop in direct sunlight.

- Keep your laptop insulated from the heat.

- Do not leave your laptop in an enclosed space, such as a car. Not only can this get very hot, but the sun's power can be increased by the vehicle's glass.

Cold

Again, it is best to try to avoid your laptop getting too cold in the first place, and this can be done by following similar precautions as for heat. However, if your laptop does suffer from extremes of cold, allow it to warm up to normal room temperature again before you try to use it. This may take a couple of hours but it will be worth the wait, rather than risking damaging the delicate computing elements inside.

Beware

If a laptop gets too hot it could buckle the plastic casing, making it difficult to close.

Hot tip

Try wrapping your laptop in something white, such as a t-shirt or a towel, to insulate it against the heat.

138

Laptops at Sea

Water is the greatest enemy of any electrical device, and laptops are no different. This is of particular relevance to anyone who is taking their laptop on vacation near water, such as on a cruise. This not only has the obvious element of water in the sea, but also the proliferation of swimming pools that are a feature of cruise ships. If you are going on vacation near water, then bear in mind the following:

- **Avoid water**. The best way to keep your laptop dry is to keep it away from water whenever possible. For instance, if you want to update your diary or download some photographs, then it would be best to do this in an indoor environment, rather than when sitting around the pool.

- **Keeping dry**. If you think you will be transporting your laptop near water then it is a good precaution to protect it with some form of waterproof bag. There is a range of "dry-bags" that are excellent for this type of occasion, as they remain waterproof even if fully immersed in water. These can be bought from a number of outdoor suppliers.

- **Drying out**. If the worst does occur and your laptop does get a good soaking, then all is not lost. However, you will have to ensure that it is fully dried out before you try to use it again.

Power Sockets

Different countries and regions around the world use different types of power sockets, and this is an issue when you are on vacation with your laptop. Wherever you are going in the world, it is vital to have an adapter that will fit the sockets in the countries you intend to visit, otherwise you will not be able to charge your laptop.

There are over a dozen different types of plugs and sockets used around the world, with the four most popular being:

North America, Japan
This is a two-point plug and socket. The pins on the plug are flat and parallel.

Continental Europe
This is a two-point plug and socket. The pins are rounded.

Australasia, China, Argentina
This is a three-point socket that can accommodate either a two- or a three-pin plug. In a two-pin plug, the pins are angled in a V shape.

UK
This is a three-point plug. The pins are rectangular.

Hot tip

Power adapters can be bought for all regions around the world. There are also kits that provide all of the adapters together. These provide connections for anywhere, worldwide.

Hot tip

If you are going on a cruise, check before you travel which type of power socket your ship has, and get the right adapter.

Airport Security

Because of the increased global security following terrorist attacks, levels of airport security have been greatly increased around the world. This has implications for all travelers, and if you are traveling with a laptop this will add to the security scrutiny you will face. When dealing with airport security when traveling with a laptop, there are some issues that you should always keep in mind:

- Keep your laptop with you at all times. Unguarded baggage at airports immediately raises suspicion and it can make life very easy for thieves.

- Carry your laptop in a small bag so that you can take it on board as hand luggage. On no account should it be put in with your luggage that goes in the hold.

- X-ray machines at airports will not harm your laptop. However, if anyone tries to scan it with a metal detector, ask them if they can inspect it by hand instead.

- Keep a careful eye on your laptop when it goes through the X-ray conveyor belt and try to be there at the other side as soon as it emerges. There have been some stories of people causing a commotion at the security gate just after someone has placed their laptop on the conveyor belt. While everyone's attention (including yours) is distracted, an accomplice takes the laptop from the conveyor belt. If you are worried about this, you can ask for the security guard to hand-check your laptop rather than putting it on the conveyor belt.

- Make sure the battery of your laptop is fully charged. This is because you may be asked to turn on your laptop to verify that it is just that, and not some other device disguised as a laptop.

- When you are on the plane, keep the laptop in the storage area under your seat, rather than in the overhead locker, so that you know where it is at all times.

At the time of printing, there are some issues with taking laptops on planes, particularly to the USA. If in doubt, contact your airline before you fly.

If there is any kind of distraction when you are going through security checks at an airport, it could be because someone is trying to divert your attention in order to steal your laptop.

When traveling through airport security, leave your laptop in Sleep mode so that it can be powered up quickly if anyone needs to check that it works properly.

Keeping in Touch

Skype has become established as one of the premier services for free voice and video calls (to other Skype users) and instant messaging for text messages. It can now be incorporated into your Windows 10 experience and used to keep in touch with family and friends, at home and around the world. To use Skype:

1 Click on the **Skype** button on the Start menu

2 If you already have a Skype account you can sign in with these details, or with your Microsoft Account details. Click on **Create a new account** to create a new Skype account

3 Recent conversations are listed in the left-hand panel

4 Click on this button to view your Skype contacts, or search for new ones. Click on one to start a voice or video call, or a text message

8 Sharing with Your Family

This chapter deals with sharing your laptop.

144 About Multiple Users

146 Adding Users

148 Family Safety

About Multiple Users

Because of the power and flexibility that is available in a laptop computer, it seems a waste to restrict it to a single user. Thankfully, it is possible for multiple users to use the same laptop. One way to do this is simply to let different people use the laptop whenever they have access to it. However, since everyone creates their own files and documents, and different people use different types of apps, it makes much more sense to allow people to set up their own user accounts. This creates their own personal computing area that is protected from anyone else accessing it. User accounts create a sense of personalization, and also security, as each account can be protected by a password.

Without user accounts, the laptop will display the default account automatically. However, if different user accounts have been set up on the laptop, a list of these accounts will be displayed by clicking on your own account icon on the Start menu.

If no other user accounts have been set up, yours will be the only one, and you will be the administrator. This means that you can set up new accounts and alter a variety of settings on the laptop.

The relevant user can then click on their own account to access it. At this point they will have to enter the correct password to gain access to their account. A user can have a Local Account or a Microsoft Account. If it is the latter, the user will have access to a selection of Microsoft services, through the Windows 10 apps. A password can be specified for either a Local Account or a Microsoft one. To see how to add new user accounts, see pages 146-147.

...cont'd

Customization

Once individual user accounts have been set up it is possible for each user to customize their account; i.e. to set the way in which their account appears and operates. This means that each user can set their own preferences, such as for the way the Start menu and Desktop background appear, and also the items on the Taskbar:

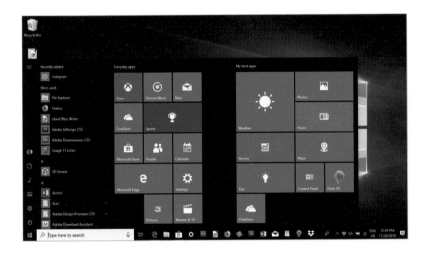

The whole Desktop environment can be customized. This is done within the **Personalization** section of the **Settings** app.

This shows two different user accounts and the changes in Settings, background and Taskbar apps.

Adding Users

If more than one person uses the laptop, each person can have a user account defined with a username and a password. To create a new user account, as either a Microsoft Account or a Local Account:

1 Access the **Settings** app and select **Accounts**

2 Click on the **Family & other users** button

3 Click on the **Add a family member** button

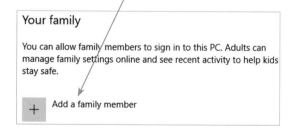

4 Select whether the account is for a child or an adult (for a child this provides online security options). Then, click **Next**

5 Enter the name of the new user, an email address and a password to create a Microsoft Account for the user

The email address is a required field when creating a new user with a Microsoft Account.

6 Click on the **Next** button to complete the setup wizard

7 The user is added to the Accounts pages

8 Click on a user to change the type of their account (e.g. from a Local Account to a Microsoft Account) or to delete their account

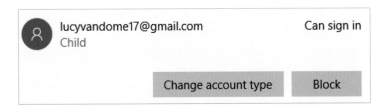

Family Safety

Once multiple user accounts have been set up, it is possible to apply separate online security settings to different accounts. This can be useful if you are going to be setting up an account for grandchildren and you want to have a certain amount of control over how they use the laptop. To do this:

1 Access the **Accounts** > **Family & other users** section of the **Settings** app

2 Select a user, and click on the **Manage family settings online** link

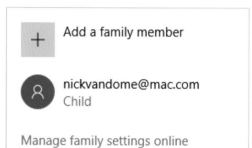

3 Click on one of the options for managing the child's profile and applying restrictions, as required (see pages 149-152)

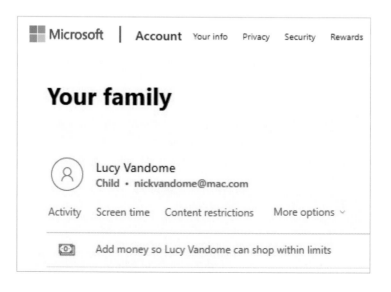

The default browser for viewing the family settings online is Microsoft Edge.

...cont'd

Recent activity controls

One of the options within the family safety controls is to view recent activity by a user. To view this:

1 In the **Manage family settings online** section, underneath **Your family** in Step 3 on the previous page, select the required user

2 Click on the **Recent activity** option and drag the **Activity reporting** button to **On**

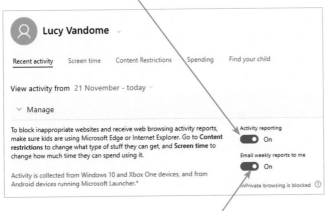

If you are setting family safety for young people, such as grandchildren, make sure you tell them what you have done so that they understand the reasons behind your actions.

3 Check **On** the **Email weekly reports to me** button to receive a weekly report about the user's computer usage

4 Scroll down the page to view and edit the other family safety options

…cont'd

Web browsing controls

The websites accessed by a specific user can also be controlled through family safety:

1 Click on the **Web browsing** option

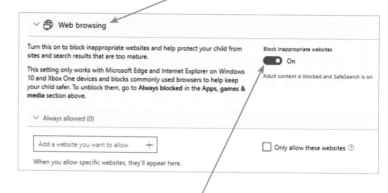

2 Drag the **Block inappropriate websites** button to **On**

3 Enter the web addresses of any websites you want to include, and click on the **+** button

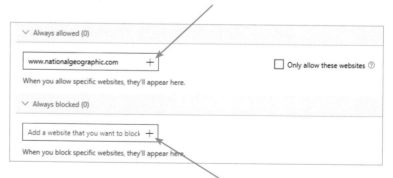

4 Repeat the process in Step 3 here, for any websites that you want to be blocked

Apps and games controls

Computer games and apps are another very popular pastime for young people. These include games that are downloaded from the web, and also those that are bought on CDs or DVDs. However, just as with movies, some games and apps are unsuitable for younger children and should have ratings to specify the age groups for which they are suitable. It is then possible to control which games are played. To do this:

1 From the **Manage family settings online** link (shown in the image in Step 2 on page 148), click on the **Apps, games & media** option to restrict the type of content the user can access

2 Drag the **Block inappropriate apps, games & media** button to **On**

3 Click on the **View allowed ratings** button in Step 1 to view the available rating levels

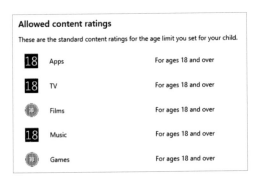

The age ratings in Step 3 will be applicable to your geographical location.

...cont'd

Screen time controls

A familiar worry when young people are using computers is the amount of time that they are spending on them. However, this can also be controlled in the Screen time controls for a selected user. To do this:

Don't forget

If time controls have been set, the affected user will not be able to access their account outside the times that have been specified.

1 From the **Manage family settings online** link (shown in the image in Step 2 on page 148), click on the **Screen time** option to specify times at which a user can use the computer

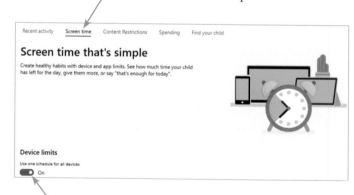

2 Drag the **Use one schedule for all devices** button to **On**

3 Select the times for using the laptop on specific days (each day can have its own times and also an overall limit per day)

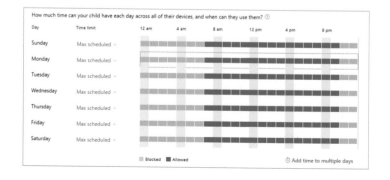

9 Networking and Wireless

This chapter shows how to use the Windows 10 networking functions, enabling you to share files and folders and use Nearby sharing.

154 Network Components

155 Going Wireless

156 Connecting to a Network

157 Sharing Settings

158 Nearby Sharing

160 Saving Files for Sharing

162 Network Troubleshooting

Network Components

There are numerous possibilities for setting up a home network. To start with, there are two major network technologies:

- **Wired** – e.g. Ethernet, using twisted pair cables to send data at rates of 10, 100 or 1000 Mbps (megabits per second).

- **Wireless** – using radio waves to send data at rates of 11 to 300 Mbps, or up to, in theory, 1 Gbps with the latest devices (although all of these are theoretical top speeds).

There are also the hardware items required:

- **Network adapter** – appropriate to the network type, with one for each computer in the network.

- **Network controller** – one or more hub, switch or router, providing the actual connection to each network adapter.

There is also the internet connection using:

- A router that connects to the internet wirelessly (using Wi-Fi) or with a cable (Ethernet).

- A modem connected to the computer and the network (this is an increasingly outdated method).

Setting up the components

The steps you will need will depend on the specific options on your system. However, the main steps will include:

- Set up or verify the internet connection. This should be provided by your Internet Service Provider (ISP).

- Configure the wireless router or access point. Most Wi-Fi routers will be automatically recognized by Windows 10.

- Start up Windows on your PC.

Windows 10 is designed to automate as much of the network setup task as possible.

The network adapter can be connected to the USB port, inserted in the PC Card slot, or installed inside your computer.

Ethernet adapters connect to a network hub, switch or wired router. Wireless adapters connect through a wireless router or a combination of router/switch.

You may already have some of these elements in operation, if you have an existing network running a previous version of Windows.

Going Wireless

For networking, "wireless" means connecting your computer to other devices using radio waves rather than cables. These can include a router for connecting to a network, a printer, keyboard, mouse or speakers (as long as these devices also have a wireless capability). For the laptop user in particular, this gives you the ultimate freedom: you can take your laptop wherever you want, and still be able to access the internet and use a variety of peripherals.

Wireless standards

As with everything in the world of computers, there are industry standards for wireless connections: for networking devices the standard is known as IEEE 802.11. The purpose of standards is to ensure that all of the connected devices can communicate with each other.

The IEEE 802.11 standard (or just 802.11) used for networks has a number of different variations (known as protocols) of the original standard. These variations have been developed since the introduction of 802.11 in 1997, with a view to making it work faster and cover a greater range. Early wireless devices used the 802.11a and 802.11b protocols, while the most widely-used protocol at the time of printing is 802.11n, with 802.11ac also beginning to be used. When you are creating a wireless network it is best to have all of the devices using the same version of 802.11. For instance, if you have a wireless card in your laptop that uses 802.11n, then it is best to have the same version in your router. However, most modern wireless cards and routers have multiple compatibility, and can cater for at least the b and g versions of the standard. If two devices use different 802.11 protocols, they should still be able to communicate, but the rate of data transfer may be slower than if both of the devices used the same protocol.

The Bluetooth standard is another method of connecting devices wirelessly. It does not have the same range as 802.11 and is now mainly used for connecting devices over short distances, such as a wireless mouse.

Very few new devices use the 802.11a version of the standard, although newer devices will usually be backwards-compatible with it.

Devices using the 802.11n protocol can communicate with each other via radio waves over distances of approximately 25 yards (indoors) and 75 yards (outdoors).

Connecting to a Network

You can connect your computers to form a network using Ethernet cables and adapters, or by setting up your wireless adapters and routers. When you start up each computer, Windows 10 will examine the current configuration and discover any new networks that have been established since the last startup. You can check this, or connect manually to a network from within the Wi-Fi settings from the Network & Internet section of Settings. To do this:

The most common type of network for connecting to is the internet.

If your network is unavailable for any reason, this will be noted in Step 2.

1 Access the **Settings** app and click on the **Network & Internet** button

2 Drag the Wi-Fi button to **On**. Under the **Wi-Fi** heading, click on one of the available networks

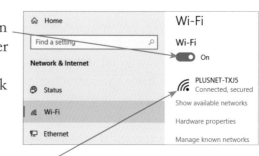

3 Click on the network and drag **On** the **Connect automatically when in range** button

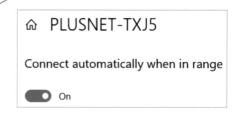

4 The selected network is shown as **Connected**. This is also shown in the Notifications area

Sharing Settings

There are also options for specifying how items are shared over the network. To select these:

1 Open **Settings** >
Network & Internet >

Status and click on the **Sharing options** link

2 Select sharing options for different networks, including Private, Guest or Public, and All networks. Options can be selected for turning on network discovery so that your computer can see other computers on the network, and for turning on file and printer sharing

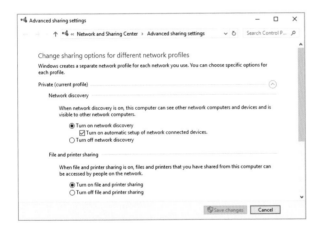

If you are sharing over a network you should be able to access the Public folder on another computer (providing that network discovery is turned on). If you are the administrator of the other computer you will also be able to access your own Home folder, although you will need to enter the required password for this.

3 Click on these arrows to expand the options for each network category

Change sharing options for different network profiles

Windows creates a separate network profile for each network you use. You can choose specific options for each profile.

Private (current profile)

Guest or Public

All Networks

   Public folder sharing

      When Public folder sharing is on, people on the network, including homegroup members, can access files in the Public folders.

      ○ Turn on sharing so anyone with network access can read and write files in the Public folders
      ◉ Turn off Public folder sharing (people logged on to this computer can still access these folders)

Nearby Sharing

The HomeGroup feature that was previously available with Windows 10 is no longer used. Instead, a feature called Nearby sharing can be used to sharing files wirelessly, either using Bluetooth or Wi-Fi. As the name suggests, the computer with which you want to share files has to be relatively close to the one that is sharing the content. Also, the other device has to support Nearby sharing (Windows 10 April 2018 Update, or later). To use Nearby sharing:

1 Access the Settings app and click on the **Shared experiences** button within the **System** section

⚙ Shared experiences

2 Drag the **Nearby sharing** button to **On**

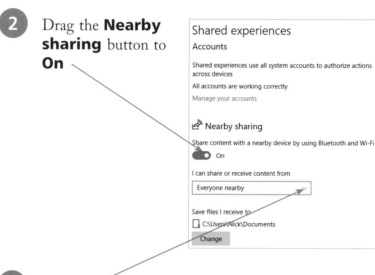

3 Select who you want to be able to share content with your PC. It can be everyone, or only your own devices; i.e. ones on which you have signed in with your Microsoft Account details

4 Under the **Save files I receive to** heading, click on the **Change** button to select a new location

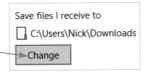

5 Select a new location for files that are shared with Nearby sharing and click on the **Select Folder** button

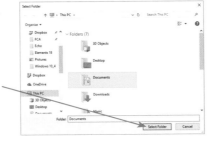

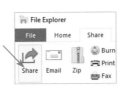

If a new folder has been selected for storing files downloaded using Nearby sharing, this will be listed under the **Save files I receive to** heading.

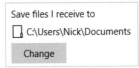

Sharing files

Once Nearby sharing has been set up it can be used to share files wirelessly with other compatible devices. To do this:

1 Access the Settings app and select **System > Notifications & actions > Add or remove quick actions** and drag the **Nearby sharing** button to **On**

2 Click on the Notifications button and click on the **Nearby sharing** button

The **Share** option in Step 3 can also be used to share a selected item in a variety of other ways, including email and social media sites.

3 Open File Explorer and select a file. Click on the **Share** button in the **Share** section of the Scenic Ribbon

4 Click on the person's name with whom you want to share the file

Saving Files for Sharing

When you want to save files so that other people on your network can access them, this can be done by either saving them into the Public folder on your own laptop or saving them into the Public folder of another computer on your network. To do this:

1 Create the file that you want to save onto the network

2 First, save the file to a folder within your own file structure; i.e. one that is within the File Explorer Libraries, not on the network. This will ensure that you always have a master copy of the document

3 Select **File** > **Save As** from the Menu bar (this is standard in most types of apps)

4 The Save As window has options for where you can save the file

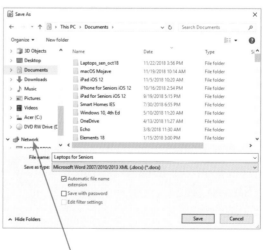

5 Click on the **Network** icon in the left-hand pane

...cont'd

6 Double-click on another computer on the network to save the file here

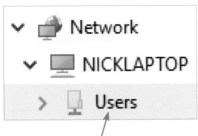

7 Double-click on the **Users** folder, then the **Public** folder

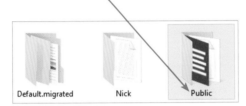

If you copy files to your own Public folder, other computers on the network will only be able to access these when your laptop is turned on.

161

8 Double-click on the folder into which you want to save the file and click on the **Save** button

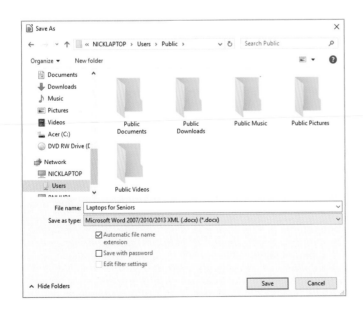

Network Troubleshooting

1 Open **Settings > Network & Internet > Status** and click on the **Network troubleshooter** link

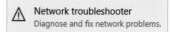

Network troubleshooter
Diagnose and fix network problems.

Don't forget

For more Windows 10 troubleshooting options, see page 175.

2 Click on the option that most closely matches your network problem

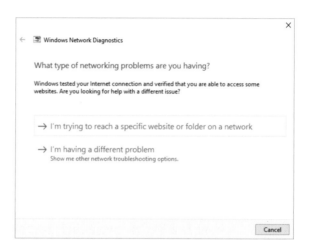

Windows Network Diagnostics

What type of networking problems are you having?

Windows tested your Internet connection and verified that you are able to access some websites. Are you looking for help with a different issue?

→ I'm trying to reach a specific website or folder on a network

→ I'm having a different problem
   Show me other network troubleshooting options.

Cancel

3 Most options have additional selections that can be made to try to solve the problem. Click on these as required

Windows Network Diagnostics

Choose the networking issue to troubleshoot

→ Allow other computers to connect to this computer

→ Connect to your workplace using DirectAccess

→ Use a specific network adapter (for example, Ethernet or wireless)

Cancel

10 Battery Issues

Battery power is crucial to a laptop, and this chapter shows how to get the best out of your battery and deal with any problems.

164 Types of Battery

165 Power Consumption

166 Battery Management

169 Charging the Battery

170 Removing the Battery

171 Dead and Spare Batteries

172 Battery Troubleshooting

Types of Battery

A laptop's battery is one of the items that helps to define its identity: without it, the portable nature of the laptop would be very different as it would always have to be connected with a power cable. Laptops have used a variety of different types of batteries since they were first produced, and over the years these have become smaller, lighter and more powerful. However, laptop batteries are still relatively heavy and bulky, and are one of the major sources of weight in the machine:

The type of battery provided with a laptop, and the approximate lifespan for each charge, should be displayed with the details about the machine on the manufacturer's website or in any promotional literature that comes with it.

164

The types of batteries used in modern laptops are:

- **Lithium-ion.** This is a type of battery that has a good weight-to-power ratio and loses its charge at a relatively slow rate. However, they can be prone to overheating if they are not treated properly or are defective.

- **Lithium polymer.** This is an advanced version of the lithium-ion battery. It is generally considered to be a more stable design.

These types of batteries are rechargeable, so they can be charged and used numerous times after they initially run out. However, over time, all rechargeable batteries eventually wear out and have to be replaced.

The quality of laptop batteries is improving all the time.

Power Consumption

Battery life for each charge of laptop batteries is one area on which engineers have worked very hard since laptops were first introduced. For most modern laptops, the average battery life for each charge is approximately between three and five hours. However, this is dependent on the power consumption of the laptop; i.e. how much power is being used to perform particular tasks. Power-intensive tasks will reduce the battery life of each charge cycle. These types of tasks include:

- Surfing the web.

- Watching a DVD.

- Editing digital photographs.

- Editing digital video.

When you are using your laptop you can always monitor how much battery power you currently have available. This is shown by the battery icon that appears at the right-hand side of the Taskbar:

If you are undertaking an energy-intensive task such as browsing the web, try to use the external AC/DC power cable rather than the battery, otherwise the battery may drain quickly and the laptop will close down.

Because of the vital role that the battery plays in relation to your laptop, it is important to try to conserve its power as much as possible. To do this:

- Where possible, use the mains adapter rather than the battery when using your laptop.

- Use the Sleep function when you are not actively using your laptop.

- Use power-management functions to save battery power (see pages 166-168).

Battery Management

Unlike desktop computers, laptops have options for how the battery is managed. These allow you to set things like individual power schemes for the battery and to view how much charge is left in the battery. This can be done from the Settings app. To access the options for managing your laptop's battery:

1 Access the **Settings** app and select the **System** section

2 Click on the **Power & sleep** link

3 Under the **Power & sleep** section, click on the **Screen** options to make selections for the period of inactivity until the screen goes to sleep, for both on battery power and when connected to the mains

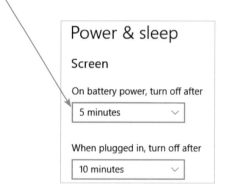

4 Select a time period for the selection made in Step 3 (this can include **Never**, if you scroll down to the bottom of the list, in which case the screen will not be put to sleep)

5 Under the **Sleep** section, click on options for putting the laptop to sleep after a period of inactivity, for both battery and mains power

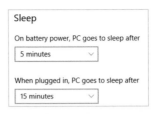

Sleep

On battery power, PC goes to sleep after

5 minutes

When plugged in, PC goes to sleep after

15 minutes

6 Select a time period for the selection made in Step 5, in the same way as for putting the screen to sleep (this can include **Never**, in which case the laptop will not be put to sleep)

25 minutes
30 minutes
45 minutes
1 hour
2 hours
3 hours
4 hours
5 hours
Never

If you don't protect your laptop with a password for when it is woken from sleep, anyone could access your folders and files if they wake the laptop from sleep.

Power settings

Additional power settings can be made from the link under Related settings at the bottom of the Power & sleep section.

1 Click on the **Additional power settings** link

Related settings

Additional power settings

2 The link opens the Control Panel **Power Options** window for creating customized power plans

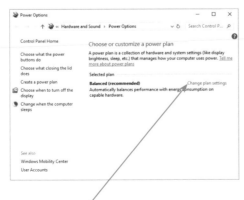

Use the links at the left-hand side of the Power Options window to access other power-management options, such as what happens when closing the lid of the laptop.

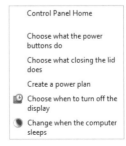

Control Panel Home

Choose what the power buttons do

Choose what closing the lid does

Create a power plan

Choose when to turn off the display

Change when the computer sleeps

3 Click here to select power plans, for balancing performance and battery consumption

…cont'd

Battery saver

Within the System Settings there are also options for viewing the current level of battery charge; the estimated time remaining on the current charge; and viewing battery usage by app. There is also an option for turning the battery saver on automatically. To do this:

1 Click on the **Battery** button within **Settings** > **System**

2 The current battery usage is shown here, with the estimated time remaining for the current charge shown below

3 Click here to view how much power currently-running apps are using

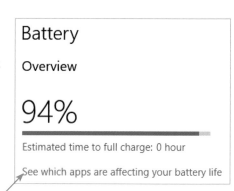

4 Under **Battery saver**, check On this button and drag the slider to specify the battery level at which the battery saver will be turned on

When the battery saver is On, background activity (such as pushing notifications and emails) is limited in order to save power.

Charging the Battery

Laptop batteries are charged using an AC/DC adapter, which can also be used to power the laptop instead of the battery. If the laptop is turned on and being powered by the AC/DC adapter, the battery will be charged at the same time, although at a slower rate than if it is being charged with the laptop turned off.

The AC/DC adapter should be supplied with a new laptop, and consists of a cable and a power adapter. To charge a laptop battery using an AC/DC adapter:

A laptop battery can be charged whether the laptop is turned on or off.

1 Connect the AC/DC adapter to the cable and plug it into the mains socket

2 Attach the AC/DC adapter to the laptop and turn on at the mains socket

3 When the laptop is turned on, the Power Meter icon is visible at the right-hand side of the Taskbar. Click on this to view the current power details

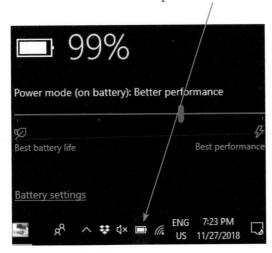

4 If the laptop is on battery power, click on the **Battery saver** button to turn this option **On**

Removing the Battery

Although a laptop's battery does not have to be removed on a regular basis, there may be occasions when you want to do this. These include:

- If the laptop freezes, i.e. you are unable to undertake any operations using the keyboard or mouse, and you cannot turn off the laptop using the Power button.

- If you are traveling, particularly in extreme temperatures. In situations such as this, you may prefer to keep the battery with you to try to avoid exposing it to either very hot or very cold temperatures.

To remove a laptop battery:

Beware

Some laptops, particularly slim ultrabooks, do not have removable batteries and they have to be replaced by the manufacturer.

1 With the laptop turned off and the lid closed, turn the laptop upside down

2 Locate the battery compartment and either push or slide the lock that keeps the battery in place

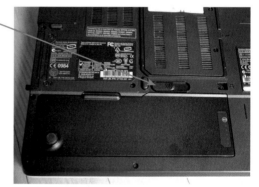

Don't forget

To re-insert the battery, or a new battery, push it gently into the battery compartment until it clicks firmly into place.

3 Slide the battery out of its compartment

Dead and Spare Batteries

No energy source lasts forever, and laptop batteries are no exception to this rule. Over time, the battery will operate less efficiently until it will not be possible to charge the battery at all. With average usage, most laptop batteries should last approximately five years, although they will start to lose performance before this. Some signs of a dead laptop battery are:

- Nothing happens when the laptop is turned on using just battery power.

- The laptop shuts down immediately if it is being run on the AC/DC adapter and the cord is suddenly removed.

- The Battery Meter shows no movement when the AC/DC adapter is connected; i.e. the Battery Meter remains at 0% and shows as not charging at all.

If you think that your battery may be losing its performance, make sure that you save your work at regular intervals. Although you should do this anyway, it is more important if there is a chance of your battery running out of power and abruptly turning off.

171

Spare battery

Because of the limited lifespan of laptop batteries, it is worth considering buying a spare battery. Although these are not cheap it can be a valuable investment, particularly if you spend a lot of time traveling with your laptop and you are not always near a source of mains electricity. In situations such as this, a spare battery could enable you to keep using your laptop if your original battery runs out of power.

When buying a spare battery, check with the laptop's manufacturer that it will be compatible: in most cases the manufacturer will also be able to supply you with a spare battery for your laptop.

Battery Troubleshooting

If you look after your laptop battery well it should provide you with several years of mobile computing power. However, there are some problems that may occur with the battery:

If there is no response from your laptop when you turn it on in battery mode, try removing the battery and re-inserting it. If there is still no response then the battery is probably flat, and should be replaced.

172

If you are not going to be using your laptop for an extended period of time, remove the battery and store it in a safe, dry, cool place.

- **It won't keep its charge even when connected to an AC/DC adapter**. The battery is probably flat and should be replaced.

- **It only charges up a limited amount**. Over time, laptop batteries become less efficient and so do not hold their charge so well. One way to try to improve this is to drain the battery completely before it is charged again.

- **It keeps its charge but runs down quickly**. This can be caused by the use of a lot of power-hungry applications on the laptop. The more work the laptop has to do to run applications, such as those involving videos or games, the more power will be required from the battery and the faster it will run down.

- **It is fully charged but does not appear to work at all when inserted**. Check that the battery has clicked into place properly in the battery compartment and that the battery and laptop terminals are clean and free from dust or moisture.

- **It is inserted correctly but still does not work**. The battery may have become damaged in some way, such as becoming very wet. If you know the battery is damaged in any way, do not insert it, as it could short-circuit the laptop. If the battery has been in contact with liquid, dry it out completely before you try inserting it into the laptop. If it is dried thoroughly, it may work again.

- **It gets very hot when in operation**. This could be caused by a faulty battery, and it can be dangerous and lead to a fire. If in doubt, turn off the laptop immediately and consult the manufacturer. In some cases faulty laptop batteries are recalled, so keep an eye on the manufacturer's website to see if there are any details of this if you are concerned.

11 System and Security

Windows 10 includes tools to help protect your online privacy, troubleshoot common problems, maintain your hard drive, protect your computer from malicious software, and back up your content.

174 Privacy

175 Troubleshooting

176 System Properties

178 Clean Up Your Disk

180 Windows Update

181 Backing Up

182 System Restore

184 Security and Maintenance

185 Windows Defender Firewall

186 Malware Protection

Privacy

Online privacy is a major issue for all computer users, and Windows 10 has a number of options for viewing details about your personal online privacy.

Click on **Privacy statement** in Step 2 to view Microsoft's Privacy Statement (this is an online statement and, by default, displayed within the Edge browser).

174

1 Open the **Settings** app and click on the **Privacy** button

2 Drag these buttons **On** or **Off** to allow advertising more specific to you; let websites provide local content based on the language being used by Windows; and let Windows track apps that are launched to make the search results more specific

General

Change privacy options

Let apps use advertising ID to make ads more interesting to you based on your app usage (turning this off will reset your ID)
On

Let websites provide locally relevant content by accessing my language list
On

Let Windows track app launches to improve Start and search results
On

Show me suggested content in the Settings app
On

Know your privacy options

Learn how this setting impacts your privacy.
Learn more
Privacy dashboard
Privacy statement

3 Click on **Privacy dashboard** to view details on the Microsoft website about how ads are used online and in Windows 10 apps

Click on **Learn more** in Step 2 to view further details about general privacy settings and options within Windows 10.

4 Click on the **Sign In With Microsoft** button to manage your own personal privacy settings, including browsing data, search history and location data

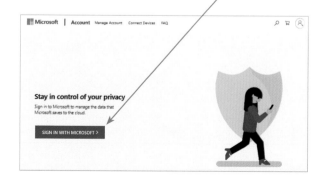

Troubleshooting

On any computing system there are always things that go
wrong or do not work properly. Windows 10 is no different,
but there are comprehensive troubleshooting options for
trying to address a range of problems. To use these:

1 Open the **Settings** app, select
Update & Security and click
on the **Troubleshoot** button

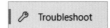

2 The range of
troubleshooting options
is displayed within the
main window

3 The top
troubleshooting
categories are displayed
at the top of the
window (other options
are shown further
down the window)

4 Click on one of the
categories to select it,
and click on the **Run
the troubleshooter** button

5 Any issues for
the selected item
are displayed, and
options for trying to
fix the issue

System Properties

There are several ways to open the System Properties and view information about your computer:

1 Select **Settings** > **System** > **About**, or

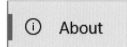

1 Press the **WinKey** + the **Pause/Break** keys, or

1 Right-click **This PC** in the File Explorer Navigation pane

2 Select **Properties** from the menu, or

1 Right-click on the **Start** button

2 Select **System** from the Power User menu

The main System panel (About) provides the Windows 10 edition, processor details, memory size and device name.

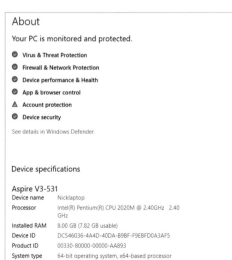

About

Your PC is monitored and protected.

- Virus & Threat Protection
- Firewall & Network Protection
- Device performance & Health
- App & browser control
- ⚠ Account protection
- Device security

See details in Windows Defender

Device specifications

Aspire V3-531

Device name	Nicklaptop
Processor	Intel(R) Pentium(R) CPU 2020M @ 2.40GHz 2.40 GHz
Installed RAM	8.00 GB (7.82 GB usable)
Device ID	DC546036-4A4D-40DA-B9BF-F9EBFD0A3AF5
Product ID	00330-80000-00000-AA893
System type	64-bit operating system, x64-based processor

Device Manager

1 Type **Device Manager** in the Settings app Search box and click on **Device Manager** to view the hardware components on your computer

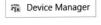

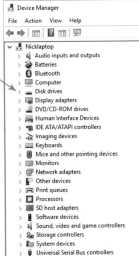

2 Select the › symbol to expand that entry to show details

3 Double-click any device to open its properties

You may be prompted for an administrator password or asked for permission to continue when you select some Device Manager entries.

4 Select the ⌄ symbol to collapse the expanded entry

5 Select the **Driver** tab and select **Update Driver** to find and install new software

6 Select **Disable Device** to put the particular device offline. The button changes to **Enable Device**, to reverse the action

Click on the **Roll Back Driver** button (if available) to switch back to the previously-installed driver for a device, if the new one for it fails.

Clean Up Your Disk

1 In File Explorer, right-click the **C:** drive and click on the **Properties** option

2 Click on the **Disk Cleanup** button

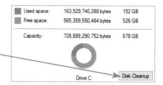

3 Disk Cleanup scans the drive to identify files that can be safely removed

Don't forget

You can have more than one hard disk on your computer.

4 All of the possible files are listed by category, and the sets of files recommended to be deleted are marked with a tick symbol

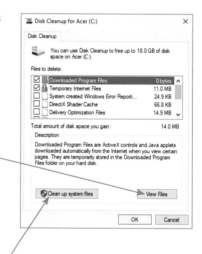

5 Make changes to the selections, clicking **View Files** if necessary to help you choose

6 Select the **Clean up system files** button, to also include these, then select **OK**

7 Deleted files will not be transferred to the Recycle Bin, so confirm that you do want to permanently delete all of these files. The files will be removed and the disk space will become available

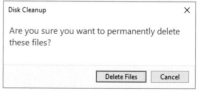

When a file is written to the hard disk, it may be stored in several pieces in different places. This fragmentation of disk space can slow down your computer. Disk Defragmenter rearranges the data so the disk will work more efficiently.

1 In the File Explorer, right-click on the **C:** drive and click on the **Properties** option

Spellings are localized.

2 Select the **Tools** tab and click on the **Optimize** button

3 The process runs as a scheduled task, but you can select a drive and select **Analyze** to check out a new drive

Only disks that can be fragmented are shown. These can include USB drives that you add to your system.

179

4 Click the **Optimize** button to process the selected disk drive. This may take between several minutes to several hours to complete, depending on the size and state of the disk, but you can still use your computer while the task is running

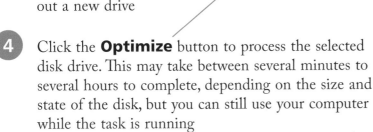

Windows Update

Updates to Windows 10 and other Microsoft products are supplied regularly to help prevent or fix problems, improve the security or enhance performance. The way in which they are downloaded and installed can be specified from the Settings app:

180

1 Access the **Settings** app and click on the **Update & Security** button

Update & Security
Windows Update, recovery, backup

2 Click on **Windows Update**

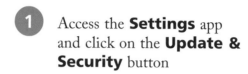
Update & Security

Windows Update

3 Click on the **Check for updates** button to see details of any updates that are waiting to be installed

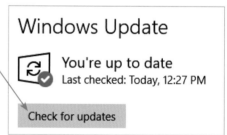
Windows Update

You're up to date
Last checked: Today, 12:27 PM

Check for updates

4 Click on the **Advanced options** button and drag the buttons **On** or **Off** for the relevant options to specify how and when updates are installed, and also **Pause updates**

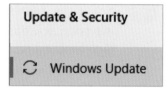

Advanced options

Update options

Give me updates for other Microsoft products when I update Windows.
Off

Automatically download updates, even over metered data connections (charges may apply)
Off

Update notifications

Show a notification when your PC requires a restart to finish updating
Off

Pause updates

Temporarily pause updates from being installed on this device for up to 7 days. When updates resume, this device will need to get the latest updates before it can be paused again.
Off

Pausing now will pause updates until 12/26/2018.

Backing Up

Backing up your data is an important task in any computer environment, and in Windows 10 this can be done from within the Settings app. To do this:

1 Access the **Settings** app and click on the **Update & Security** button

○ Update & Security
Windows Update, recovery, backup

2 Click on the **Backup** button

↑ Backup

3 Drag the **Automatically back up my files** button to **On** to back up your files whenever the

Backup

Back up using File History
Back up your files to another drive and restore them if the originals are lost, damaged, or deleted.

Automatically back up my files
⬤ On

More options

external drive is connected. After the initial backup, each further one will be incremental; i.e. only new files that have been added or changed will be backed up, not the whole system

4 Click on the required external drive

Select a drive

Seagate Slim Drive (E:)
63.6 GB free of 465 GB

5 Click on the **More options** button in the main Backup window to view backup options. Click on the **Back up now**

⌂ Backup options

Overview
Size of backup: 0 bytes
Total space on Seagate Slim Drive (E:) (E:): Disconnected
Your data is not yet backed up.

Back up now

button to perform a manual backup

Don't forget

The **Recovery** option in **Update & Security** has a **Reset this PC** option that can be used to reinstall Windows and select which files you want to keep.

System Restore

Windows 10 takes snapshots of the system files before any software updates are applied, or in any event once every seven days. You can also create a snapshot manually. The snapshots are known as Restore Points and are managed by System Restore.

Hot tip

System Restore returns system files to an earlier point in time, allowing you to undo system changes without affecting your documents, email, and other data files.

1. From the Control Panel, open **System** under **System and Security** and select **System protection**

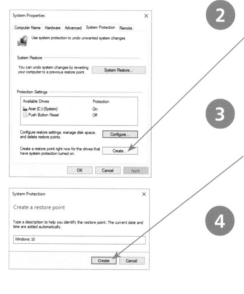

2. Select the **Create...** button, to create a Restore Point manually

3. Provide a title for the Restore Point and click **Create**

4. The required data is written to disk and the manual Restore Point is set up

Beware

System Restore is not intended for protecting personal data files. For these you should use Windows Backup (see page 181).

Using Restore Points

The installation of a new app or driver software may make Windows 10 behave unpredictably or have other unexpected results. Uninstalling the app or rolling back the driver (see page 177) can correct the situation. If it doesn't, use an automatic or manual Restore Point to reset your system to an earlier date when everything worked correctly.

1 Select **System protection** and click the **System Restore...** button

2 By default this will offer to undo the most recent change. This may fix the problem

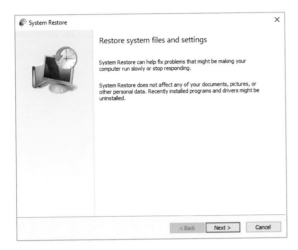

You can also run **System Restore from Safe Mode**, the troubleshooting option. Start up the computer and press **F8** repeatedly as your computer reboots, to display the boot menu, then select **Safe Mode**.

3 Otherwise, click a suitable item to use as the Restore Point

If the selected Restore Point does not resolve the problem, you can try again, selecting another Restore Point.

4 Follow the prompts to restart the system using system files from the selected date and time

Security and Maintenance

The Security and Maintenance section in the Control Panel monitors security and delivers alerts for security features.

You can learn more about maintaining your Windows 10 system in our companion title: Windows 10 in easy steps – Special Edition. Visit www. ineasysteps.com to find out more about this book.

1 In the Control Panel, click on the **Security and Maintenance** link in **System and Security**

2 Select the **Change Security and Maintenance settings** link

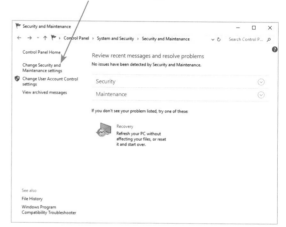

In the Security and Maintenance settings you can also **Change User Account Control settings**, from a link at the side of the window.

3 Check the settings **On** or **Off** as required

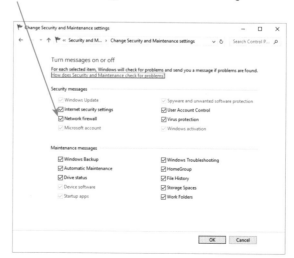

Windows Defender Firewall

1 Open the Control Panel, select the **System and Security** category and select **Windows Defender Firewall**

Windows Defender Firewall
Check firewall status
Allow an app through Windows Firewall

2 Select **Turn Windows Defender Firewall on or off** to customize settings for private (home and work) and public networks

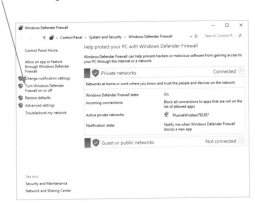

3 Select **Allow an app or feature through Windows Defender Firewall**, to view the allowed apps

Allow an app or feature through Windows Defender Firewall

4 Click on the **Change settings** button to allow or restrict apps

Change settings

5 Check apps **On** or **Off** to allow or remove them from the allowed list. Click on the **OK** button to apply the changes

Hot tip

The Windows Defender Firewall can be used to provide a level of protection against malicious software and viruses.

Don't forget

Firewall is on by default in Windows 10, but you can turn it off if you have another firewall installed and active.

Beware

Only add apps to the allowed list if you are advised to do so by a trusted advisor, or if you trust their origins.

185

Malware Protection

The Windows Security app, which is pre-installed with Windows 10, can be used to give a certain amount of protection against viruses and malicious software. To use it:

Don't forget

Malware (malicious software) is designed to deliberately harm your computer. To protect your system, you need up-to-date antivirus and anti-spyware software. Windows Security can provide this, and you can also install a separate antivirus app.

1 Select **Settings > Update & Security > Windows Security**

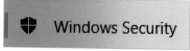

2 Click on **Open Windows Security**

Open Windows Security

3 The Windows Security window contains options for a range of security services

4 Click on one of the security options to view its details. The **Virus & threat protection** option can be used to scan your PC for viruses. Click on the **Quick scan** button to scan your system

Index

A

Action Center	68-69
Adding notes to web pages	101
Adding users.	See Users: Adding
All apps	
Grid	85
Viewing	85
App list	
Minimizing	85
Apps.	See also Windows 10 apps
About	78-79
Alphabetic list	85
Buying	89
Closing	83-84
Installing	91
Maximizing	83
Menus	83
Minimizing	83
Moving	82
Pin to Start menu	38
Pin to taskbar	38
Reinstalling	90
Searching for	86
Uninstalling	92
Using	82-83
Windows 10 apps	78
Windows classic apps	78
Windows Store	87-90
Windows Store apps	78

B

Background	
Setting	46
Backing up	181
Backpacks	136
Battery	
AC/DC adapter	169
Charging	169
Icon	165
Life	165
Lithium-ion	164
Lithium polymer	164
Management	166-168
Power	10
Rechargeable	164
Re-inserting	170
Removing	170
Spare	25, 171
Troubleshooting	172
Bookmarking web pages	100
Books	133
Buying	133
Books button	
In Edge browser	133
Buying apps	89

C

Calendar	120-122
Adding events	122
Carry case	24
CDs/DVDs	26
Loading	55
Players and re-writers	21
CD writers	13
Central Processing Unit (CPU)	12
Cleaning material	26
Clean up your disk	178-179
Cloud clipboard	32
Connectivity.	See Laptops: Connectivity
Cookies	106
On online shopping sites	107
Cortana	64-67
Does not understand	66
For shutting down	67
From the Lock screen	66
Searching with	66
Setting up	64
Setting up the microphone	65
Using	65-67

D

Dark Mode	32, 70
Desktop	40
Accessing	35
Accessing with shortcuts	40
Desktops	
Deleting	41
Device Manager	177
Disk Defragmenter	179
Dry-bags	139
DVDs/CDs	26
DVD writers	13

E

Ease of Access	
From login screen	58
Edge browser. *See* Microsoft Edge browser	
Energy intensive tasks	165
Ethernet	21, 154

F

Facebook	113
Family history	109
Family Safety	148-152
Apps and games controls	151
Recent activity controls	149
Screen time controls	152
Web browsing controls	150
File Explorer. *See also* Library	
Opening	72
Quick Access	73-74
This PC	72
Firewall. *See* Windows Defender Firewall	
Flashdrives	56
Frequently used apps	
On the Start menu	36

G

Gaming	134
Achievements	134
Activity feed	134
Clubs	134
My games	134
Genealogy	109
Gmail	110
Graphics card. *See* Laptops: Graphics card	
Groove Music app	130
Accessing Spotify	130
Adding music from your laptop	131
Playing music	131
Streaming music	130

H

Hand position	19
HDMI	21
Headphones	26
Hotmail renamed	110
Hotspots	22
Hybrids	11

I

IBM	8, 9
IEEE 802.11	155
Instagram	113
Installing apps	91
Internet Explorer	94
Internet Service Provider (ISP)	94

K

Keyboard	19

L

Language
  Display — 64
  Speech — 64
Laptop case — 136
Laptop position — 16
Laptops
  Avoiding water — 139
  Carrying — 18
  Cleaning — 23
  Connectivity — 13
  Desktop replacements — 11
  Drying out — 139
  Functionality — 10
  Graphics card — 13
  Hybrids — 11
  IBM-compatible — 9
  Insulating against heat — 138
  Keeping dry — 139
  Memory — 12
  Netbooks — 11
  Notebooks — 11
  Optical Drive — 13
  Pointing device — 13
  Portability — 10
  Ports — 13
  Power — 10
  Processor — 12
  Safety on vacation — 137
  Screen sizes — 11
  Size — 14
  Storage — 12
  Transporting — 136
  Ultrabooks — 11
  Webcam — 13
  Weight — 14
  Wireless — 13
Library
  File menu — 75
  Home menu — 75
  Manage menu — 76
  Menu options — 76
  Share menu — 76
  View menu — 76

Library tools — 75
Live Tile functionality — 39
  Calendar — 39
  Groove Music — 39
  Mail — 39
  Money — 39
  News — 39
  People — 39
  Photos — 39
  Sport — 39
Live Tiles — 39
Local Account sign-in — 59
Locking your computer — 58
Lock screen — 58
  Settings — 48-49
Logging in — 58-59
Login settings — 59
Luggables — 9

M

Mail — 110-113
  Accounts — 110
  Formatting — 113
  POP3 account — 110
  Sending — 112-113
  Setting up — 110-111
Malware protection — 186
Memory.   *See* Laptops: Memory
Memory card reader — 21
Metal case — 136
Microsoft Account — 44
  Creating — 44-45
  Email address — 147
  Prompted to create — 44
  Services — 44
Microsoft Edge browser
  About — 94
  Accessing favorites — 103
  Adding Notes — 101-102
  Bookmarking pages — 100
  Browsing history — 103
  Clear history — 103
  Downloads — 103

Homepage button   96
Hub   103
Importing favorites   96
Reading list   103-104
Reading view   105
Set aside tabs   99
Setting a homepage   96
Smart address bar   95
Tab previews   98
Tabs   97
Microsoft Store
  About   87-89
  Buying apps   89
  Downloaded apps   90
  Featured apps   87
  Ratings and reviews   88
  Reinstalling apps   90
  Viewing your apps   90
Microsoft Store apps   79
Microsoft Surface   29
Microsoft website
  For downloading Windows 10   31
Mouse
  External   20, 26
  Wireless   20
Movies and TV
  Viewing   132
Multi-card reader   21, 26
Multiple users
  Customization   145
  Overview   144-145
Music
  Playing   131

N

Nearby sharing   158-159
Network
  Components   154
  Troubleshooting   162
Networking
  Saving files for sharing   160-161
  Wireless   155

Notifications   68-69
  Settings   69
Notifications area
  On the Taskbar   40

O

OneDrive
  Adding items to File Explorer   115
  Adding items to OneDrive online 116
  Adding items to the OneDrive app 116
  Online   114
  Overview   114
  Settings   117
  Sharing   116
Opening a laptop   28
Optical Drive.   See Laptops: Optical Drive
Optimizing folders   76
Outlook   110

P

Padlock   24
Parental controls.   See Family Safety
People app   118-119
  Adding contacts manually   119
  Finding people   118-119
Personalization   46-47
Photos
  App   124-129
  Draw button   128
  Editing   128-129
  Importing   124
  Sharing   127
  Viewing   124-126
Picture password   59
PIN   59
Pinterest   113
Pin to Start menu   38
Pin to Taskbar   38
Pointing device. See Laptops: Pointing device
Ports.   See Laptops: Ports

Posture	15
Power	
Conserving	165
Usage	165
Power cable	25
Power off button	58
Power options	34
Power sockets	140
Power User menu	35
Pre-install	31
Processor.	*See* Laptops: Processor

Q

Quick access folder	74

R

Random Access Memory (RAM)	12
Recycle Bin	178
Removing users.	*See* Users: Removing
Restart	43
Restart for updates	43
Restore point	182
Ribbon.	*See* Scenic Ribbon
Run function	91

S

Safe Mode	183
Scenic Ribbon	75-76
Screen adjusting	17
Screen glare	17
Screen resolution	52
Screenshots	33, 71
Searching	62-63
Asking a question	63
Over your laptop	63
Text search	62
The web	63
Seating position	15
Security and Maintenance	184
Security at airports	141
Settings	60-61
Accessing	60
Adding to the taskbar	60
Sharing files	159
Shopping online	106-107
Shoulder strap	24
Shutting down	43
Sign-in options	58-59
Skype	142
Sleep	43
Snapchat	113
Snapshots with System Restore	182
Snip & Sketch	33, 71
Snipping	71
Social media	113
Spotify	130
Start button	34-35
Functionality	34-35
In previous versions	79
Shutting down from	43
Using	34
Start menu	36-39
Frequently used apps	36
Power button	36
Resizing tiles	38
Shutting down from	43
Storage	53. *See also* Laptops: Storage
Storage sense	53
Structure of the Desktop	40
Surface Pro	32
System properties	176
Device Manager	177
System Restore	182-183
For creating Restore Points	182

T

Tablets	29
Tabs	
Using in Microsoft Edge	97

Taskbar   40
  Notifications area   40
  Viewing open windows   40
Task View   41-42
Task View button
  Showing or hiding   41
Temperature extremes   138
Text searches   67
Themes   50-51
This PC
  For accessing Properties   176
Timeline   42
Touch pad   19
Touchscreens   29
Travel   108-109
Troubleshooting   162
Turning off   43
Twitter   113

U

Uninstalling apps   92
Update Assistant
  Windows 10 October 2018 Update 31
Updates
  Restarting   43
USB   13, 21
USB Type-C   21
Users
  Adding   146-147
  Removing   147
Using Restore Points   182

V

Vacation
  Booking   108-109
  Cruises   109
  Hotels   109
Voice calls with Skype   142
Voice search with Cortana   66-67
Volume adjustments   54

W

Web-cam.   *See* Laptops: Webcam
Web searches   63
Wi-Fi   22
Windows 8   30
Windows 10   9
  About   30
  Installing   31
  Obtaining   31
Windows 10 apps   78, 80-81
Windows 10 October 2018 Update   30
  About   32-33
Windows apps   79
Windows Defender Firewall   185
Windows Hello   59
Windows Insider Program   180
Windows Key (WinKey)   32, 40, 58, 72
Windows Update   180
  Pause Updates   180
  Windows 10 October 2018 Update 31
Windows updates
  Restarting   43
Wireless   22.   *See also* Laptops: Wireless
Wireless network   154
Wireless networking   155
Working position   15
Wrong password when signing in   58

X

Xbox   134